MINERALS
OF
CALDBECK
FELLS

MINERALS OF THE ENGLISH LAKE DISTRICT

CALDBECK FELLS

M P COOPER
AND
C J STANLEY

NATURAL HISTORY MUSEUM PUBLICATIONS
LONDON

Designed by Michael Morey
© British Museum (Natural History) 1990
Cromwell Road, London SW7 5BD

British Library Cataloguing in Publication Data
Cooper, M.P. (Michael P.)
 Minerals of the English Lake District -
 Caldbeck Fells.
 1. Cumbria. Caldbeck. Mineral deposits
 I. Title   II. Stanley, C.J.
 553'.09427'87

ISBN 0-565-01102-2

Typeset by Advanced Filmsetters (Glasgow) Ltd,
in Photina and Helvetica
Printed by Craft Print Pte Ltd

Frontispiece DALE BECK VALLEY: a wide-angle photograph looking south towards Iron Crag in the centre of the photograph. The results of centuries of mining can be seen in the rubble-strewn bed of Dale Beck, composed largely of debris washed down from the Roughton Gill mine dumps under Iron Crag.

CONTENTS

INTRODUCTION

The mines and mineral veins of the Caldbeck Fells have produced some of the finest mineral specimens ever found: pyromorphite, plumbogummite, mimetite, linarite, hemimorphite and other species from the area grace public and private collections the world over. Among British mineral collectors, Caldbeck is one of the most popular collecting areas in the country, sometimes referred to as the 'Cornwall of the North'. But the Caldbeck Fells are not only of appeal to the amateur, their complex geological history and the relationships between the mineral deposits and their host rocks have presented a stimulus and challenge to professional geologists and mineralogists from the early days of these sciences.

As producers of fine specimens, the mines of Caldbeck have been justly famous for over 150 years but their history dates back much further than this and can be traced at least to the sixteenth century when German miners contracted with Elizabeth I to work copper and silver there. The smelter they built at Keswick was the largest in Europe at the time and the oft-quoted proverb

> Caldbeck and the Caldbeck Fells
> Are worth all England else
>
> (Hutchinson, 1794)

is supposed to have originated in this period. Although most of the mines that produced fine specimens have been closed for more than 100 years, new mineralogical discoveries are still being made.

In this book we have attempted to provide comprehensive coverage of the mineral occurrences of the area,

Fig. 1 ROUGHTON GILL: the beck drops some 120 metres (400 feet) in a series of attractive waterfalls between Iron Crag on the east and Balliway Rigg on the west. Mineral veins crossing the gill have been worked for centuries, making and losing fortunes in the process. The earliest workings were from the beckside at the top of the gill; the most recent were from the 90 fathom cross-cut driven near the foot of the lowest waterfall (just off the left of the photograph). Roughton Gill has not seen the bustle of miners and smelters for over a century but remains famous for the rare and beautiful mineral specimens it produced.

combining information from previous publications with our own and others' unpublished observations, and a thorough study of many public and private collections of specimens and memorabilia. We hope that everyone from the beginner to the experienced mineralogist will gain an appreciation of the minerals for which the Caldbeck Fells are renowned.

CALDBECK FELLS MINING DISTRICT

The Caldbeck Fells mining district occupies approximately 25 sq km in the north-east of the English Lake District, some 12 km north-north-east of Keswick. Before 1974 the fells were in the county of Cumberland, since merged with Westmorland and part of Lancashire to form the new administrative county of Cumbria.

It is an area of high ground, once described as 'desolate and mountanous' [*sic*], lying to the south of the village of Caldbeck, and the commonly inclement weather led the same observer to note that 'the property of the Arctic Circle is not confined to those unhappy regions which lie within 23 degrees of the pole' (Anon, 1747: 522). Indeed the first recorded building at Caldbeck was a hospice, built c.1112 by the Prior of St Mary, Carlisle, under licence from Ranulph Engayne chief forester of Inglewood, as a refuge for travellers oppressed by the climate or 'benighted from the hands of prowling freebooters' (Mannix & Whellan, 1847: 458–459; Wiseman, 1987: 86–87).

The fells are essentially treeless, except for the few rowans and sycamores in the steep-sided ravines ('gills'), that cut through the fellsides. It was in these gills that the old men found the mineral veins that made the Caldbeck Fells famous. Now that the miners are gone the district relies almost wholly on farming and the fells are given over to sheep-walk. In the old days it was said that 'the teeth of the sheep are remarkably tinged with a gold colour, supposed to be by the water issuing from the veins of copper' (Nicholson & Burn, 1777). Be that as it may, the mineralogy of the rocks may have a bearing on the health of the sheep: the relative lack of calcium in the

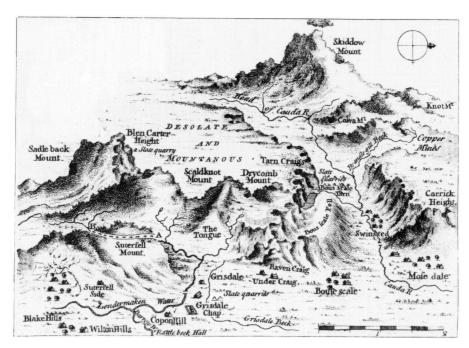

Fig. 2 CALDEW VALLEY: a westerly view up the Caldew Valley showing 'Carrick Height' and the 'Copper Mines' in a grotesquely exaggerated landscape. From *A Journey to Caudebec Fells . . .* (Anon, 1747).

Fig. 3 THE CALDBECK FELLS: a panoramic view of the Fells from the north shows the treeless grassy moorland rising behind enclosed agricultural land. The distance from Carrock End to Red Gill is about 6 km (3.7 miles).

country rocks and veins discourages the growth of fresh-water snail colonies—an essential vector in the life cycle of the sheep liver fluke.

The Caldbeck parish boundary includes most of the mining district, but the southern slopes of Carrock Fell, including Brandy Gill and the Carrock tungsten mine, are part of Mungrisdale parish. For our purposes the fells are taken to extend from Brae Fell in the west to the precipitous end of Carrock Fell in the east, the southern border following the River Caldew from Mosedale hamlet (below Carrock Fell) to the foot of Great Calva about 9 km south of Caldbeck. The ground reaches its highest point at High Pike (647 m) approximately in the centre of the district. The fells were thoroughly scoured by glaciers in the Pleistocene Ice Age and have a generally rounded appearance, although the eastern slopes of Carrock Fell, and Iron Crag above Roughton Gill, are rocky and steep, the home of ravens and rare birds of prey. Boulder clay and peat blanket much of the ground, in places to a great depth. The resulting poor and acid soil supports a typical moorland flora of grasses, mosses, heather, heaths and berries nurtured by a high annual rainfall of 125–150 cm (Pearsall & Pennington, 1973).

Although of great interest to those concerned with the natural sciences, mining history, or archaeology (Turner, 1987), the Caldbeck Fells have been largely ignored by the hordes of tourists, past and present, who were, and still are, drawn to the more dramatic scenery of the central Lake District. Caldbeck is, however, bereft neither of history nor attractions outside the mining story (see, for instance, Hutchinson, 1794, Vol. 2: 374–396; Allen, 1987). Its most notorious son was the celebrated huntsman and drunkard, John Peel (1776–1854). He is buried in Caldbeck churchyard, a last resting place shared with, among others, Mary Robinson (d.1837), the 'Beauty of Buttermere', who survived her calamitous early life as a victim of celebrity to wed a Caldbeck farmer (Nicholson, 1955). More pertinent to this book are two other people: Bryce McMurdo Wright (c. 1814–1874), the eminent Victorian mineral dealer who was born in Hesket Newmarket, Caldbeck (Anon, 1875), and John Dalton (1766–1844), 'the father of modern chemistry'

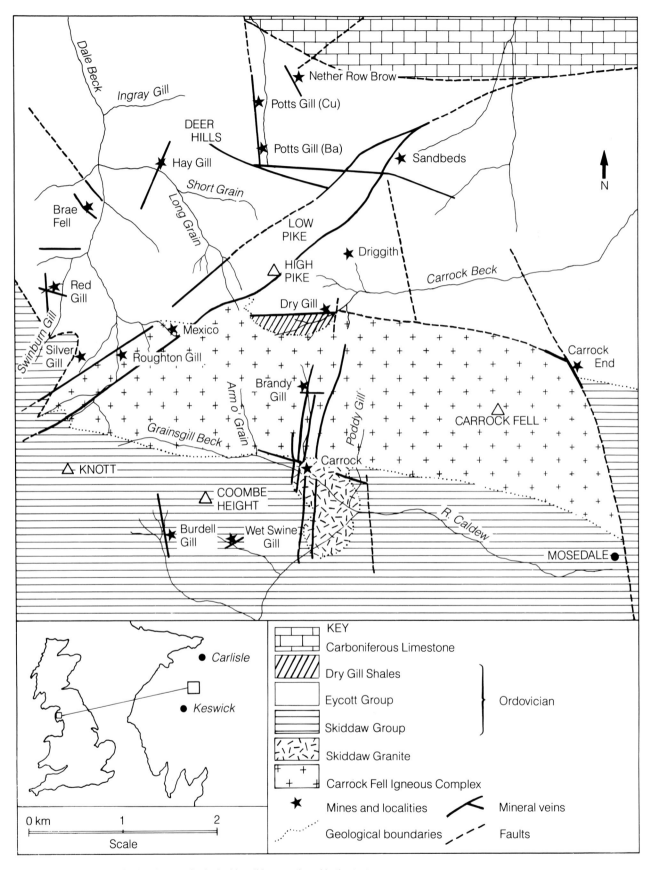

Fig. 4 CALDBECK FELLS: sketch map of principal localities mentioned in the text.

and founder of today's atomic theory, who once lived at Greenrigg, Caldbeck—the home of his maternal ancestors for more than 200 years (Parkin, 1921).

In the eighteenth and nineteenth centuries the new tourists, drawn to whatever was 'picturesque', visited Caldbeck to view the dramatic Howk (Mannix & Whellan, 1847: 461), a limestone ravine scooped out by the River Caldbeck. Victorian visitors could gape at 'Red Rover' the new water wheel of the Caldbeck bobbin mill reputed to be the largest in the country; the earlier wheel had once provided power at Driggith mine (Allen, 1987: 13). The more hardy could climb Carrock Fell for its superb views and its mysterious summit ruins (now believed to be the remains of an Iron Age hill fort) or visit nearby 'bottomless' Bowscale Tarn, on the opposite side of Mosedale, in the hope of seeing the stars reflected in its depths at midday (Anon, 1747: 523) or of catching a glimpse of its legendary pair of trout, immortalized by Wordsworth in *Song at the feast of Brougham Castle*.

The inveterate walker Charles Dickens, accompanied by a less enthusiastic Wilkie Collins, visited Caldbeck in 1857. In Dickens' amusing account of their stay they climbed Carrock Fell, 'a trumpery little mountain of fifteen hundred feet', in a 'fine, soft, close, drowsy, penetrating rain'. They made their way over 'irritating, comfortless rocks, littered about anyhow by Nature; treacherous, disheartening rocks of all sorts of small shapes and small sizes, bruisers of tender toes and trippers-up of wavering feet' until, in a thick mist, they reached the summit and became hopelessly lost. During their tortuous and difficult descent they came across a mine 'exhausted and abandoned; a dismal ruinous place, with nothing but the wreck of its works and buildings left to speak for it' (Dickens, 1857: 11–19).

Although we do not know which mine they encountered we can be fairly certain that, scattered amongst mineral collections far and wide, there is sure to be rather more 'to speak for it' than Dickens thought.

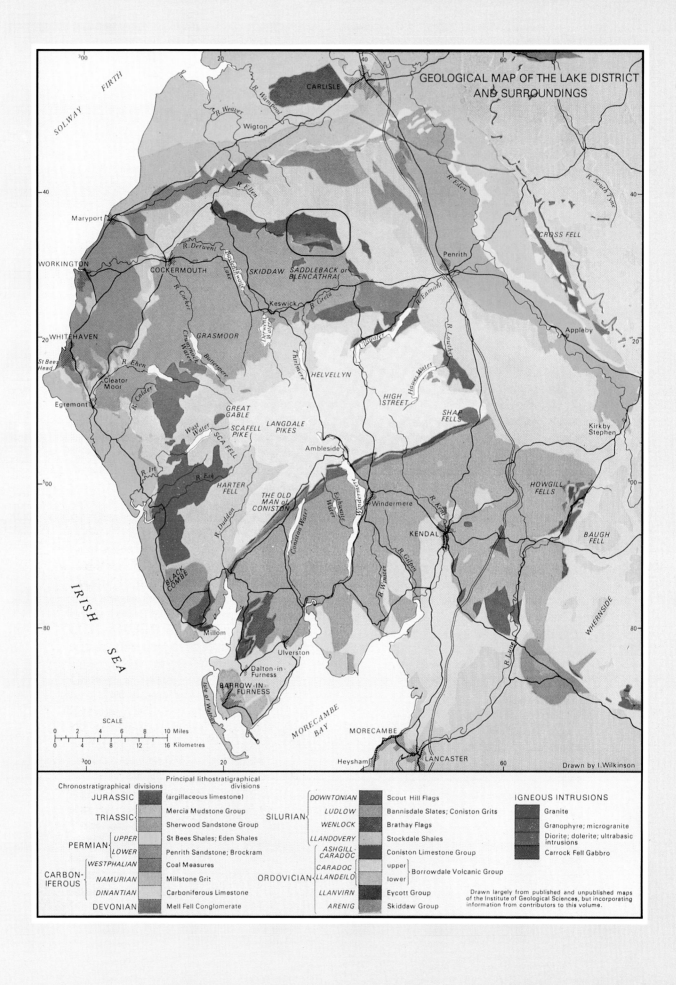

GEOLOGICAL MAP OF THE LAKE DISTRICT
AND SURROUNDINGS

SOLWAY FIRTH

IRISH SEA

CARLISLE

R. Weaver

Wigton

Maryport

R. Ellen

R. Derwent

WORKINGTON

COCKERMOUTH

SKIDDAW

SADDLEBACK or
BLENCATHRA

R. Cocker

Bassenthwaite

R. Greta

Keswick

R. Eden

CROSS FELL

Penrith

R. Eamont

Appleby

R. Lowther

WHITEHAVEN

R. Ehen

GRASMOOR

Crummock Water

Derwent Water

Thirlmere

HELVELLYN

Ullswater

Haweswater

St Bees
Head

Cleator
Moor

Buttermere

R. Calder

HIGH
STREET

SHAP
FELLS

Kirkby
Stephen

Egremont

West
Water

GREAT
GABLE

SCA FELL

SCAFELL
PIKE

LANGDALE
PIKES

R. Irt

R. Esk

Ambleside

HARTER
FELL

THE OLD
MAN of
CONISTON

Coniston Water

Esthwaite
Water

Windermere

Windermere

R. Kent

HOWGILL
FELLS

R. Duddon

BLACK
COMBE

R. Winster

R. Gilpin

KENDAL

BAUGH
FELL

Millom

Ulverston

R. Leven

WHERNSIDE

Dalton-in-
Furness

Isle of Walney

BARROW-IN-
FURNESS

MORECAMBE
BAY

MORECAMBE

WHERNSIDE

SCALE
0   2   4   6   8   10 Miles
0   4   8   12   16 Kilometres

Heysham

LANCASTER

Drawn by I.Wilkinson

Chronostratigraphical divisions

Principal lithostratigraphical
divisions

JURASSIC   (argillaceous limestone)

TRIASSIC   Mercia Mudstone Group
                       Sherwood Sandstone Group

PERMIAN   UPPER   St Bees Shales; Eden Shales
           LOWER   Penrith Sandstone; Brockram

CARBON-   WESTPHALIAN Coal Measures
IFEROUS   NAMURIAN   Millstone Grit
           DINANTIAN   Carboniferous Limestone

DEVONIAN   Mell Fell Conglomerate

SILURIAN   DOWNTONIAN   Scout Hill Flags
           LUDLOW   Bannisdale Slates; Coniston Grits
           WENLOCK   Brathay Flags
           LLANDOVERY   Stockdale Shales

ORDOVICIAN ASHGILL-   Coniston Limestone Group
           CARADOC
           CARADOC   upper
           LLANDEILO   lower   Borrowdale Volcanic Group
           LLANVIRN   Eycott Group
           ARENIG   Skiddaw Group

IGNEOUS INTRUSIONS

           Granite

           Granophyre; microgranite

           Diorite; dolerite; ultrabasic
           intrusions

           Carrock Fell Gabbro

Drawn largely from published and unpublished maps
of the Institute of Geological Sciences, but incorporating
information from contributors to this volume.

GEOLOGY

It was the distinguished and controversial geologist Adam Sedgwick, Professor of Geology at Cambridge, who in 1831 first acknowledged Jonathan Otley's major contribution to the understanding of the geology of the Lake District. Their friendship had begun some years earlier and was to end only with Otley's death in 1856 at the age of 90. Otley, who lived in Keswick for much of his life, recognized (1820: 257–258) that in the Lake District

> Granite is understood to occupy the lowest place in the series of rocks which have hitherto been exposed to human observation, it may be called the foundation rock upon which all the others rest . . . The rocks which succeed, and have been confounded together under the general name of slaty rocks may be classed in three divisions.

These groups he called the Clayslate, Greenstone and Greywacke divisions, the first representing the slates and other sediments of what is now referred to as the Skiddaw Group; the second representing the cleaved tuffs and lavas of the Borrowdale Volcanic Group; and the last, the Coniston Limestone and Silurian rocks (Windermere Group; Moseley, 1984) of the southern Lake District. In addition, he first drew attention to the fundamental distinction between cleavage and bedding (Ward, 1876–1877).

Otley's simple, but carefully recorded, observations formed the basis of his book, published in 1823 *A concise description of the English Lakes and adjacent mountains with general directions to tourists: and observations on the mineralogy and geology of the district.* Such was the friendship between Sedgwick and Otley that the former later expressed his regret at having promised to write some geological notes in a book written and published by Hudson of Kendal in 1842 *A complete guide to the Lakes, comprising minute directions for the tourist with Mr Wordsworth's description of the scenery of the country etc. and three letters on the geology of the Lake District by the Rev. Prof. Sedgwick.* Although the main competition to Otley's book, Sedgwick need not have worried, for Otley's book appeared in eight editions between 1823 and 1849 selling nearly 9000 copies in all.

It was Otley, in fact, who had introduced Sedgwick to the area in 1823. Interestingly, their first excursion was in the Caldbeck Fells area, following the Caldew river upstream from Mosedale to the mineral veins in Grainsgill. How many times must this same journey have been undertaken by succeeding generations of geologists, mineralogists, mining engineers and students? In 1842 Sedgwick (*in* Hudson, 1842: 230) remarked of this first visit:

> None of the veins were worked to profit when I last visited the spot, nearly twenty years since. They

Fig. 6 ADAM SEDGWICK: aged 47, from a portrait painted by Thomas Phillips R.A., 1832, reproduced in Clark & Hughes, 1890, frontispiece.

Fig. 5 (*opposite*) **GEOLOGICAL MAP:** the Lake District with Caldbeck Fells area in box. (Reprinted from Moseley (Ed.), 1978).

13

were, however, occasionally opened by mineral dealers: for they contain apatite, schorl, tungsten, wolfram, and several other minerals in considerable abundance.

Sedgwick also observed some similarities between these veins and mineral deposits he had seen in Cornwall:

> I was struck with the close resemblance of the mineralised portion of Skiddaw Forest to certain parts of Cornwall near the junction of granite and slate.
>
> *(in* Hudson, 1842: 230)

Although lacking in tin, the greisen-bordered tungsten veins have much in common with those found in SW England.

Fig. 7 ADAM SEDGWICK: on a geological excursion, believed to have been drawn by Mr J. E. Davis. (From Clark & Hughes, 1890: 255).

Unusually, for so prominent a man, Sedgwick had a well-refined sense of humour, with little trace of pomposity. There is no doubt that he recognized himself in the amusing story of 'Joe and the Geologist' written in Cumberland dialect:

> ... T' gentleman was a queerish like oald chap, wid a sharp leuk oot, grey hair and a smo' feàce—drist i'black, wid a white neck-cloth like a parson, an' a par of specks on t'top of a gay lang nwose' at wasn't set varra fair atween his e'en, sooa'at when he leuk't ebbem at yan through his specks he rayder turn't his feàce to t'ya side ...
>
> (Clark & Hughes, 1890: 253)

J. Clifton Ward documented much of the correspondence between Sedgwick and Otley in 1876–1877 and was perhaps the foremost of a succession of eminent geologists who worked in the Lake District in the latter part of the nineteenth century. In addition to the Geological Survey memoir of the Keswick area published in 1876*a* he wrote many papers including one on the granitic rocks of the Lake District, published in two parts, with an account of the Skiddaw Granite (1875; 1876*b*). J. G. Goodchild (1882, 1884, 1885) produced a series of contributions on the topographical mineralogy of the region updating the earlier work of Greg & Lettsom (1858); while Postlethwaite's *Mines and Mining in the Lake District, An Essay* (1877, 1889, 1913) remains a much sought after reference on the mines. The gabbros of the Carrock Fell Igneous Complex were the subject of a detailed study by Harker in 1894 who followed it up in 1895 with a paper on the alteration of the Skiddaw Granite to the 'quartzo-micaceous granite' or 'greisen' in Grainsgill.

In the early part of this century J. E. Marr, R. H. Rastall, A. M. Finlayson, T. Eastwood, C. S. Hitchen and G. H. Mitchell all made considerable advances in certain aspects of the geology of the Lake District and the Caldbeck Fells. It would be invidious to comment on the contributions of the many living geologists, their works are widely referred to in the brief review below. Suffice to say that the more the Lake District and Caldbeck Fells are studied, the more problems arise, and the greater is the opportunity for diverse opinions and controversial debate.

Some assessment of the progress made in nearly 200 years of scientific study can be gauged by comparing the geological maps of the Caldbeck Fells. The earliest (Fig. 8) was that of William Smith whose map of Cumberland on a scale of 1:210 000 was published in 1824. That this great man visited the Caldbeck Fells in 1821 is related by Ward (1876–1877) who remarked that Smith and his nephew John Phillips stayed at the Queen's Head, Hesket Newmarket (near Caldbeck) having business in connection with the 'High Pike mine'. It was not until much later that the Geological Survey first mapped the Keswick area (Old Series Sheet 101 SE; New Series Sheet 29) with an accompanying memoir (Ward, 1876*a*) and subsequently produced the hand-coloured map of the Caldbeck Fells as part of the Cockermouth sheet (Old Series Sheet 101 NE; New Series Sheet 23). The latter (Fig. 9), on a scale of one inch to the mile, was published in 1890 but with no memoir. A revised solid edition of the one inch map was published in 1959 and the explanatory memoir appeared belatedly in 1968 (Eastwood, Hollingworth, Rose & Trotter). Figure 10 is of the recently enlarged metric (1:50 000) edition of this map.

For those readers who wish to study the geology of the Caldbeck Fells in greater detail than is given here, Smith (1974), Eastwood *et al.* (1968) and Moseley (1978)

Fig. 8 GEOLOGICAL MAP: Caldbeck Fells by William Smith (1824). From part of the 1:210 000 Cumberland sheet published by G. and J. Cary, London

Fig. 9 GEOLOGICAL MAP: Caldbeck Fells. The 1:63360 Cockermouth sheet 23 of 1890. Geological Survey.

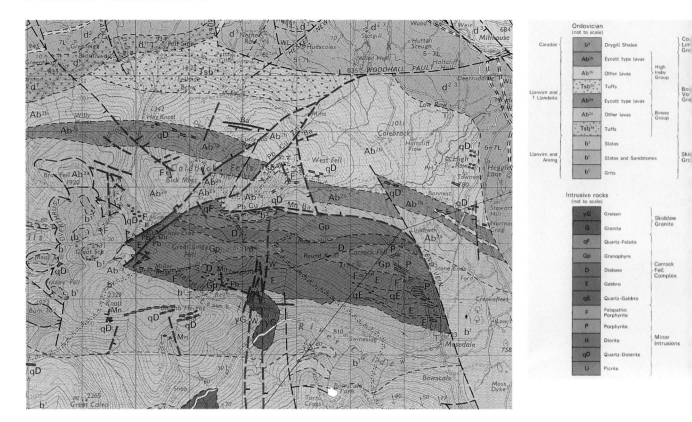

Fig. 10 GEOLOGICAL MAP: Caldbeck Fells. Part of the 1: 50 000 solid edition of the 1959 Cockermouth sheet 23, British Geological Survey. Rocks shown here as the Borrowdale Volcanic Group are now referred to the Eycott Group (see text). The Key refers to the pre-Carboniferous rocks only.

will prove invaluable sources in combination with the more recent literature.

Of the three rock units of Lower Palaeozoic age which make up the central and southern Lake District, the Skiddaw Group, the Borrowdale Volcanic Group and the Coniston Limestone Group (the latter now part of the Windermere Group; Moseley, 1984), only the first is represented in the Caldbeck Fells, the geological history of which is given below in its generally recognized stratigraphic sequence (Table 1 – opposite).

SKIDDAW GROUP

The nature of the pre-Ordovician basement rocks of the Lake District is not known and the earliest rocks exposed are those of the Skiddaw Group of Tremadoc and Arenig (c. 500 – 485 Ma) age (Molyneux & Rushton, 1985) which have a total thickness of several thousand metres. In the Caldbeck Fells, two of the four formations recognized elsewhere in the Lake District are present. The oldest, exposed west of the Carrock Fell Igneous Complex, is the Loweswater Flags: these sediments accumulated on the continental slope, or further seaward, as a result of periodic sediment flow (turbidity currents) forming turbidite sequences (Jackson, 1978). Such sandy (arenaceous) sediments were derived from older Cambrian and Pre-

cambrian outcrops along the southern margin of the proto-Atlantic Ocean (Iapetus). However, these sediments are unrepresentative of the Skiddaw Group as a whole, most of which formed through slow settling of clay and silt in relatively deep water conditions. The Kirk Stile Slates Formation exposed south of the Carrock Fell Igneous Complex is typical of this type of sedimentation and, although it contains some arenaceous beds, it is composed predominantly of black shales. Subdivisions of these formations are made on the basis of their graptolite fauna.

EYCOTT GROUP

There appears to have been no break in sedimentation between the Skiddaw and Eycott Groups and the arbitrary boundary is taken where the volcanic content of the sequence becomes dominant (Wadge, 1978).

The earliest of the volcanic eruptions were submarine in character, and sedimentary fragments and ash were interstratified with mud deposits and occasional lava flows. Eventually, the main mass of Eycott volcanic rocks accumulated subaerially on the newly emerged land mass.

The Eycott Group includes all interbedded volcanic and sedimentary sequences which may be correlated with the successions of Eycott Hill and the Caldbeck Fells. It was first recognized as being older (Llanvirn c.485–475 Ma) than the main volcanic outcrop of the Lake District (the Borrowdale Volcanic Group of Llandeilo–Caradoc age and not exposed in the Caldbeck Fells area) on microfossil (acritarchs and chitinozoa) evidence (Downie & Soper, 1972). Previously, it had been noticed by Fitton & Hughes (1970) that the volcanic rocks of the Caldbeck Fells were distinct both petrographically and geochemically from those of the main outcrop in the central Lake District. The former consist dominantly of basalt and basaltic andesite flows with a few tuff and agglomerate horizons and occasional rhyolites. Rocks of the Borrowdale Volcanic Group on the other hand contain less iron and titanium and have rather more andesite and dacite flows, showing a calc-alkaline geochemistry compared with the transitional tholeiitic to calc-alkaline trend of the Eycott Group (Millward et al. 1978).

At this stage of the Ordovician, the Caldbeck Fells were probably part of an island arc over an active subduction zone, with the Eycott Group volcanics extruded above a thin continental crust (Bamford et al., 1976).

DRY GILL SHALES

The Dry Gill Shales form a small outlier (1 × 0.25 km) on the northernmost flank of the Carrock Fell Igneous Complex. Little of the outcrop is fresh, but in their unaltered condition the rocks are grey to black calcareous ashy mudstones and shales which dip south-south-east at 50–70°, except in the north-west part of the outcrop where the dip is to the north at 40°. Extensive alteration, mostly bleaching, has developed from joints, cleavages and bedding planes to affect the whole rock.

The shales contain a trilobite and brachiopod fauna diagnostic of an Upper Ordovician or Caradocian age. As such the outcrop is of great importance in the stratigraphic correlation of the period. Dolerite is associated with the shales in Dry Gill and Eastwood et al. (1968) considered that both were emplaced at the time of the intrusion of the nearby Harestones felsite of the Carrock Fell Igneous Complex. Their preservation is ascribed to general subsidence of the roof rocks of the igneous complex.

The Dry Gill Shales and other late Ordovician and Silurian sediments were deposited unconformably on the Lower Ordovician sediments and volcanic rocks. Ingham & McNamara (1978) suggest that the marine transgression responsible for their deposition progressed from north to south, and the mostly shallow-water fauna indicates a marine shelf environment. Moseley (1978) considers that, with the cessation of volcanicity, subduction had virtually ceased and that the American and European plates were now in close proximity.

Evidence of the extent of deposition of late Ordovician and Silurian rocks in the northern Lake District and Caldbeck Fells has yet to be found and may not exist.

Table 1 Simplified stratigraphic relationships in the Lake District and the Caldbeck Fells from Ordovician to Triassic times.

Ma	SYSTEM	LAKE DISTRICT	CALDBECK FELLS
200	TRIASSIC	ST BEES SANDSTONE	
	PERMIAN	PENRITH SANDSTONE	
		——— H E R C Y N I A N O R O G E N Y ———	
300	CARBONIFEROUS	COAL MEASURES	(eroded)
		MILLSTONE GRIT	
		CARBONIFEROUS LIMESTONE	CARBONIFEROUS LIMESTONE
		COCKERMOUTH LAVAS	BASEMENT CONGLOMERATE
		MELL FELL CONGLOMERATE	
	DEVONIAN		[Skiddaw Granite intruded]
400		——— C A L E D O N I A N O R O G E N Y ———	
	SILURIAN	WINDERMERE GROUP	
			DRY GILL SHALES
		BORROWDALE VOLCANIC GROUP	[Carrock Complex intruded]
	ORDOVICIAN	EYCOTT GROUP	EYCOTT GROUP
		SKIDDAW GROUP	SKIDDAW GROUP
500		(base not seen)	(base not seen)

CARROCK FELL IGNEOUS COMPLEX

The constituent rocks of this plutonic intrusive complex form a series of narrow, steeply inclined sheets which lie parallel to the east–west strike of the adjacent sediments. A great variety of rock types is present ranging from melanocratic ilmenite-rich gabbros near the southern margin through banded quartz gabbros to leucocratic quartz gabbro rich in feldspars. The iron content of the gabbros increases markedly close to the granophyre which varies from hedenbergite-rich to albite-rich (Eastwood *et al.*, 1968). Other rock types included in the complex are diabase, which is later than the gabbros and possibly postdates the granophyre, and the Harestones felsite regarded as later than all these. The Arm o'Grain microgranite is poorly exposed near the southern margin. Several minor porphyritic and quartz dolerite intrusions cut the complex and adjacent country rocks.

Rafts of Eycott-type lavas of the Eycott Group included in the gabbros have undergone metamorphism to pyroxene granulites and this is consistent with the K–Ar age for the gabbros of 468 ± 10 Ma (Rundle, 1979), i.e. post-Eycott Group. A somewhat younger Rb–Sr age (416 ± 20 Ma) for the granophyre may be erroneous due to partial isotopic resetting associated with the emplacement of the Skiddaw Granite (O'Brien *et al.*, 1985).

Chemically, the rocks of the complex show a tholeiitic trend similar to that of the Eycott Group volcanics and the inference is that they are related (Firman, 1978). The granophyre has a trace element content distinct from the gabbros and also from other Lake District granitoid rocks, but has close geochemical links with the ferrogabbros and hybrid varieties (O'Brien *et al.*, 1985). This is consistent with the observations of Eastwood *et al.* (1968) that the layering shown by the intrusion is the result of separate intrusions of magma from depth rather than having been produced by the more usual mechanisms of *in situ* magmatic differentiation. Harris & Dagger (1987) interpret the complex as a multiple sub-horizontal sheet intrusion which was subsequently rotated into its present near-vertical position.

At the southern margin of the complex the contact with the slates of the Skiddaw Group above Mosedale is welded and the slates are bleached and hornfelsed, commonly with pinkish porphyroblasts of garnet, sodic plagioclase and chloritoid. This increase in sodium content is attributed to mild soda-metasomatism of adinole type. Elsewhere, the metamorphic effects of the gabbro have been obliterated to some degree by the later intrusion of the Skiddaw Granite.

OROGENY

Earth movements in Ordovician and early Silurian times, probably the consequence of widespread magmatic activity in the Lake District, resulted in folding of some of the less competent strata of the Skiddaw Group. This, however, was but a prelude to the main period of tectonic activity towards the end of the Silurian ($c.410–420$ Ma) when continental collision occurred. This resulted in the destruction of the great ocean Iapetus as the American and European plates fused together, and led to polyphase deformation of the rocks of both continental margins. In the Caldbeck Fells the most intense folding occurred in the slates of the Skiddaw Group, where tight folds, such as those seen in the Caldew valley, developed (Roberts, 1971). This was accompanied by regional metamorphism to greenschist facies and cleavage formation. The principal compressive forces were north-north-west to south-south-east in direction leading to roughly east–west folds. A major anticlinal axis runs east–west along the Caldew valley and, to the north of this axis around Great Sca Fell, the anticlinal structure has been ruptured and the competent Loweswater Flags overthrust onto the volcanic rocks of the Eycott Group (Eastwood *et al.*, 1968).

Much of the composite granite batholith which underlies the Lake District (Bott, 1974) was emplaced before this end-Silurian deformation, and the end of the orogeny in the Caldbeck Fells was marked by the intrusion of the Skiddaw Granite which overlapped the final stages of cleavage formation (Soper & Moseley, 1978).

Firman & Lee (1986), on the basis of analogy with Peru, state that perhaps 16 or 17 separate intrusions might reasonably be expected to underlie the Lake District and that the known Lower Devonian granites of Shap (393 ± 3 Ma, Wadge, Gale, Beckinsale & Rundle, 1978) and Skiddaw (392 ± 9 Ma, Shepherd, Beckinsale, Rundle & Durham, 1976) were intruded peripherally to the main batholitic granite.

SKIDDAW GRANITE

The name Skiddaw Granite refers to three distinct outcrops, connected at shallow depth, of greyish biotite granite intruded into country rocks of the Skiddaw Group. The most northerly of these outcrops, in Grainsgill, appears to be an elongate dome and, from evidence in Carrock mine, forms a lobate intrusion underlain and overlain by hornfelsed slate. In part, this Grainsgill intrusion has been altered to a muscovite-quartz rock known as 'greisen' and this may be the result of metasomatism *in situ*, or be due to late fluids concentrating against the less permeable rocks of the Carrock Fell Igneous Complex to the north. When unaltered, the Grainsgill Granite is a white rock with oligoclase, orthoclase, quartz, muscovite, and chlorite.

The thermal aureole of the granite includes rocks of the Skiddaw Group, Carrock Fell Igneous Complex, Eycott Group and Dry Gill Shales, the last two metamorphosed, perhaps by a deep northerly extension of the granite or extensively metasomatized by later, widely penetrating hydrothermal solutions.

In the Skiddaw Group, outer zones of metamorphism are characterized by spotting of the slates and the formation of andalusite (chiastolite) which sometimes may replace graptolites (as on Bowscale Fell). Progressive hardening occurs closer to the granite with, ultimately, well formed crystals of cordierite and clear to translucent porphyroblasts of andalusite in a tough hornfels.

A remarkable variety of altered gabbro is exposed in Brandy Gill. Close to the southern margin of the complex, biotite extensively replaces the primary mafic minerals, and sericitization and albitization of plagioclase feldspar has occurred. Further from the contact, actinolite is common as a replacement of the primary amphiboles and pyroxenes, chloritization of the feldspars is almost complete and ilmenite is altered to titanite.

In the Dry Gill Shales, widespread bleaching is the main change observed, and in the Eycott Group metamorphic effects include the alteration of chlorite to biotite in the rhyolites and andesites, and epidotization of feldspar phenocrysts. In these rocks, however, it is difficult to distinguish between alteration due to the Carrock Fell Igneous Complex, or the Skiddaw Granite, and the widespread hydrothermal rotting of the country rocks by later mineralizing fluids.

In Grainsgill, the tungsten mineralization formed soon after the greisen and is dealt with in the chapter on Mineral Deposits.

DEVONIAN, CARBONIFEROUS AND LATER

As a result of the continental collision the Old Red Sandstone continent was formed and widespread desert conditions prevailed. In the Caldbeck Fells, there was rapid erosion of the newly formed mountains but there is no evidence of deposition before the Carboniferous period (c.360–280 Ma). The land had been extensively weathered and deeply reddened under oxidizing conditions and the matrix of the Carboniferous Basement Conglomerate is a reddish mudstone or sandstone deposited unconformably on the earlier strata. West of the Caldbeck Fells a minor episode of volcanism led to the formation of the Cockermouth Lavas at about the same time.

The Carboniferous sea bounded the Caldbeck Fells to the north and east and the Carboniferous Limestone was deposited on the conglomerate. Mitchell, Taylor & Ramsbottom (1978) suggest that towards the end of Lower Carboniferous times the Lake District was submerged and that the Millstone Grit and Coal Measures rocks of Upper Carboniferous age were deposited over the whole area, subsequent erosion removing them from the Caldbeck Fells; their outcrop is now about 7 km to the north.

The Carboniferous period was terminated by Hercynian earth movements with uplift, folding and widespread faulting. Oxidizing conditions prevailed on the rapidly denuded landmass in an arid climate, with substantial reddening of the rocks beneath the pre-Permo-Triassic (New Red Sandstone) land surface. The sedimentary basins which developed to the north and east of the Caldbeck Fells were infilled mostly by sandstones and shales with extensive evaporite sequences.

Erosion has removed these Permo-Triassic rocks from the Caldbeck Fells and the central Lake District, and there is little evidence of the geological events which took place over the period of some 180 million years between the Triassic and the Quaternary periods. Post-Triassic earth movements, possibly in the Tertiary, are cited by many as being responsible for the gentle doming of the Lake District and may be the result of isostatic adjustments following rapid erosion.

Extensive glaciation occurred in the Quaternary Ice Age, the glaciers exploiting the geological weaknesses, faults, anticlinal axes, softer rock types etc. to form the spectacular scenery, more subtle in the Caldbeck Fells than in the central Lake District, but no less impressive. Typical glacial features abound, the craggy corrie and moraine-dammed tarn of Bowscale Fell, the narrow U-shaped valley of the Caldew from Grainsgill to Mosedale with glacial striae on the large gabbro and hornfels boulders. To the north of the boulder-strewn plateau of Carrock Fell, the valleys are characteristically infilled with morainic debris while boulder clay has been smeared over the fell sides; large erratic boulders are common.

Fig. 11 CARROCK MINE AND MOSEDALE: view of the U-shaped glacially eroded valley of the Caldew looking east towards Carrock Fell and Mosedale. In the foreground are the tailing ponds and mill of Carrock mine. Since this photograph was taken, in March 1987, the buildings have been removed and the tailings ponds bulldozed.

MINERAL DEPOSITS

The metalliferous mineralization of the Caldbeck Fells is broadly typical of such mineralization elsewhere in the Lake District, where the dominant ore minerals are sulphides of lead, copper and zinc, with lesser amounts of antimony- and arsenic-bearing sulphides and sulpho-salts. A notable exception to this is the Carrock Fell tungsten deposit. The principal gangue mineral in all the veins is quartz: fluorite and carbonates such as calcite and dolomite, so spectacularly developed elsewhere in Cumbria (as in the Alston Moor area in the east, and in the West Cumbria hematite deposits), are much less common in the Lake District.

Other metalliferous deposits in the Caldbeck Fells include extensive manganese oxide mineralization, and locally high (< 20–30%) concentrations of ilmenite and, rarely, chromite in the gabbros of the Carrock Fell Igneous Complex. None of these occurrences has been worked commercially. The titanium and chromium minerals are of magmatic origin, formed by various concentration mechanisms in the magma chamber, and are, therefore, not considered in the following discussion of the vein deposits.

Although many of the early descriptions of the geology of the Lake District listed the main minerals present in the metalliferous deposits, few paid much attention to the processes involved in their origin and concentration. Kendall, who attempted a simple classification in 1884, was one of the first to discuss the mineralization in scientific terms. He recognized five types of deposit, based on the dominant metal present, namely: lead, zinc, copper, iron and manganese. The Carrock tungsten mineralization, although undoubtedly known to him, was omitted, probably since it was, at that time, little more than a mineralogical curiosity of more interest to collectors than miners. Subsequently, the tungsten veins and their relationship with the Skiddaw Granite became one of the most studied geological features of the Caldbeck

Fells and the deposit is regarded as a fine example of hydrothermal mineralization associated with a granite intrusion (see e.g. Finlayson, 1910; Hitchen, 1934; Fortey, 1978; Shepherd et al., 1976; Moore, 1982).

While Kendall (1884) argued that the Lake District veins had formed in situ by 'metamorphism and substitution', authors both before (e.g. De la Beche, 1839; Geikie, 1882) and since (e.g. Eastwood, 1921; Firman, 1978; Stanley & Vaughan, 1982) are in general agreement that the veins are epigenetic infillings of either normal faults or, less commonly, tear faults. During this century researchers have been concerned with establishing the ages of the deposits, the sources and nature of the mineralizing fluids, the relationship of the veins to local and regional structures, and the controls exercized by host rock lithology and the underlying composite granite batholith. The extraordinary variety of the minerals encountered in the geographically small area of the Caldbeck Fells can be attributed to four factors:

i the variety of chemically different mineralizing fluids.
ii the number of episodes of mineralization.
iii the many different host rocks.
iv the intense alteration both of the host rocks and of the primary mineral assemblages leading to the formation of secondary or supergene assemblages.

CLASSIFICATION OF THE MINERALIZATION

A classification scheme for the Caldbeck Fells mineral deposits can be attempted based on the following criteria:

i the mineralogy of the veins.
ii the spatial distribution and geological setting of the veins.
iii the age relationships of the veins inferred from field relations and radiometric ages.

This classification is presented in Table 2 (p. 22) and is discussed in detail below.

1 TUNGSTEN-BEARING VEINS AT CARROCK MINE

The major tungsten-bearing veins are the Smith, Harding, and Emerson veins (Fig. 25) which cut the greisenized

Fig. 12 CARROCK MINE: exposure of the Harding vein in the roof of the No. 1 level; the vein being approximately 1.5 m wide at this point. Black wolframite blades are well developed, particularly near the boundary of the vein with the greisen wall-rocks and are commonly associated with scheelite.

Table 2 Classification of Caldbeck Fells mineral deposits

TECTONIC AND IGNEOUS ACTIVITY	AGE OF MINERALIZATION	TYPICAL MINERAL ASSEMBLAGE	EXAMPLES
Tensional regime as Europe and America separate. Post-Triassic earth movements	? Jurassic and later c.190–180 Ma	Pyromorphite $\pm$ mimetite $\pm$ covelline $\pm$ djurleite $\pm$ anglesite $\pm$ malachite $\pm$ cerussite $\pm$ linarite $\pm$ smithsonite $\pm$ lanarkite $\pm$ hemimorphite $\pm$ caledonite $\pm$ leadhillite $\pm$ mattheddleite $\pm$ goethite $\pm$ 'psilomelane' $\pm$ 'limonite' and many other species	Oxidation assemblages at Potts Gill, Roughton Gill, Driggith, Dry Gill, Red Gill, Brae Fell, Poddy Gill, Brandy Gill Lead mine etc.
ESE–WNW faults Uplift due to Hercynian Orogeny Olivine dolerite dykes	Upper Carboniferous to Permian c.290–230 Ma	Baryte $\pm$ quartz $\pm$ calcite $\pm$ galena	Potts Gill, Sandbeds
E–W to NE–SW normal faults End Devonian—L. Carboniferous earth movements Cockermouth lavas	? Lower Carboniferous c.360–330 Ma	Quartz $\pm$ chalcedony $\pm$ galena $\pm$ sphalerite $\pm$ chalcopyrite $\pm$ tetrahedrite $\pm$ pyrite $\pm$ native antimony $\pm$ bournonite $\pm$ calcite $\pm$ baryte $\pm$ dolomite $\pm$ fluorite	Roughton Gill, Driggith, Silver Gill, Red Gill, Brae Fell, Carrock E–W lead vein, etc.
N–S to NE–SW faults	? Lower to Upper Devonian	Quartz $\pm$ arsenopyrite $\pm$ stibnite $\pm$ fülöppite $\pm$ berthierite $\pm$ jamesonite $\pm$ zinckenite	Wet Swine Gill, Grainsgill
N–S faults	? Uncertain	Quartz $\pm$ 'psilomelane' $\pm$ pyrolusite $\pm$ manganite and other manganese minerals	Higher Brandy Gill, Burdell Gill, Arm o'Grain
N–S (to NNE–SSW and NNW–SSE) faults	Lower Devonian c.390–370 Ma	Quartz $\pm$ chlorite $\pm$ arsenopyrite $\pm$ pyrite $\pm$ chalcopyrite $\pm$ sphalerite $\pm$ galena	Potts Gill Copper vein, Carrock End, Hay Gill
Intrusion of Skiddaw Granite at c.400 Ma End of Caledonian orogeny		Quartz $\pm$ muscovite $\pm$ apatite $\pm$ wolframite $\pm$ scheelite $\pm$ arsenopyrite $\pm$ $\pm$ pyrrhotine $\pm$ columbite $\pm$ chalcopyrite $\pm$ cubanite $\pm$ native bismuth $\pm$ bismuthinite $\pm$ bismuth sulphotellurides $\pm$ sphalerite $\pm$ ankerite	Carrock N–S tungsten veins

Skiddaw Granite in Grainsgill, passing northwards successively through cordierite–andalusite hornfels (contact metamorphosed Skiddaw Group slates) and altered gabbros, diabase, and granophyre of the Carrock Fell Igneous Complex. The veins are of the order of 0.75–2 m thick in the greisen of Grainsgill, have sharp well-defined margins and appear to have formed in open fractures rather than normal faults; in the gabbros the veins are thinner and strongly braided. South of Grainsgill, tungsten values fall off rapidly outside the area of greisening on the flank of Coomb Height, while to the north Shepherd & Waters (1984) suggest a limit to the economic mineralization 500–600 m north of the granite contact where the veins split into strings, approximately half way up Brandy Gill on the surface.

Broadly, the sequence of deposition is as described by Hitchen (1934) with early quartz vein formation and the growth of wolframite in sometimes thick blade-like crystals from vein margins into the vein (Fig. 12), followed by sulphide, sulpharsenide and, finally, carbonate deposition. Ball, Fortey & Shepherd (1985) refined this sequence and suggested that, initially, quartz, wolframite, apatite, muscovite, sericite and minor scheelite were deposited in

open fractures. Subsequently, scheelite, pyrite. arsenopyrite, chalcopyrite, pyrrhotine, cubanite, molybdenite, sphalerite, native bismuth, bismuthinite, and bismuth sulphotellurides formed. Finally, a carbonate-dominated mineralization with 'ankerite' or ferroan dolomite was deposited in vughs in the main veins and in cross-cutting faults.

The mineralization is no older than Lower Devonian: Shepherd et al. (1976) obtained isotopic (K–Ar) ages of 386 and 388 $\pm$ 6 Ma on muscovite from barren quartz veins thought to represent the earlier phases of vein mineralization (Hitchen, 1934). A U–Pb isotopic date of 375 $\pm$ 10 Ma obtained on uraninite from greisenized wall rock (Beddoe-Stephens in Ball et al., 1985) is in reasonable agreement with this.

2 CHALCOPYRITE–PYRITE–ARSENOPYRITE VEINS

The Hay Gill, Carrock End and Potts Gill copper veins lie outside the aureole of the Skiddaw Granite and away from its immediate influence. However, mineralization here is probably of similar age to that at Carrock mine and occurs predominantly in N–S to NNW–SSE fractures. It is characterized by simple primary mineral assemblages of quartz, pyrite and chalcopyrite, with or without arseno-pyrite, and apparently lacking tungstates, molybdenite and bismuth sulphotellurides. Elsewhere in the Lake District similar veins have been important producers of copper, notably at Coniston and in the Vale of Newlands, south-west of Keswick (Stanley & Vaughan, 1982).

3 MANGANESE VEINS

At the northern end of Brandy Gill, the N–S veins mined for tungsten in Grainsgill are barren and consist of quartz with pyrolusite, 'psilomelane' and other manganese minerals. South of Grainsgill, manganese-bearing veins occur in Wet Swine Gill (Shepherd & Waters, 1984) and Burdell Gill. Other occurrences are N–S veins in Arm o'Grain and Poddy Gill, and in the E–W Dry Gill vein. The manganese oxides from the N–S veins carry significant arsenic and tungsten values (Hitchen, 1934; Appleton & Wadge, 1976), and are considered by several authors to represent an outer fringe of

the wolframite–scheelite mineralization (Hitchen, 1934; Eastwood et al., 1968; Shepherd & Waters, 1984). However, some at least of the manganese mineralization in Dry Gill is undoubtedly later than the formation of secondary lead phosphate and arsenate minerals (see below) and there may have been more than one period of manganese mineralization.

4 ANTIMONY MINERALIZATION

Stibnite was listed from 'Carrock Fells' by Greg & Lettsom in 1858, but Kingsbury & Hartley (1956b) suggested that zinckenite, jamesonite and boulangerite were more common than stibnite at Carrock mine, and that they may have been mistakenly identified for it. These sulphosalts were found in quartz stringers cutting the greisen in Grainsgill. Stanley & Vaughan (1981) described native antimony, bournonite, and tetrahedrite as early minerals in many of the lead–zinc veins and suggested that the antimony mineralization of the area, although of

Fig. 13 CARROCK MINE AND BRANDY GILL: view north to Carrock mine and beyond up Brandy Gill in August 1976. Carrock mine worked three major N–S veins; surface workings on two of these can be seen to the west (Harding vein) and to the east (Emerson vein) of Brandy Gill.

uncertain age, is likely to pre-date the lead–zinc mineralization. This relative chronology is supported by the recently described antimony mineralization in Wet Swine Gill (Fortey, Ingham, Skilton, Young & Shepherd, 1984) where an early Sb–Fe–As assemblage (arsenopyrite–stibnite–berthierite) gives way to an Sb–Pb assemblage (zinckenite–fülöppite–semseyite). Additional minor antimony occurrences are given below.

5 LEAD–ZINC MINERALIZATION

Economically and historically this has proved the most important of the various types of mineralization in the Caldbeck Fells. The veins generally have an E–W or NE–SW direction with a primary mineral assemblage of galena, sphalerite and chalcopyrite in a quartz matrix. Minor amounts of native antimony, bournonite and tetrahedrite occur as inclusions in galena (see above) together with pyrite. That this area in particular was known for its

'antimonial lead deposits' is recorded in Lysons & Lysons (1816) and it may well have been the antimony in the Caldbeck Fells ores that the master smelter Joachim Gaunse referred to in 1581 as one of the nine 'infectyve and evil humours' present in copper ore worked by the Company of Mines Royal. The actual source of the ores was not specified (Abrahams, 1899–1901).

Unlike the well known deposits of the Alston area which have a similar sulphide mineralogy, fluorite is known only from Carrock mine in the Caldbeck Fells and is generally uncommon elsewhere in the Lake District. Carbonate gangue minerals are, likewise, not common although some calcite and dolomite occur in the Roughton Gill South vein and in the Carrock E–W vein.

The veins are almost entirely in rocks of the Eycott Group and the Carrock Fell Igneous Complex. In general, the Lake District lead–zinc mineralization is thought to have an early Carboniferous age of $c.360–330\,\mathrm{Ma}$

Fig. 14 CARROCK E–W LEAD VEIN: seen here in a drive on the Harding vein ('Canadian' level) of Carrock mine, the vein is 1 m wide with brecciated hornfels wall rocks; it contains thin (1–2 mm) stringers of galena and sphalerite in a gangue of quartz and dolomite.

(Stanley & Vaughan, 1982), however, isotopic ages obtained from the Caldbeck Fells deposits are not in agreement with this: Moorbath (1962), using lead isotope data from galena, obtained ages of 210 ± 70 Ma for the Carrock mine E–W vein; 220 ± 40 Ma for Roughton Gill; and 260 ± 90 Ma for Driggith. Ineson & Mitchell's (1974) K–Ar isotopic ages from wall-rock illites gave a range from $178-231$ Ma. The variability of these ages may reflect either the episodic nature of the lead–zinc mineralization of the area, or the dubious authenticity of isotopic ages derived from galenas and wall-rock illites in areas which have undergone widespread alteration. Unfortunately, the only direct evidence of age for the lead–zinc mineralization is relative, in that it is later than the tungsten mineralization in Grainsgill, where the N–S tungsten veins are cut and displaced by E–W lead–zinc veins. Also, with baryte appearing in vughs or in the centres of several of the lead–zinc veins, it seems likely that the latter formed before the major Potts Gill and Sandbeds baryte veins.

6 BARYTE MINERALIZATION

Quartz, carbonates, and galena are minor constituents of the large (<1.5 m wide) baryte veins at Potts Gill and Sandbeds. These predominantly ESE–WNW veins lie outside the area of intense alteration around Roughton Gill and High Pike and, although there is 'considerable decomposition of the country rock' (Eastwood et al., 1968: 241) in the immediate vicinity of the veins, this appears to be directly related to the baryte mineralization rather than to be the result of later alteration. Therefore, the K–Ar ages ($249-229$ Ma) of wall rock illites, suggesting an Upper Carboniferous to Permian age (Ineson & Mitchell, 1974), may have more significance than the corresponding isotopic dates given for the lead–zinc mineralization. North of Caldbeck village, baryte occurs in joints in the Carboniferous Limestone.

7 ALTERATION ASSEMBLAGES

Assemblages of secondary lead, copper, and zinc minerals, mostly phosphates, arsenates, sulphates, and carbonates, occur in cavities in many of the lead–zinc veins particularly around Roughton Gill. It is possible that these alteration assemblages are related to a widespread pervasive sericitic alteration of the host rocks (notably the volcanic rocks of the Eycott Group in the High Pike area), and local kaolinization of the granophyre and Harestones Felsite of the Carrock Fell Igneous Complex. This alteration may be of Jurassic age as represented by the K–Ar ages of c.$190-180$ Ma obtained by Ineson & Mitchell (1974) on illites from Roughton Gill. Such alteration could also account for the type of chemical interaction found, for instance, in Brandy Gill where stolzite and arsenate minerals occur close to intersections of E–W lead veins with the N–S tungsten–arsenic veins.

Deposition of the metalliferous and gangue minerals in veins requires:

   i the availability of fractures.

   ii a heat source to circulate hot aqueous (hydrothermal) fluids; this is in general initially provided by magmatic activity and maintained by decay of radioactive minerals or by further pulses of magma.

   iii a source of metals, usually minerals in the wall rocks, that is susceptible to alteration by chemically active fluids thus releasing the metals into solution.

   iv a transport mechanism for the released metal cations such as chloride and bisulphide complexing agents.

   v a concentrating or precipitating mechanism resulting in ore deposition in the open fissures to form veins.

Samples of the hydrothermal fluids responsible for such mineralization became trapped during crystal growth and now form 'fluid inclusions' in the host mineral. Such inclusions are best examined in the transparent vein minerals such as quartz and fluorite and, using certain microscopic techniques, can give valuable information on the salinities, dissolved gas content and formation temperatures of the mineralizing fluids. The temperatures obtained directly from the microscope heating stage are referred to as homogenization temperatures and require pressure corrections to give the probable formation temperatures.

LOWER DEVONIAN MINERALIZATION

Evidence from fluid inclusions in minerals from the Carrock tungsten veins (Shepherd & Waters, 1984) suggests formation temperatures of c.$370°C$ for apatite and c.$305°C$ for quartz (assuming 800 bars pressure, Shepherd et al., 1976) with wolframite formation at intermediate temperatures. The salinities of the fluids are typically low with < 10 equiv. wt% NaCl and they have relatively high CO_2 contents.

Although no comparable data exist for the Lower Devonian copper veins of the Caldbeck Fells, Stanley & Vaughan (1982) suggest a lower range of temperatures from $200-350°C$ and, on the basis of fluid inclusion data (T. J. Shepherd, pers. comm.), salinities of $5-10$ equiv. wt% NaCl for other Lake District copper veins with a similar mineralogy.

The buried Lake District batholith, of which the partially exposed Skiddaw Granite is a part, has been shown to have high heat production capacity in this northern part of the Lake District (Lee, Brown, Webb, Wheildon & Rollin, 1987) and thus it is not too surprising that the earliest period of hydrothermal mineralization is directly related to the establishment of circulatory systems following granite emplacement. Most recent workers have recognized this: for example, Firman (1978) proposed that the granite batholith was the source of heat for the circulation of hydrothermal fluids through channelways in the country rocks and in the granites themselves; Stanley & Vaughan (1982) suggested that the Lower Devonian veins of the Lake District had a magmatic component dependent on their proximity to the granitic intrusions in addition to a non-magmatic component perhaps derived from metamorphosed black shales of the Skiddaw Group, or from the volcanic rocks of the Eycott, or Borrowdale Volcanic, Groups. At Carrock, Shepherd & Waters (1984) favour a magmatic origin for tungsten involving the melting and incorporation into the magma of tungsten-enriched volcanic rocks and associated sediments.

Quartz-manganese veins in Upper Brandy Gill, Wet Swine Gill, Poddy Gill, and Burdell Gill are considered to be an outer fringe of the tungsten mineralization (Shepherd & Waters, 1984) on the basis of their N–S trend, the presence of significant tungsten values in the manganese oxides, and gas analysis results from fluid inclusions in quartz, which show a close affinity with the late-stage quartz of the main Carrock tungsten veins.

ANTIMONY MINERALIZATION

Fluid inclusion studies on quartz associated with the Wet Swine Gill antimony mineralization indicate a range of homogenization temperatures of 166–287°C and a narrow range of salinities from 7–11 equiv. wt% NaCl (Fortey et al., 1984). The fluids differ from those of the tungsten mineralization in being CO_2-poor and possibly $MgCl_2$-rich. The low salinities are consistent with these veins being of roughly similar age to the Lower Devonian veins, although Fortey et al. (1984) suggest that the later antimony–lead assemblage at Wet Swine Gill may represent later remobilization of the earlier assemblage by lead-bearing fluids of the Carboniferous mineralization episode.

The source of the antimony is in some doubt. Certainly, the presence of Mg in the fluids might indicate leaching from a basic source rock such as the gabbros of the Carrock Fell Igneous Complex, the volcanic rocks and volcanic-derived sediments of the Eycott Group, or ashy Silurian rocks since removed by erosion.

LEAD–ZINC MINERALIZATION

Pale blue-green fluorite from the vughs in a vein breccia in the E–W galena–sphalerite–dolomite vein in Carrock mine contains fluid inclusions which yield homogenization temperatures of about 120°C (Stanley, 1979). Shepherd & Waters' (1984) data for their fluorite–carbonate stage of mineralization at Carrock are in good agreement with this; the salinities of the fluids are high, > 23 equiv. wt% NaCl, and are interpreted to consist of 12 wt% NaCl and 15 wt% $CaCl_2$. This represents a fundamental difference between the compositions of the fluids thought to have been involved in the deposition of the lead–zinc mineralization in this area and the earlier low-salinity, high-temperature fluids responsible for the tungsten and copper mineralization. Such a change could have occurred when fractures were opened — on uplift of the Lake District towards the end of the Devonian (Firman, 1978), or through tensional tectonic activity in the early Carboniferous — permitting the hydrothermal circulation of Carboniferous seawater (Stanley & Vaughan, 1982). Fluids of such contrasting composition might be expected to leach different sets of elements from the local country rocks.

LATER MINERALIZATION

Little work has been done on the baryte mineralization. Smith (1973) obtained homogenization temperatures of 122.3°C for inclusions in quartz from the Sandbeds baryte vein.

Fissures probably opened, or in some cases reopened (as baryte is commonly found in the centre of the lead–zinc veins) in response to Hercynian earth movements. As the Permian basins developed to the east and north of the Caldbeck Fells, concentrated sulphate-rich fluids could have been drawn into the area and circulated to leach barium and subsequently deposit baryte. The local, but extensive, alteration of the Eycott Group volcanic wall rocks adjacent to the Sandbeds and Potts Gill veins suggests such leaching has occurred here and thus these may have been the source of the barium.

The origin of the phosphate-, arsenate-, and sulphate-rich fluids which altered the primary mineralization of the Caldbeck Fells to form the assemblages of secondary lead and copper minerals is uncertain. One suggestion is that phosphate may have been leached from the predominantly igneous wall rocks with sulphate and arsenate minerals forming as a result of the decomposition of sulphides and sulpharsenides.

Later weathering by groundwater circulation would be facilitated by the higher permeability of the altered host rocks and permit the formation of late stage iron and manganese oxide minerals.

SUMMARY

The vein mineralization in the Caldbeck Fells area has recently been interpreted (e.g. Moore, 1982; O'Brien et al., 1985) as the result of several individual convective systems or 'hydrothermal cells', possibly of the type now active in modern geothermal fields such as Wairaki and Broadlands in New Zealand. Clearly, many years of erosion in the Caldbeck Fells have seen the removal of the upper levels of these fossil hydrothermal systems leaving only the mineralization at lower structural levels.

The most important factors in the establishment and maintenance of such hydrothermal cells are the presence of open fissures and channelways produced by tectonic activity, and a suitable source of heat to circulate the fluids. Ultimately, though, it is the extent of active tectonism which governs whether or not hydrothermal circulation can occur, since the sealing of fractures through ore and gangue mineral deposition progressively inhibits fluid flow and therefore such circulation is a declining geological process.

Within the small area of the Caldbeck Fells, a prolonged high heat flow regime and regular earth movements produced, or in some cases reactivated, fissures and led to the formation of successively lower temperature mineral deposits. It is clear from recent work in the North Pennines (Brown, Ixer, Plant & Webb, 1987) and in SW England (Durrance, Bromley, Bristow, Heath & Penman, 1982; Moore, 1982; Thorne & Edwards, 1985) that high heat flow regimes in these regions resulted in broadly similar sequences of hydrothermal mineralization.

MINES AND MINING

INTRODUCTION

The history of mining in the Caldbeck Fells is long, complex, and incomplete. New information on the work of the 'old men' (as miners traditionally call their predecessors) is still being discovered in archives around the country or on the fellsides themselves. There are scores of levels, shafts, and trials on the Caldbeck Fells; almost every gill contains a working of some sort and the fellsides are variously scarred with hushes*, leats†, prospects, and mine dumps. The excellent examples of hand-cut 'coffin-levels'‡ to be seen in some workings attest to the antiquity of the mines. Many of the smaller sites have long since become grassed over and are almost invisible to the inexperienced eye.

We cannot describe, or even list, all of the traces of mining on the fells, but the following review includes all those of economic or mineralogical importance. The larger sites are described in some detail, including the deposits worked, the extent of the mine (where known), and the important events in their history. Less information is given for the smaller sites or for those mines that produced little of interest to the collector. The National Grid Reference is given in square brackets after each locality.

Our knowledge of the early history of many of the mine workings is only fragmentary; the few records found in old archives give an incomplete picture and mining may, in some cases, have been more continuous than is suggested here. Even the nineteenth century records are imperfect; most frustrating is the lack of contemporary mine plans, drawings or photographs.

Fig. 15 'THE MYNES' AT 'CLADBECK': The activities of the Elizabethan Company of Mines Royal at Caldbeck ('Cladbeck') are shown here on one of the earliest published maps of Cumberland, that of the renowned cartographer John Speed, in *The Theatre of Great Britain Display'd* of 1610. At Keswick, the headquarters of the miners, one of the most advanced smelters in Europe had been built to process ore from Caldbeck and other Cumbrian mines. The precise location of many of the Elizabethan mines has been lost, for although detailed maps of the mines and smelt works are mentioned in contemporary documents none seem to have survived.

For further information the reader is referred to the general mining histories of Postlethwaite (1913), Shaw (1970), and Adams (1988), the last being a particularly useful field guide to the lesser sites and to the complex remains of the larger mines. The many writers who have discussed the activities of the Company of Mines Royal in sixteenth century Caldbeck are cited in the *Mining History* section.

The mineral deposits and their workings were reviewed for the Geological Survey by Carruthers, Eastwood, Wilson, Pocock & Wray (1915), Dewey & Dines (1923), Dewey & Eastwood (1925), Dunham & Dines (1945), Eastwood (1921) and Wilson, Eastwood, Pocock, Wray & Robertson (1922). Their future prospects were discussed in Eastwood (1959) and the output figures, ownership, and workforce details published from 1845–1913 have been collated by Burt, Waite & Burnley (1982); the period 1848–1881 is also dealt with in Lawson (1972).

The more determined researcher may wish to consult original documents, letters, and reports produced by the mine operators: a brief discussion of public archives with important holdings of Caldbeck mining documentation is given in the bibliography.

MINING HISTORY

The heyday of the Caldbeck mines was in the nineteenth century but their origins are much further back in time. Many of the vein outcrops on the fells must have been clearly defined from the earliest period, their signs unmistakeable to ancient prospectors. The Romans are supposed to have exploited several Lake District metal

---

* *hushing* is an early prospecting technique in which the fellside was cleared to the bed rock by digging channels, down which a torrent of water was then diverted. The resulting gully is known as a 'hush',

† *leat* — a channel dug across a hillside to carry water from a stream or adit usually to an ore-dressing site where it was used to power machinery via a water wheel. Driggith and Carrock End mines suffered particularly from water shortages and long leats can be traced to them across the fellsides.

‡ *coffin levels* were cut through the solid rock by hand, using hammers, picks, and a series of iron wedges known as a 'stope and feather'. To save on the labour, only the minimum of rock would be cut away leaving the level wide at shoulder height and tapering to the roof and floor to give a coffin-shaped cross-section.

deposits and it has been suggested by Sir Ian Richmond (quoted in Pearsall & Pennington, 1973: 219) that the Roman fort at Caermote (on the Carlisle–Keswick road about 10 km west of Roughton Gill) controlled lead mining interests in the Caldbeck Fells. There is, unfortunately, no direct evidence to substantiate this, but part of the ancient east–west highway through Caldbeck ('the old King's road' as it was called in 1219) is known as 'The Street' which suggests a Roman connection (Last, 1945).

Shaw (1970) states that the Caldbeck mines may have been worked in the twelfth century — there was a heightened demand for lead for building at this time — and goes on to make the perhaps more historical claim that the silver–lead mines of 'Silver Beck and Minersdale', referred to in a fourteenth century charter of Edward III, were those of Silver Gill and the Dale Beck valley in Caldbeck. There are many references to Cumbrian mines in such early charters and estate papers: 'the mine at Keswick' and 'the silver mine of Carlisle' figure prominently but these are workings in the Newlands valley (Bean, 1958) and on Alston Moor (Walton, 1946) respectively. It is not until 1537 that there is actual documentary evidence of mining in Caldbeck when the presence of a valuable silver mine in the parish (and of another in Braithwaite to the south-west) is stressed in a report by a Royal Commission Survey of the northern estates (Bean, 1958: 51). These mines may also have been worked in the fifteenth century: the Duke of Northumberland, who owned the estates, appointed a Supervisor of mines in 1453 who was probably responsible for metal mines in the 'Skiddaw area' (i.e. the Caldbeck Fells and adjoining districts). However, the available records do not show the extent of any working (Bean, op. cit.).

Although these tantalizing fragments of information suggest the possibility of a longer history of mining, the story can only truly begin in 1563 with the arrival of mining experts from Germany and the subsequent foundation of the Company of Mines Royal. Much has been written about this unprecedented enterprise and we can give below only a sketch of the Company's remarkable history, abstracting from an extensive literature such information as relates to the Caldbeck workings. Unfortunately, it has not been possible to examine all the numerous original documents extant in record offices and libraries throughout Great Britain. For a fuller discussion and for citations of Elizabethan papers the reader is referred to the contemporary accounts of Pettus (1670) and Stringer (1713), although due consideration must be given to these authors' vested interests when reading their claims; to the financial analysis by Scott (1911); to the technical considerations of Hamilton (1926); to the seminal work by Collingwood (1912) based on translations of the original German account books; and to the numerous lesser papers cited below. Donald (1955) gives an overview of the whole operation with extensive quotations from Elizabethan documents*; Hammersley's (1973) work is important for his view of the Company's decline.

In 1563 the German mining engineer and smelting expert Daniel Höchstetter came to England to prospect for metallic ores. He was a representative of the powerful finance house of Haug Langnauer and Company of Augsburg who had extensive mining interests elsewhere in Europe at Schwatz (Tyrol), Joachimstal (Bohemia) and Neusohl (Hungary). Germany had a long tradition of exporting her mineral skills to technically backward countries, and Great Britain was certainly lacking in such expertise at that time. Indeed, Höchstetter's father, Joachim, had been involved in gold mining in Scotland in 1526 and was surveyor of mines to Henry VIII in 1528. The latter association ended abruptly in 1529 when the profligate Joachim returned to Germany following the collapse of the Scottish mining enterprise and the failure of his family's firm in Germany. He then became involved in the Neusohl mines but Donald (1955: 36) suggests he may have returned to Germany in part to grab what he could of the assets of the failing company.

Political, economic and religious problems were prominent throughout Europe during the reign of Elizabeth I. The development of Britain's indigenous resources would have been beneficial to national security and the promotion of home industry. The expansion of metal mining would have the additional advantage of improved royalties due to the Crown particularly through the privilege of Mines Royal whereby the output of precious metals from any mine automatically became a Royal prerogative.

Grants were made to Daniel Höchstetter, Thomas Thurland (Master of the Savoy Hospital), William Humphreys (Assay Master at the Mint), Thomas Smythe (Collector of Customs in the Port of London) and others authorizing them to 'search, dig, try, roast, and melt all manner of mines and ures of gold, silver, copper, and quicksilver' in Cumberland, Cornwall, Wales and elsewhere. That the Crown reserved 'preferment in the Bying of all Pretious stones or pearl [!] . . . found in the working of these mines' (Collingwood, 1910: 370) demonstrates England's need for expert guidance. The findings, particularly in Cumberland, were highly praised by Höchstetter on his return to Germany. Haug Langnauer expected sole rights to the British mines but Sir William Cecil, the Home Secretary, was advised it would be prudent to include some English shareholders. Consequently, in 1564, an indenture was signed between the Queen, Höchstetter

---

* It should be noted, however, that Donald had the unfortunate habit of 'improving' the language of his transcripts, thus losing much of the flavour and occasionally the meaning, of the Elizabethan originals.

Fig. 16 SILVER GILL: interior of a well preserved hand-cut 'coffin-level' cross-cut to the Silver Gill vein in the east side of Silver Gill. The neatly spaced pickmarks of the 'old men' can easily be seen on the left-hand wall and the roof. This beautifully worked level, probably dating from the seventeenth century or earlier, has been widened by nineteenth century blasting where it meets the vein. The workings are now collapsed.

Fig. 17 THE ARMS OF THE SOCIETY OF THE MINES ROYAL: given Aug. 26 1568. Anno 10. Eliz. As they are Blazon'd.

Silver with a Mount Vert. A Man working within a Mine, with two Hammers and a Lamp, all in their proper colours on a Chief Azure. A cake of Copper between a Bezant and a Plate on a Wreath Silver and Azure. A Demy man (called in Dutch the Schicht Master) with an Escocheon on his Breast Or and Azure per Bend inverted; in one of his Hands an Instrument called a Wedge, and in the other Hand a Compass, Gold mantled, Silver doubled Azure, supported with two Men, the one called the Hammer-man, with a Hammer on his Shoulder; and the other the Smelter, with a Fork in his Hand; all in proper colours. (From Pettus, 1670: 22–23; in this work the Arms of the Society of the Mines Royal and the Arms of the Society for the Mineral and Battery works have been inadvertently transposed.)

and Thurland, and 24 shares were distributed between the Germans and various English businessmen, aristocrats and statesmen including Cecil himself. The 14 shares sold in England cost their holders £1200 each (Collingwood, 1928).

Höchstetter's grants gave the prospectors extensive privileges and allowed the Crown the right to buy metals at advantageous prices. They also admonished the miners not to work 'under castles, nor in houses, gardens or orchards' without the goodwill of the owner. One landowner whose goodwill they did not have was Percy, Earl of Northumberland, who, in 1566, objected to the mines on his estates—particularly 'God's Gift'* the rich copper mine at Newlands in Derwentfells—being declared Mines Royal because of their alleged gold content. The arguments of the Crown against Northumberland were heard in a famous court case before all the judges of England and the Barons of the Exchequer. Northumberland's case was carefully argued but, despite the lack of

* The original German name 'Gottes Gab' (God's Gift) has since been corrupted to 'Goldscope'.

proof of the precious metal content of the predominantly copper-bearing ores, the Crown's case was upheld. This judgment gave great strength to the principle of Mines Royal and was not to be reversed until the Mines Royal Act was passed in 1693. Northumberland's final skirmish with the crown had a more permanent conclusion: following his involvement in an attempt to place the Catholic Mary Queen of Scots on the throne, he was beheaded in 1572.

After the judgment of 1568, Höchstetter and his associates were incorporated as the 'Governors, Assistants, and Commonality of the Company of Mines Royal' (Collingwood, 1912), the first company of its kind to be set up in England. In the preceding four years, with the help of miners and smelters brought from Germany, they had begun work on many mines in the Lake District, particularly at Newlands and Caldbeck. The 'Kolbeckh' mines are mentioned in the German accounts for the first time in 1566 when £55 was spent on them. In all, seven Caldbeck mines are named in the accounts (e.g. St Emanuel, Lower Nick, New Adit and Fortune's Adit) but cannot now be assigned to any particular working (Collingwood, 1912: 12). A report made in 1602 by Company agents Bowes and Nedham (see below) makes it clear that these mines had been worked 'before these Germans comeing to Keswick' (Collingwood, 1912: 14).

Ore samples were sent to Germany for assay and, following favourable results, the construction of a smelter was begun at Brigham on the River Greta near Keswick. The lease for this site survives (see Crosthwaite, 1883). The smelter and its asssociated works were to become the largest in Europe and 'maintained no less than 4000 Artificers and Labourers daily' according to Pettus (1670: 32), although this figure must include associated outworkers throughout the county. 'The smelting houses were so many that they looked like a little town...' wrote Sir Daniel Fleming in 1671 (Ferguson, 1889: 13); with their 'forcible Stream, and their inventions... for easy Bellows-work, Hammer-works, Forge-works, and sawing of boards' admired by all who saw them (Holland, 1610).

The German experts had many problems to contend with: the localities were remote, they were assailed by floods, drought, and bitter cold that froze their water wheels; the ores were complex and difficult to smelt (Abrahams, 1899–1901; Graves, 1928); supplies of raw materials, particularly wood, were scarce and expensive, partly due to profiteering by local landowners and partly through the prodigious cost of overland transport. In addition there was distrust and discord amongst the English shareholders and intense local prejudice against the 'Almaynes' or 'Dutchmen', as the immigrant miners were called, which on at least one occasion erupted in violence and murder. The interference by the Earl of Northumberland has already been mentioned. The

Germans were accused of concealing the proper value of the minerals, or of incompetence in smelting, but there was also disagreement amongst the English as to their true worth. Thomas Thurland, one of the initiators of the mining enterprise, was arrested several times for personal debts and financial irregularities (including the pawning of silver from St Paul's Cathedral). Humphreys left the partnership in 1565 to set up the Society of the Mineral and Battery Works (Scott, 1911: Vol. 2, 413–429; Donald, 1961) having previously complained to Cecil: 'I say unto you most instantly that every cwt. of that copper ore holds more pounds in every cwt. that they [i.e. Höchstetter and others] have written in ounces' (Donald, 1955).

Nevertheless, mining, smelting, and construction carried on. Much money was being spent on the enterprise and, although no profit was forthcoming, the economy of the region was expanding rapidly. Many hundreds of men, women, and children worked as miners and labourers (though the former were mostly the more experienced Germans), as suppliers of wood, charcoal, peat, building materials, and transport. Local prejudice against the Germans abated and the immigrants began to marry into the Keswick community. Surnames of Germanic origin still survive in the district (see Crosthwaite, 1876; 1883; Collingwood, 1910; 1912).

The year 1567 was important: in September, Höchstetter wrote to Elizabeth I: 'Although ... we have found it a great and chargeable enterprise to set up and erect the perfect making of copper, we have now (at the last) attained to the perfection thereof. But as the natures of the ores thereof here gotten ... do differ much from others the like in other countries, and also in themselves, here differ from one another, so has it compelled us to have spent more time in bringing to pass that which is now done than we ourselves did make account of in the beginning. It may please your majesty the 19 day of this month of September we obtained the perfect finishing of some copper.' The process took 18 weeks and 5 days, and involved 16–18 separate firings to make 70 cwt. [c.3.5 tonnes] of 'good malleable copper' (Donald, 1955; see also Graves, 1928).

The Caldbeck ores were particularly troublesome: George Nedham wrote in 1581 'of the riche Copper ure gotten in the mynes of Caldbeck being enfected with such Corruptions, that hetherto Mr Danyell or his sonn Coulde never smelt them alone ... but were forced to myngle them with rosted stone of the first smelting of godes gifte ure' (Abrahams, 1899–1901). The lead–silver ores were likewise difficult to process and much metal was lost. In 1579, 'Certaine leade yewres gotten in Caldbeck' were used to test processes newly-developed to smelt ores brought by Martin Frobisher from 'Meta Incognita' in the New World (McDermott, 1986). The roasting process invented by Henry Pope proved useful but Frobisher's

gold ore appears to have been worthless ultrabasic rock. The Caldbeck lead ores were primarily of interest for their silver content; the lead was also useful for extracting silver from copper ores although a German assay of 1567 claimed that the low silver content of the Cumbrian copper ores would not pay the expense of extracting it. An interesting observation in the light of the court case with Northumberland.

Extravagant claims of the potential value of copper, silver, and gold (over £13 000 a year) were not being met by actual output. There was no gold; the silver furnace was dogged by problems. In a good year the company would realise only £4000. Moreover, sales were very slow. Calls on shareholders for more money failed to raise the full amount: by 1569 an extra £850 per share had been demanded to meet the heavy development costs and fees for the court case but thereafter 'the English partners seeing no hope of profitt, but great Charges & continuall Disbursements contrary to their Expectations ... stay'd their hands from further Disbursements' (Collingwood, 1928: 25). The company was more than £22 000 in the red. Höchstetter tried various ways to sell copper and restore confidence (Scott, 1911: Vol. 2, 388–394), but with only limited and belated success. The most promising outlet was through the manufacture of beaten copper and brass ware (battery ware) and, accordingly, a permit was obtained in 1575 from the Mineral and Battery works who held the monopoly for brass making and battery. Yet more expense was incurred in setting up the new metal-working machinery.

These new and promising developments came too late for the German partners. In 1570 a distracted Hans Langnauer, his credit fast waning, wrote to Hans Loner the Company's London agent 'I beseech you ... explain our distress to the Queen, and Mr. Secretary, and the Earl of Leicester, and beg them to justify the confidence with which we ventured into this labyrinth with our own and other people's money ... Believe me I don't know what to do ... nobody who has not been in the business with me can believe — Ach Gott! — how frightened I am, I would rather be dead than lose credit like this' (Collingwood, 1912: 97). The shortage of money was so acute in 1572 that the mines were on the point of closure. Loner wrote to Sir William Cecil (the then Lord Burghley): 'The copper lies dead upon our hands and in the meantime the works suffer great loss and hindrance through lack of money'. As proof of the potential of the mines he enclosed an ingot of silver 'gotten in the mines at Caldbeck' (Donald, 1955). There was to be no improvement: Haug Langnauer and Company failed in 1574 and were taken over by their creditors. By 1576 the debt of the Company of Mines Royal had risen to £32 000; Hans Loner was dismissed, accused of incompetence.

In 1577, the German financiers withdrew completely leaving the Company in the hands of the English shareholders and such of the Germans who chose to remain. Chief amongst the latter was Daniel Höchstetter, whose family had joined him in Keswick in 1571. Why he chose to remain is not clear; he was perhaps committed morally and financially to the Keswick works (see Collingwood, 1928: 25) and considered that the elusive commercial success was within his grasp. His critics considered his motives to have been less altruistic: accusations of profit-taking were renewed and the Company obtained an independent assay of the Cumberland ores but nothing came of the over-optimistic result.

Acting on a suggestion by Höchstetter, the Society leased the mines to Thomas Smythe (one of the original prospectors) and himself in 1580 for a period of five years. This enabled the Company to make money on rents and transfer the financial burden of running the mines on to the lessees. The partners appear to have done well enough to pay off past debts (Collingwood, 1928). Daniel Höchstetter died in 1581 and was succeeded by his son Emanuel and son-in-law Mark Steinberger. An inventory of the Cumbrian mines was made in 1580 and showed the Caldbeck workings to be idle at that time: at 'the foote of the gill of the meynes', the stamping house, 'the walls of lime and stone builded with good timber and slated over' was 'decayed for lack of occupying' (Donald, 1955).

The report of George Nedham in 1581 also comments: 'the rich leade myne at Caldbeck, w'ch houldeth good quantity of silver, and hath cost the company great sommes of mony: Lieth now unwrought' but went on to say that newly improved smelting techniques would ensure 'great gaynes' should it be reopened. These new techniques, developed by Nedham's colleague Joachim Gaunse, promised much improved efficiency but do not seem to have been adopted at Keswick (Abrahams, 1899–1901).

Details of the mines are scanty during the turmoil of the following years. Thomas Smythe became increasingly interested in developing copper mines in Cornwall and Wales and lost a great deal of money in the process. Presumably, the Höchstetters (Daniel junior joined his brother Emanuel in 1597) and Steinberger carried on at Keswick. They took out new leases in 1590 and 1597, the year in which an epidemic decimated the Keswick population (Crosthwaite, 1876). A commission sent by the Company in 1600 recommended certain improvements at Caldbeck and God's Gift; and a second commission in 1602, led by George Bowes and Francis Nedham (son of George Nedham) viewed the new work. Two transcripts of their long and detailed report have been published* (Collingwood, 1928; Wildridge, 1975). Bowes and Nedham found the Caldbeck mines being cleaned out: 'the Stamping House, the Washing Boards and Sumpths, which were greatly decayed . . . [are now set] in reasonable good repair for they have taken down almost halfe of the washing-house and two of the washing tables by reason there was little or small use for so many'. Of the three levels they examined, the lowest (New Stoln [Stoln from the German Stollen = adit]) and one above it (Emanuel Stoln) were in reasonable repair but Fortune's Stoln was 'wholly decayed'. Very rich silver ore had formerly been won from the New Stoln. Bowes and Nedham considered that further rich ore could be raised by cutting a new lower level to drain the ground below New Stoln or by hushing the ground 'to discover the Veins in the topp about the Lodgeing-house of the Miners'. The lessees were more pessimistic and complained that they 'have no hope of comfort in this work of Caudbeck, but think the cost . . . bestowed there utterly lost'. George Bowes was later 'bruised to death' in an accident in 'the deepe pits' at Keswick in which Daniel Höchstetter [Jr] was also injured (Atkinson, 1619).

At about this time the rich deposits at Coniston in the south of the county were discovered (or rediscovered) and Davies (1693) suggested that many men were transferred there from Caldbeck and elsewhere.

By 1618, at the latest, Caldbeck was back in work again: Hammersley (1973: 13) quotes a letter to the Governors of the Mines Royal 'For Caudbeck wee found yt full as good as we left it and Rather better' yet the New and Emanuel workings were still troubled with water and again the need for a lower level was raised.

Although heavy losses had been sustained in the closing decades of the sixteenth century the Höchstetter brothers (and later Emanuel's son Joseph) were now managing to show a profit. They were selling, from various sources, over £2000 worth of copper a year from 1601 to 1624 and, in the same period, had produced 1363 pounds $10\frac{1}{2}$ ounces of silver from the Caldbeck mines. Hammersley (1973: 13) estimates their profits as, at most, £350 a year, the equivalent of a 'solid country gentleman', and hardly sufficient to accommodate large development costs or reversals in their fortunes due to accidents or the inhospitable climate.

The Höchstetters continued working in Cumberland through the 1630s but seem to have closed the Caldbeck mines sometimes before this. In 1630 (following the chronology of Hammersley above) the mines were reported as 'left and given over' and the proposed new low level was still not driven. An estimate for this new level, 15 fathoms below New Stoln was for a cross-cut 43 fathoms through hard rock to reach the vein 'being wrought upon night & day by 3 pickmen everyone working 8 hours will nearly finish it in 12 months and

*These transcripts appear to be copies of a mixture of items: the original of the 1602 report is not known. The MSS are dated 1616 but Collingwood and Wildridge date them on internal evidence to 1600. Donald (1955) and Hammersley (1973) date them as 1602; moreover the last section of the MSS 'A true report of Caudebeck Mines . . .' is dated by Hammersley (op. cit.: 13) to 1630.

that will cost at the least £129' (Collingwood, 1928: 26).

At the outbreak of the Civil War in 1642 the Keswick mines and works were closed. In 1649 the Company of Mines Royal noted that the Keswick works were 'ruinated and spoyld since the beginning of these troubles'. Just what had happened is open to debate. The received wisdom is that the mines and works were broken down and the miners killed or conscripted by Cromwell's army but this is not substantiated by contemporary observation or claims for compensation. It appears likely that the mining enterprise was already considerably run down, or even halted, before the war began. In Pettus' (1670: 32) view, the collapse was due to 'the death of the first German Artizans, and the neglect of a continued stock, and the want of Fuel in those parts, and the succeeding wars'. Each of these elements has been expounded by later historians. Hammersley (1973) considered that the failure of the third generation Germans to build on the technical and mercantile genius of the elder Höchstetters was enough to destabilize the fragile business. He argues that the collapse of the Company of Mines Royal was of no great surprise: more remarkable is how they kept going for so long in view of their considerable difficulties in winning and smelting what were, by continental standards, poor and difficult ores, in a remote area, at a time when the market for their principal product was so depressed.

During the war the Royalist sympathies of the major shareholders militated against the Company; in addition the Keswick works were on land owned by the Catholic Radcliffes whose estates were sequestered for 'recusancy and delinquency' in 1650 (Thompson, 1904). On the other hand, the miners, at least those of German origin, were all Protestants and would thus be expected to lean to the Parliamentarians. Indeed, Nathaniel Nicholson, Daniel Höchstetter senior's grandson, was a Parliamentarian officer in the Civil War (Collingwood, 1910) and Daniel Höchstetter III was rector of Bolton near Caldbeck and witness, in 1642, to the 334 men of Caldbeck who made 'protestation of attachment to the Protestant faith' (Brown, 1921).

In 1675 Edmund Sandford wrote of the Brigham site: 'Heer was the bravest water mille of the dutch invented: Daniel and Manell [Emanuel] came from beyond seas in Queen Elizabeths Time for the smelting and fining of Cooper Ore: gott in the mountains here about: but now the woods are gone and the works decayed Though I thinke the mines be as much in the montains as ever they were' (Ferguson, 1890: 12). Sandford's comment on the woods is a significant one: each ton of ore smelted consumed a half-acre of trees in the form of charcoal and further supplies were required for building and mine timbering. The impact on the landscape of this deforestation must have been considerable. Hammersley (1973: 19) plays down the importance of fuel shortages

in the decline of the Mines Royal but his complex calculations take no account of the depletion of woodland for purposes other than smelting. The Höchstetters complained frequently of the lack of wood, or of peat due to wet weather. As early as 1615 the local timber shortage was so acute that Cumbrian iron works were restrained by law from using charcoal and many were forced to close down (Gentle & Feild, 1975). Nonetheless, for whatever reasons, the copper boom was over. Depopulated by the closure of the mines, the ravages of war and plague, Keswick was reduced to a single street (Bouch & Jones, 1961).

Dr Martin Lister of the Royal Society attempted to resurrect the Company of Mines Royal in 1683 and enquired of the local expert David Davies of Braithwaite as to the state of the Cumberland mines. Of Caldbeck, Davies replied 'there is no shafts in being ... at Caldbeck ... and if there hath been any, they are all filed [sic] up, and will be of no use ... There is part of an Addit wrought, but how much it wants to be finished I know not'. At that time he could find no miner alive that 'did work in those mines; and if there are any, they are so old that they are not capable to direct others'. He considered an expenditure of £10 000 over 6–7 years necessary to set the mines to work again, but that this would be a much more efficient venture than under 'Hextecher's' management, when, he says, 'the mines might have been wrought with one third [of the outlay] to better purpose' (Davies, 1693). This view of the work necessary to reopen the Caldbeck mines may have dissuaded potential operators, for the major thrust of development seems to have been towards Coniston and Newlands, although neither was successful at the time (Grant, 1985).

In 1692 the newly formed Company of Royal Mines, Copper leased mines at Caldbeck and, by 1698, was smelting ore at 'the copper works, Corbeck' (Jenkins, 1938). Dr Edward Wright of the company was experimenting with smelting using coal and may have smelted lead slags at Caldbeck (Grant, 1985: 145), besides mining copper at Carrock End mine (Shaw, 1970: 47). The Company surrendered the leases in 1698, but lead ore from 'Caudbeck' is mentioned in their accounts in 1702 (Jenkins, ibid.).

In the 1690s, there was a great deal of speculative investment in metal mining in Great Britain. Of particular note were the rich silver–lead mines of Esgair-Hir in Wales from which large profits were made. The positive effects of this boom were, however, largely outweighed by subsequent large-scale fraud by the mine owners (see Scott, 1911:443; Lewis, 1967:74). One side-effect of the numerous controversies surrounding this enterprise was the overthrow of the Mines Royal monopoly following a court case over mineral rights. The political climate no longer favoured the old company and, despite the fact that silver-poor ore samples, possibly from Derbyshire (Stringer, 1713), were substituted in evidence for highly argentiferous Welsh ore, the courts found in favour of the miners. The Mines Royal Act of 1693 closed the door on the 1568 right of Mines Royal. Henceforth, landowners were able to develop their own mines free from what Heton (1707) melodramatically described as 'the Terror of the Mines Royal'. This freedom is often seen as a prime reason for the subsequent increase of interest in metal mining although, as pointed out by Hammersley (1973: 18), the depressive effect of the old monopoly was probably over-rated. More important in the resurgence of mining were to be the technical improvements of the age*: the development of smelting with coal and the reverberatory furnace (Grant-Francis, 1881; Hamilton, 1926); the invention of efficient pumps to dewater mines and the increasing use of gunpowder (Burt, 1982a); and improvements in ore dressing technology (Burt, 1982b). All of these provided a great stimulus to the stagnant mining industry.

In the early eighteenth century there was considerable interest in the Caldbeck mines, but available evidence is fragmentary. A report of c.1700 by one Anthony Pratt (MS) gives a general review of many Caldbeck properties including Red Gill, Sandbeds, Driggith, Silver Gill, and Carrock End ('Dutchman's Moss') as well as several lesser or unidentified sites including the oddly-named 'Knockerhole' near Red Gill. Subsequent, or concurrent, interest is demonstrated by crude sketch maps of 'The Great Lead Silver Mine of Golden [H]ugh and Silver Gill' in 1710 (Walker, MS) and of ' . . . Brandygills Vein and Workings' in 1724 (Benson MSS, D/Ben/3120) by Thomas Hillary who was mine agent to the Duke of Wharton, then owner of the land and mineral rights in the manor of Caldbeck. Hillary worked mines at Brandy Gill, Red Gill, Long Grain, 'Burch' [Birk?] Gill, Silver Gill, Golden Hugh, Driggith, Todd Gill, 'Yalld Stele' [Yard Steel?], and 'Duchmoss'. Wharton's agents may have worked the Caldbeck mines from 1722 to 1730 or there-abouts (see below under Brandy Gill) but the only proof of mining during this period is that contained in the ac-counts kept by Hillary from September 1724 to December 1726 for the mines and trials mentioned above (Benson MSS, D/Ben/3116–3122). In July 1726, Wharton's Head Agent, Thomas Smales, instructed Hillary to 'Give Over the Worke' at Brandy Gill and Long Grain, but

---

* For an overview see Hunt (1884). The techniques used by the Elizabethan miners are probably similar to those described in elaborate detail in the contemporary book by Agricola (1556). The developments of geological knowledge and mining technology in sixteenth and seventeeth century England are reviewed by Scott (1972; 1973).

Fig. 18 DAILY MAIL: Saturday 5 August 1899. A typical 'puff' or overstatement of the case in an attempt to attract venture capital into a speculative mining project. The reference to 'wolfram' and the other minerals places the locality firmly in the Caldbeck Fells.

ROMANCE OF A MINE.

A DISCOVERY THAT MAY MAKE CUMBERLAND'S FORTUNE.

("Daily Mail" Special.)

Quite a romance encircles a mining dis-covery which has recently been made on the Cumberland hills.

For the past quarter of a century an elderly gentleman named Bird has paid periodic visits to these hills. His relatives evinced some surprise at the persistency of his visits, and were inclined to laugh at the suggestion that the county contained rich mineral mines which merely wanted exploit-ing.

Mr. Bird was originally largely influenced in his researches by the folklore of the dis-trict, but on examination of the mountain-ous region in and about Penrith, he gradu-ally satisfied himself that the trace of minerals was sufficient to warrant him in pursuing his investigations more thoroughly.

In the meantime he was written down as a mining maniac by those most closely con-nected with him, but in spite of it all he persevered, and sometime ago he took into his confidence Professor Grey, the well-known analyst, and a mining engineer named Wm. Hastings, a man of over thirty years' experience.

In November last the trio began a series of mining experiments, which gave such results that they sought and obtained a lease of a stretch of land about five square miles in area.

This property has since been exploited in various directions, and the adits have shown results which read more like a chap-ter from the "Arabian Nights" than an actuality.

The veins which have been sampled show that the galena ore contains nearly 82 per cent. of lead, carrying

13¼ OUNCES OF SILVER PER TON,

the iron-stone which can be quarried works out at 36 per cent. of iron, the copper pro-duce is 13 per cent., partly carbonate and partially sulphide, the tin ore shows 24 per cent. of pure metal, while antimony averages 36 per cent., arsenic is present in the pro-portion of 45 per cent., and wolfram carries over 60 per cent.

The discovery has not unnaturally created a good deal of stir among mining experts and big metal men.

In the opinion of those who have surveyed the district Cumberland and Westmorland are considered to be in their infancy in re-gard to mining industry, and the discoveries of the last few months have convinced many metallurgical authorities that the counties of Westmorland and Cumberland are des-tined to become perhaps the richest mining districts in the world.

Mr. Charles Cotterill, of Birmingham, who has been directing the investigations, in-forms our Birmingham correspondent that the discovery will give a new lease of life to the mining industry of this country.

Wolfram, which is becoming a scarce com-modity and which plays such a prominent part in steel manufacture, has already at-tracted the attention of Continental manu-facturers. Indeed, a firm in Hanover was anxious to land an order for 200 tons at once.

The railway company having lines in the vicinity of the mines have notified their willingness to spend £10,000 in order to faci-litate the work of getting the ores, which appear to be so plentiful and rich.

Driggith and the Golden Hugh were continued, the latter 'being our Greatest hopes' (Benson MSS, D/Ben/3119). The subsequent history of Hillary's exploitation of the Caldbeck deposits is unknown but in 1747 a traveller observed: '... in Brandlegillbeck [Brandy Gill] and the Northern descents [of the Caldbeck Fells], copper has formerly been dug, but the mines are long since worn out.' (Anon, 1747). Some time after this the land and mineral rights passed separately to the Earl of Egremont and to Lord Pomfret respectively and, although Pomfret is reputed to have allowed a trial to be made at Arm o'Grain about 1774, nothing further is known of the Caldbeck mines until the 1790s by which time smelters were at work at both Roughton Gill and Driggith, no doubt stimulated by the increased demand for lead resulting from the French and Napoleonic Wars and other factors (see Burt, 1984). By the turn of the eighteenth century mining at Hay Gill and Carrock End had

also been resumed. During the nineteenth century the mines were exploited vigorously, if not always profitably. Roughton Gill was particularly prosperous from the 1820s to about 1870; Driggith worked continuously for many years. Other mines were worked more intermittently. Detailed accounts of all these ventures are given below under mine headings.

Most of the mines had been given up as worked out before 1870; thereafter, plummeting metal prices, due to the exploitation of rich and easily won ores in America and Australia, made those that were working uneconomic. By 1876 Roughton Gill was finished as a metal mine and its owners bankrupt. Although Driggith produced small amounts of ore in the early 1900s the closure of Roughton Gill effectively marked the end of the mining of metals (other than tungsten) in the Caldbeck Fells.

From the latter part of the nineteenth century baryte

Fig. 19 THE DALE BECK VALLEY: from just below the outcrop of the Roughton Gill (South) vein on Iron Crag, the foreground strewn with fragments of vein quartz. The main Roughton Gill mine dump is in the centre of the photograph; to the right and left are Peteraw and Yard Steel and in the distance is Brae Fell. On this scale even the relatively large Roughton Gill dump seems an insignificant part of a landscape now valued more for its solitude than its mineral wealth.

became an increasingly important resource in the area. Rich deposits were worked for many years in Potts Gill and Sandbeds. These mines produced tens of thousands of tons of high grade baryte and finally closed, worked out, in 1966. Since that time the only working mine has been the Carrock Fell tungsten mine which was reopened in 1971 after lying idle for 25 years. Interest in this deposit only truly began at the beginning of this century, and was reawakened during each of the World Wars. Its most recent working, started in response to high tungsten prices, was not successful. The mine was 'left and given over' in the 1980s and in 1988 the mill was demolished and the adit level sealed.

Of the mines, little remains: notoriously unstable vein walls have collapsed into old stopes and waste heaps have been washed away from run-in level mouths. Many people, of course, are not sorry to see these remains disappear: complaints of corruption and pollution, moral and ecological, have always trailed after mines and miners; there will ever be a divide between those who regard the traces of mining as unsightly scars and those who see them as worthy relics of the 'old man's' industry. Perhaps it is worth a moment when turning over mineral specimens to reflect with an old Caldbeck preacher:

the shepherd grows old, and the ploughman grows strong, but the miner is gone to his grave ere long

(Pool, 1862)

Without them the specimens described here might never have seen the light of day.

LOCALITY NAMES

Fortunately, or not, depending on one's point of view, there are not as many mineral localities in the Caldbeck Fells as there are names to define them. A great many synonyms and erroneous names exist in the literature or upon old (and even recent!) specimen labels and it is in the hope of preventing further confusion that we explain some of the most common or persistent of them.

Synonymous locality names fall into two categories: spelling variants—generally the less confusing of the two—and differences of opinion or interpretation.

Place names in this part of Cumbria are mostly Old Norse (ON) or Old Welsh (OW) in origin (Table 3) and the written forms in current use are more or less corrupt versions of these old words. It follows that there are often several equally acceptable ways of spelling the same name and precedent cannot be established. The synonymy of most of the commonly encountered variants is obvious e.g. Roughton/Roughten* or Driggith/

* There is a Roughten Gill, a tributary of Glenderaterra Beck, 7 km SSW of High Pike [NY 296 276]. Although best known for the 'chiastolite' slate exposed here, there is also an old lead mine (Glenderaterra mine or Brundholme mine, see Postlethwaite, 1913: 101 – 103) south of the confluence.

Table 3 ETYMOLOGY OF CALDBECK LOCALITY NAMES

Showing the elements of the names, their meanings and derivations. Sources are abbreviated to: ON Old Norse, OE Old English, OW Old Welsh. Taken from Brearley (1974) and Armstrong *et al*. (1950–1952).

beck (ON *bekkr*) a brook or stream
fell (ON *fell, fjall*) a mountain; now wild high ground
gill (ON *gil*) a cleft or ravine; now often a stream in a deep ravine
grain (ON *grein*) a branch of a stream or valley
moss (OE *mos*) a marsh or bog (in Caldbeck would denote a peat bog)

Balliway Rigg A **rigg** (ON *hryggr*) is an elongated hill with steep sides. **Balliway** may derive in part from ON *bali* (= a gentle slope) which is a fitting description of the northern extension of the rigg.
Brae Fell 'Broad Fell' from ON *breiðr*
Brandy Gill Perhaps 'Steep Gill' from OE *brant*
Caldbeck The 'Cold Stream' from ON *caldr*. **Caldew** is similarly derived.
Carrock Fell 'Rocky Fell' from OW *carrec* (= a rock) in allusion to its boulder-strewn slopes.
Driggith 'The Deer Paddock' from OE *deora* (= deer) and ON *garðr* (= paddock).
Grainsgill 'The Shieling on the Tributary' from ON *grein – skáli*; the Norse *skáli* being a rough hut or shieling.
Hare Stones 'The Boundary Stones' from OE *hār – stān*. An alternative interpretation is the 'Grey Stones' but since Harestones Felsite is pink and the outcrop is indeed on the parish boundary the former derivation seems more likely.
Hay Gill A *hay* was land enclosed for hunting.
Iron Crag Perhaps a corruption of *Erne Crag* (ON *erne* = eagle), or an allusion to the hardness of the rock. A further possibility may refer to the iron-stained outcrops of the Roughton Gill veins on the crag.
Poddy Gill From the dialect word *paddock* = toad.
Potts Gill No explanation has been found. Was *Potskailles* in 1592.
Roughton Gill 'The Roaring Gill' from ON *rautan* in allusion to the noise of its several waterfalls, especially in wet weather.
Todd Gill Perhaps 'The Foxes' Gill' from *tod* the dialect name for the fox, from ON *toddi*, a mass or bale of wool, alluding to the animal's bushy tail.

Driggeth. Occasionally, names are run together as in Roughtongill instead of Roughton Gill. The names used in the present work are mostly those adopted by the Ordnance Survey in their latest maps of the district.

The word *gill* (from ON *gil*, a steep-sided valley or ravine) is sometimes rendered *ghyll*—fondly assumed to be an early form. This is not borne out by a study of its origins or of early literature and the variant is, in fact, believed to be a pseudo-antiquarian conceit coined by the Lakeland poet Wordsworth. It is most consistently used for *Potts Ghyll Baryte mine* in Potts Gill, but may substitute in any other locality at the whim of the author. It is interesting to note that the 'gill' of *Grainsgill Beck* derives from a different root: *skáli*, ON for grazing land or rough hut (shieling) on such land. In 1568, the stream's name was closer to its roots as *Graynscalebeck*. Presumably, the name has been corrupted to gill in false analogy to other names but the Grainsgill Beck valley is too gentle to be a true gill. For a discussion of the historical significance of Lake District place names see Pearsall and Pennington (1973: 240–245).

Some names are merely misspelt: *Battiway*, *Balloway* or *Batteway* for *Balliway Rigg*; *Grange Gill* for *Grainsgill*; *Roughen Hill* or *Wroughten Gill* for *Roughton Gill*. J. G. Goodchild used the ancient forms *Rowtin Gill* (*Roughton Gill*), *Cawda* (*R. Caldew*), and *Carrick* (*Carrock Fell*) in several publications.

More serious for the mineralogist are the number of vague, ambiguous, or inaccurate names that appear in publications or collections. Kingsbury & Hartley commented in several of their papers on the unreliability of Caldbeck Fells locality data on old specimen labels. Hartley (1984) summarized the problem: '... it became obvious that amongst the many examples of well known minerals from the area to be found in collections and recorded in the literature, a large proportion were labelled, or stated to be from localities, from which they almost certainly did not originate, and in some cases could not have originated. Localities such as "Keswick", "Roughtongill", "Carrock Fells", "Brandy Gill" were used in such a loose manner that no reliance could be placed, in most cases, on the locality being the true provenance of the specimen. In many records the localities Carrock Fells, Grainsgill, and Brandy Gill were found to be virtually synonymous.' On several occasions, Kingsbury & Hartley collected specimens which were so similar to others previously described from a different locality that they were convinced that their site must have been the original source. This was especially noted with specimens from Potts Gill Baryte mine (particularly atacamite and brochantite specimens). In part, such confusion may have resulted from deliberate mis-labelling by dealers anxious to protect their source. The Victorian dealer Bryce Wright has frequently been accused of this. He was not alone, and it must be stated that Kingsbury & Hartley themselves were sometimes less than forthcoming over the precise locality details of many of their more interesting finds.

Some of the diversity of names has arisen through problems of identity: the lack of some distinctive character or named mine at a site when a record was made has led writers to interpret the same location in different ways. Although the resulting locality descriptions may not be intrinsically wrong, the subsequent uncritical cataloguing of these names may result in an apparent proliferation of localities from the one original site. Apart from the deliberate vagueness resorted to by some collectors, inaccurate localization should have become a thing of the past with the advent of the National Grid. There can be no excuse for confusion if Grid references, to at least six figures, are used when recording the source of specimens.

The various difficulties associated with Caldbeck localities are discussed below under the site names:

Brandy Gill and Carrock mine Two sets of veins have been exploited in and around Brandy Gill: the N–S tungsten veins and E–W lead veins. It is current practice among collectors to refer to the workings on the latter veins near the head of Brandy Gill as *Brandy Gill mine* or *Brandy Gill Lead mine* and the workings on the tungsten veins at the foot of Brandy Gill (and on the south side of Grainsgill Beck) as *Carrock* or *Carrock Fell mine*. Nineteenth century writers made no such distinction and 'Brandy Gill' was used for minerals from both sets of workings. Greg & Lettsom (1858: 349) were completely misled by records of species from the tungsten veins; their entry under molybdenite from Cumberland demonstrates their difficulties: '... near Keswick. At Carrock Fells. At Brandygill. In ... granite, near the source of the Caldew, four miles S.W. from Hesket Newmarket. At Caldbeck Fell ...' All five localities refer to the present Carrock mine site. Kingsbury & Hartley occasionally refer to the Carrock mine site as 'Grainsgill'.

Driggith–Sandbeds mine The Driggith–Sandbeds lode was exploited from both ends, the workings being essentially one mine. They are, however, commonly treated as separate entities, a usage that has been continued in the present work. The Sandbeds end of the mine is sometimes referred to as *Old Sandbeds* to distinguish it from the workings on the cross-cutting baryte veins (*Sandbeds East* and *Sandbeds West* mines) that were opened from levels nearby.

Dry Gill The characteristic 'campylite' from Dry Gill is occasionally seen labelled 'Dry Gill, Alston Moor'. This surprisingly persistent error seems to have originated with Breithaupt's original description of 'kampylite' in 1841 where he gave 'Alston More' [*sic*] as the locality.

Mexico mine Greg and Lettsom's (1858: 407) location of the Mexico mine as 'on the road from Hesket Newmarket to Roughton Gill' has led some collectors, among them Kingsbury, to identify it as an old name for Brae Fell mine. It would appear, however, that Greg and Lettsom's records of species for the Mexico mine are correct although their geography may be suspect. Kingsbury & Hartley did not refer to the real Mexico mine at all but their records for gold, plumbogummite and other species from 'a cross-cut to the North vein at the foot of Todd Gill' actually refer to the Mexico mine low level (Kingsbury & Hartley MS; Kingsbury MS 2).

Potts Gill Baryte mine The large Potts Gill baryte lodes are intersected by veins carrying lead, zinc and copper minerals, and it is from one or more of these that the remarkable suite of copper-bearing secondary minerals found by Kingsbury & Hartley is supposed to have originated. It is apparent from a study of Kingsbury's MSS notes (BM(NH)) and from discussion with Hartley, that all their material came from the dumps outside the no. 1 level of Old Potts Gill mine (some of Kingsbury's notes and labels refer to 'no. 2 level' but this has been corrected to 'no. 1' in his most up to date listings). In some of their joint papers, however, they give the occurrence in a variety of ways: the 'copper vein near Potts Gill' (1956a, 1957b, 1957d) and the variously described veins 'cut by the old no. 1 cross-cut' (1957e, 1958, 1960); all refer to material found on the above mentioned dump. The source, or sources, within the mine is a matter of conjecture. This site is also claimed by the same authors as the original source of some brochantite and atacamite previously ascribed to Roughton Gill.

Roughton Gill mine Roughton Gill probably has the greater share of wrongly localized specimens. Records of fine linarite and caledonite from here have been queried by several authors (who thought Red Gill more likely as the source), and claimed occurrences of scheelite, atacamite, and some brochantite specimens have also been doubted or denied. It is probable that some specimens originating elsewhere in the Roughton Gill sett (which included Mexico mine and mines in Silver Gill, Red Gill, and Swinburn Gill) may have been given the non-specific locality Roughton Gill; or that ore brought to the Roughton Gill dressing plant from these other mines is the cause of such confusion. The physical extent of Roughton Gill proper also requires careful scrutiny. Beyond the steeper parts of Roughton Gill, in the hanging valley forming the higher reaches of the gill, the stream bed flattens out and eventually splits into three. These latter three valleys are known as the Thief Gills (so called, it is said, from their use as an escape route by thieves high-grading the ore dumps below). The Roughton Gill South lode crops out along the west bank of the hanging valley and continues into the northern Thief Gill. There are several ancient levels and workings along the vein outcrop in this area that yield a rich variety of minerals. We refer to this part of the mine, as did Kingsbury & Hartley, as 'higher Roughton Gill'. It is also known to various writers as 'the S.E. flank of Balliway Rigg' (or just Balliway Rigg) or 'Thief Gills' or 'Thief Gills (northern)'. The last names are ambiguous and, in some cases, may actually mean the Thief Gills above the splitting of the valley.

The most corrupt version of Roughton Gill seen on a specimen is 'Roughen Hill, Cornwall' on an absolutely typical Roughton Gill mine plumbogummite. The confusion of Cumberland with Cornwall has been noted on Cumbrian calcites also, and Greg & Lettsom (1858: 353) gave a misspelt Godolphin's Bal [Cornwall] as a Cumbrian locality for wolframite.

The nomenclature of the veins worked from the Roughton Gill and Silver Gill mines is discussed under Roughton Gill in the chapter on *The Mines*.

Silver Gill The name 'Golden Hugh' given to the highest, and probably the oldest, working in Silver Gill is an enigma. Shaw (1970) suggests it may have been the Golden Vugh—*vugh* being a Cornish miner's term for a cavity in a vein—which he may have derived from misreading the Walker MS of 1710. However, references to the mine by Thomas Hillary in 1724 (Benson MSS, D/Ben/3116–3119) are unequivocally 'Hugh' and the Pratt MS of *c.* 1700 renders it, presumably phonetically, as 'Hue'. A possible derivation of Hugh is from the Scottish dialect word *heugh*, variously defined as a steep-sided ravine, a craggy or rugged cliff, or an excavation (although the last is properly one for coal).

Tenter Gill Greg & Lettsom (1858: 228) recorded 'Tenter Gill, Carrock Fells' as a source of tourmaline and quartz but no such locality is known in the area, nor is there any other reference to it. A 'Tenter Hill' has been identified about 5.5 km west-south-west of Roughton Gill [NY 247 322], but this is outside the Caldbeck Fells and, as yet, tourmaline has not been confirmed here.

LOCALITIES

ARM O'GRAIN

A N–S manganese-bearing vein and an E–W lead-bearing vein crop out in this tributrary of Grainsgill. The lead vein is probably the westward extension of the vein that cuts through the Carrock mine tungsten veins at the foot of Brandy Gill. In a plea concerning land rights in 1797, the counsel for the defendant claimed that '... ab^t 22 or 23 years ago [i.e. 1774–1775] a Mine was attempted to be Worked at Arnah Grain under a contract with Lord Pomfret who is entitled to the Lead Mines within the Manor ...'. The accompanying plan confirms the identity of 'Arnah Grain' and Arm o'Grain (Benson MSS, D/Ben/3126; D/Ben/3115).

A small dump from a trial still exists in the gill [NY 316 333] and is noted for small crystals of mottramite and beudantite, first found here about 1974 (D. R. Middleton, *pers. comm.*).

BIRK GILL

'Birk Gill vein' was described by Pratt (MS) in about 1700: 'here is no Oars to be seen but the finest Soyle that wee have seen in the Liberty in any of the dead veins, and it runs directly into the Hill so that it would try the verry bowels of Petra [Peteraw], the name of the hill.' Thomas Hillary's records of working in 'Burch Gill' may refer to the same site (Benson MSS, D/Ben/3116). Nothing further is known of the site until about 1861 when work was done by the lessees of Hay Gill mine. Traces of three levels may still be seen: one at [NY 302 357] and two at [NY 305 354]. Their extent is unknown and no minerals of interest have been reported.

Fig. 20 BRAE FELL MINE: looking west from Birk Fell. There are two adits to be seen, marked by fans of waste that suggest that the mine is relatively extensive. Below and to the left of the dumps is a small platform that probably marks the old ore dressing floor. It is likely that only basic dressing was carried out here before carting the ore to the main works at Roughton Gill. Notable features are the dry gullies running diagonally across the fellside: these are the trenches ('hushes') made by early miners when prospecting for the vein.

BRAE FELL MINE

Little is known of the history of this mine. In the nineteenth century it formed part of the same sett as the Red Gill mine and was explored by the Red Gill Mining Company in 1866 but nothing further was done. A speculator cleaned up the workings in 1882 and tried, but failed, to sell it. Since then, the site has been neglected; the now run-in levels have not been open in living memory.

The mine was worked from two or three levels [NY 298 357] driven on an ESE–WNW lead vein. The dumps are not extensive but have yielded some good specimens of leadhillite, lanarkite, anglesite and pyromorphite. Unique specimens, for the district, of acicular cerussite with prismatic green pyromorphite were found in the 1950s by Kingsbury. The occurrence of matthedd-leite here, the first in the Caldbeck Fells and the second

worldwide, was recorded by Cooper *et al.* (1988).

The locality is also notable for the fine 'hushes' which run down the fell side on each side of the old levels.

BRANDY GILL LEAD MINES

Two major E–W lead veins with subsidiary stringers cross Brandy Gill; both have been worked. The southern vein cuts the tungsten veins of Carrock Mine and outcrops in the west in Arm o'Grain and in the east in Poddy Gill where trials have been made. The east side of Brandy Gill has also been tried and the 'cross-cut at, or near, the junction of the east–west lead veins with the Emerson vein at the foot of Brandy Gill' (Hartley, 1984) may be part of this working. The northern vein crops out near the head of the gill [NY 3225 3385] and was worked from levels on both sides of the narrow valley.

According to Whellan (1860: 226) it is 'on record'

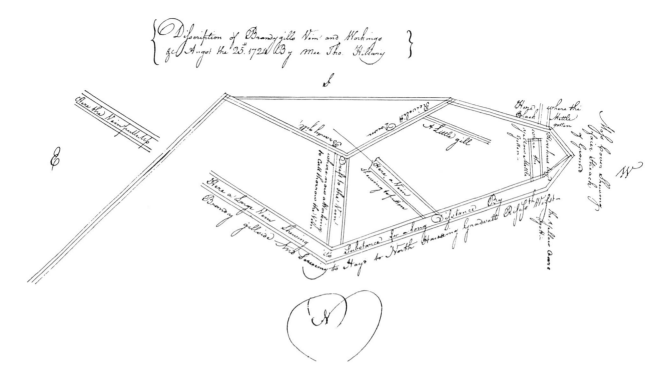

Fig. 21 'BRANDYGILLS VEIN AND WORKINGS': a late eighteenth century copy of Thomas Hillary's 1724 plan of a lead and copper mine in Brandy Gill. (Benson MSS, D/Ben/3120).

that the Lord of the Manor was mining 'at or near' Brandy Gill in the sixteenth century, but no original records are known before the eighteenth century when Lord Wharton's Mine Agent, Thomas Hillary, was working mines here and elsewhere in Caldbeck. Hillary's plan *The Disscription of Brandygills Vein and Workings &c August 25th 1724'* showing 'where the Black Mettle . . . [and] . . . the yellow Mettle gotten' still exists (Benson MSS, D/Ben/3120), but has so far defeated efforts to relate it to known workings (Fig. 21). In a plea concerning land rights on the south side of Carrock Fell in 1797 the existence of 'a very considerable Lead Mine within the Limitts claimed' is referred to as 'Working from the years 1722 to 1730 or thereab[ts]' (Benson MSS, D/Ben/3162), but surviving account sheets by Hillary date only from 1724 to 1726 (Leconsfield MSS, D/Lec/219; Benson MSS, D/Ben/3116–3118; 3121; 3122). In June 1726 he was instructed by Wharton's Head Agent, Thomas Smales, 'to Give over the Worke in Brandy Gill' (Benson MSS, D/Ben/3119), however, payments for work done in Brandy Gill, including 'driving ten fathom* in y[e] mid[e]llevel drift at 21 shilings per fathom' and sinking 5 fathoms in a sump, entered in the July to December accounts of that year, suggest that the work continued.

Nothing further is known of Brandy Gill's mining history for over 100 years. In 1852 F. W. Emerson began working the lead deposits but was forced by legal

problems to turn to mining tungsten from the N–S vein that now bears his name. His venture had ended by 1858. Leicester, Hutchinson & Co. took the lease in 1863. A small output of 4 tons of lead ore is recorded from 'South Carrock and Brandy Gill' in 1872 and a further 5.5 tons for Brandy Gill in 1874 (Burt et al., 1982). The first Ordnance Survey 6 inches to 1 mile map of the area shows lead workings in higher Brandy Gill and at the gill's foot in 1861.

The northern mine, Brandy Gill Lead mine, was worked from two levels connected by a short shaft, running into the west bank and a third, drift, level in the east. The latter is long run-in but may connect with the lowest level which runs under Brandy Gill. The mine is not extensive; there are probably no more than 300 m of level cut. The upper west level was barren but some stoping was done on the lower level.

In terms of mineral specimens, however, the mine came into prominence in the late 1940s when W. F. Davidson and A. W. G. Kingsbury and their co-workers discovered the suite of rare copper and lead supergene minerals for which the locality is now well known. Balydonite, stolzite, various vanadates, and the extremely rare mineral lindgrenite were found here. This interesting mineral assemblage is probably the result of interaction of fluids derived from the N–S tungsten–molybdenum–arsenic suite with those from the E–W lead–copper vein. All of Davidson and Kingsbury's specimens came from the old dumps; Davidson and Thomson dug out the mine

*Level depths were measured in fathoms (fm), where 1 fathom = 6 ft = 1.8 m.

but apart from the imprints of the 'old men's' 'duck-nebbed' clogs on the floor of the level found nothing of interest (W. F. Davidson *pers. comm.*). Modern collecting has been more fruitful, some good stolzite and hedyphane (the first British occurrence) have been found but, generally, good specimens are hard to come by.

A short distance downstream of the mine, a dry and shallow tributary valley joins Brandy Gill on the east side. At the head of this tributary [NY 3240 3385] several veins crop out, one of them similar in appearance to the outcrop of the main E–W vein above the eastern level of the lead mine in Brandy Gill proper. Recent collecting here has revealed a few small specimens of crystallized mimetite, beudantite, and carminite (Fig. 59, p. 87).

The extent of working on the southern lead vein at the foot of Brandy Gill is unknown, but is likely to be very small as the vein exposed in Carrock mine is almost barren (see Fortey, 1978). It is possible that evidence of mining on this vein is buried under waste from nearby

workings on the Emerson vein. Kingsbury & Hartley reported a suite of minerals similar to that from Brandy Gill Lead mine from a locality 'at, or near, the junction of the east–west lead veins with the Emerson vein at the foot of Brandy Gill' (Hartley, 1984). The exact source of their specimens can no longer be identified and no further material has been reported from this general area.

BURDELL GILL

A roughly N–S vein appears to have been tried near the head of the gill [NY 307 324]. The vein is predominantly of a hard gossany nature with spongy quartz impregnated with iron and manganese oxides. The locality is well known as a source of good, though small, crystals of pharmacosiderite. Several other arsenates and phosphates occur here and the locality has received a good deal of attention from collectors.

CARROCK MINE

Outside Devon and Cornwall, Carrock mine is the only British mine to produce commercial quantities of tungsten ore; it lies in Grainsgill at the foot of Brandy Gill and exploits three main veins, from west to east the Smith, Harding, and Emerson veins. There are a number of smaller veins, the Waterfall vein, Wilson vein, Nicholson vein, and 'Molybdenite' vein, but these have yielded insignificant amounts of ore. The southern extension of the Harding vein in Coomb Height was once called Coombside vein and the Emerson vein was once known as the Brandy Gill vein (Dewey & Dines, 1923) but these names are no longer in use. The mineralogy of the deposit and its relationship with the Skiddaw Granite have been the subject of papers by Hitchen (1934). Ewart (1957, 1962), Shepherd *et al.* (1976), Appleton & Wadge (1976), Fortey (1978), Beddoe-Stephens & Fortey (1981), Shepherd & Waters (1984) and Ball *et al.* (1985).

The Harding and Emerson veins account for most of the production from the mine. The former was worked from several levels to the valley floor and was stoped to surface on both sides of Grainsgill. The Emerson vein had some rich bunches of wolframite on the north but was barren in the one level driven south of Grainsgill Beck. Smith vein contained large amounts of arsenopyrite as well as tungsten minerals and has been worked for both.

Mining at Carrock has been sporadic; the deposit is not rich and has been worked during times of war or when the tungsten price has permitted. The strong quartz veins running N–S across Grainsgill must have been obvious to the 'old men' but it was probably the lack of any significant lead or copper that led to them being ignored until the nineteenth century. The first real interest in these veins was from mineral collectors who sought the excellent crystals of apatite and scheelite and the, then, rare mineral molybdenite from about 1809 (see p. 66). F. W. Emerson worked the vein which bears his name in

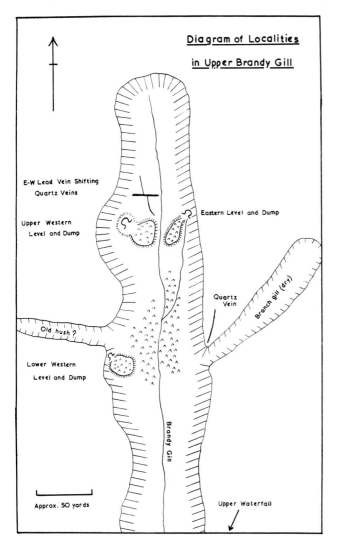

Fig. 22 BRANDY GILL LEAD MINE: diagram drawn by Kingsbury & Hartley for a proposed article on Brandy Gill.

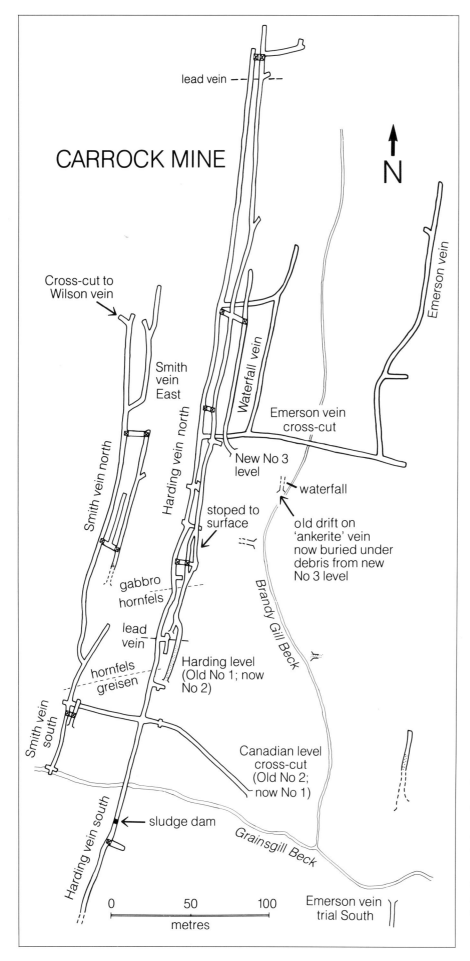

Fig. 23 CARROCK MINE VEINS: plan of recent workings.

CARROCK MINE

lead vein – –

N

Cross-cut to
Wilson vein

Smith
vein
East

Emerson vein

Waterfall vein

Harding vein north

Smith vein north

Emerson vein
cross-cut

New No 3
level

waterfall

stoped to
surface

old drift on
'ankerite' vein
now buried under
debris from new
No 3 level

gabbro
hornfels

Brandy Gill Beck

lead
vein

hornfels
greisen

Harding level
(Old No 1; now
No 2)

Smith vein south

Canadian level
cross-cut
(Old No 2;
now No 1)

Harding vein south

sludge dam

Grainsgill Beck

0   50   100

metres

Emerson vein
trial South

Fig. 24 *(opposite)* **CARROCK MINE:** looking approximately north-east from the site of the World War I ore-dressing plant at the foot of Coomb Height towards the 1971 mill (pictured in 1985). The grey pipe half-way down the photograph leads in to the adit level entrance which is just out of the frame. Although the new mill site has now been cleared the earlier ruins remain.

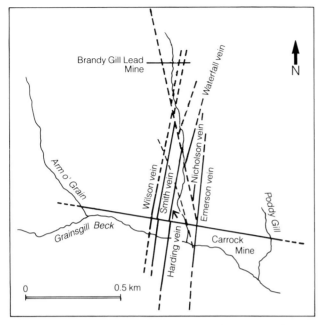

Fig. 25 CARROCK MINE VEINS: after Shepherd & Waters (1984).

1854, after having been driven from his original search for lead and copper in Brandy Gill by leasing problems. There was little market for tungsten at that time and the mine seems to have been quickly abandoned. An attempt to work the Harding vein on Coomb Height in 1872 was also short-lived.

James Harding of Penrith, operating as Carrock Mines Ltd, began work in 1902 but did little. The German-run Cumbrian Mining Company took over in 1906 and produced some 90 tons of tungsten concentrates and 4 tons of arsenic up to 1912. The strategic importance of tungsten was belatedly realized by the British Government just before the outbreak of the Great War; the newly formed Carrock Mining Syndicate headed by Anthony Wilson began mining about 1913, partly funded by the Government. During the war years, Carrock mine produced nearly 14 000 tons of undressed ore yielding about 100 tons of tungsten concentrates. The mine closed in 1919 and lay idle until war again stimulated demand. The Government-financed Non-Ferrous

Fig. 26 CARROCK MINE: the 'Canadian' cross-cut adit was driven in 1942 to intersect the Harding and Smith veins below old workings north of Grainsgill Beck. It has remained the principal mine entrance. Shortly after the photograph was taken all the rails and pipework were removed and, in 1988, the entrance was sealed and is likely to remain shut unless there is a substantial long-term increase in the price of tungsten.

Metals Development Corporation re-opened the mine in 1942 using Canadian Army engineers to develop the property. A new low-level adit was driven [NY 3225 3295] and a good deal of exploratory driving done on the Harding and Smith veins. This enabled the Ministry to prove the ore reserves, but no stoping was done. To help in the search for scheelite a portable UV-light prospecting lamp was specially developed by the General Electric Company; with batteries it weighed nearly 74 lbs (Rabone, 1945). By 1943 the tungsten supply position had improved and the Government decided that further work was not necessary.

The mine was promoted during the Korean War but the conflict ceased before negotiations to work the site (now inside the National Park boundary) could be completed. It was not until 1971 that the deposit again became a commercial prospect. The escalation of the price of tungsten, following the U.S. Government's cessation of sales of the metal from their strategic stockpile, prompted the Colorado-based WECO Development Corporation to take a lease on the mine. They examined the deposit and built a mill on the site through their British subsidiary Worldwide Energy (U.K.) Ltd (for details see Anon., 1977), but a year later the work was put on standby when the tungsten price fell.

The newly formed Carrock Fell Mining Co., a subsidiary of Amalgamated Industries Ltd, reactivated the dormant mine and mill in 1976 under lease from WECO and began work on the Harding and Smith veins. In 1979–1980 they also made an exploratory drive to the Emerson vein from the Harding adit level. Although this work continued until 1981, the venture was only briefly profitable before once again falling to market pressures. The mine was placed on care and maintenance, ownership passing to Minworth of Derbyshire in 1982 (Blundell, 1987).

In 1985, the dismantling of the mill began and much equipment was also stripped from the mine. The old stone-built miner's hut or smithy, refuge of many a bedraggled fell-walker or mineral collector, was removed in the same year. The remains of the mill were taken away in 1988, the settling ponds and dumps were bulldozed over, and the adit level entrance was sealed.

Carrock mine has been a favourite collecting site for generations of mineralogists: more species have been recorded from here than from any other locality in the area. The excitement generated by the discovery of molybdenite, scheelite, and apatite in the eighteenth century has already been discussed. Good scheelite was also produced during the latest phases of mining but very little apatite of any merit, although occasional minute gem-like crystals are a favourite with micro-mounters. Well developed arsenopyrite and small pyrrhotine crystals have been removed from the Smith vein by collectors, but the bismuth sulphide and sulphotelluride minerals for which the mine is well known have rarely been found. The mine is no longer safely accessible: not only does the sealed adit restrict entrance but the resulting lack of ventilation can only aggravate earlier problems with gas emanating from mill slimes which were pumped into the southern part of the Harding vein during the last period of working.

CARROCK END MINE

Carrock End mine, also known as the Queen mine, lies at the north-western margin of Carrock Fell [NY 352 342] near the bog once known as Dutch (or Dutchman's) Moss. Copper ores occur here along the apparently faulted boundary of the Carrock Fell Igneous Complex and Eycott Group rocks. The vein, which may continue westwards to Dry Gill mine, contained some rich bunches of ore, but fruitless driving in barren ground usually used up any operating profit (Shaw, 1970).

The mine is believed to have been worked by the Elizabethans but there is no definite evidence for this, although the name Dutchman's Moss implies exploration or trials here by Höchstetter and his men. The earliest known records date from the eighteenth century, but Pratt's report (MS) of about 1700 records 'Old Mans working' above the contemporary levels at 'Dutch Moss vein'. By Pratt's time the vein had 'been Wrought for about 300 yards in length, the shafts and open casts being about 30 or 40 yards between'. A lower level had been started but not finished and the mine was evidently idle. Thomas Hillary's accounts for 1724 contain regular payments for 'Carriage of Ore from Duch Moss' but no piece work ('Fathum Worke') payments for mining; presumably the Dutch Moss miners were on 'tribute' being paid only for the ore they extracted (Benson MSS, D/Ben/3116).

William Roe and Thomas Smythe took up Carrock End along with Driggith in 1790. According to Hutchinson (1794: Vol. 2, 682), a rich copper vein was found in 1793 from which 'two workmen got to the value of [£80] of copper-ore [in] one afternoon', but the report ends: 'we have since heard that the vein has not turned out so well as expected' (op. cit., 389). About the year 1813 'Currock-end . . . produced some thousand pounds worth of copper ore' (Watson, 1843: 58) but the writer concludes: 'The sett is very extensive, and several lodes in it, but never has been worked to a profit'. The mine was leased by the Rev. Francis Thompson from 1839 to 1863 who worked the property by a new shaft and raised some 70 tons of copper ore. From 1863 the successive lessees of Roughton Gill mine also held Carrock End but despite some exploratory work nothing of note was achieved. It was last worked in 1869.

Malachite was noted by Greg & Lettsom (1858); chrysocolla and massive chalcopyrite can still be found on the dumps.

and refining mill at 'Roughtongill Head' [probably on the site of the old lead dressing works at the foot of Roughton Gill] powered by a 'light over-shot water-wheel, 30 feet in diameter ... removed from Redgill, where it had been used for crushing lead ore'. The raw umber was brought from the mine by an 'overhead tramway' (Addison, 1889–1890). Plans and sections of the plant are given by Addison (*op. cit.*), who designed it. In 1884–1885 the mine was closed and the milling machinery was sold; a full inventory is given in the Leconfield MSS (D/Lec/MB/8/1).

The lode is part of the Roughton Gill (South) vein, here containing considerable quantities of umber and 'a type of china clay' formed from alteration of the wall-rock (Shaw, 1970). There is a large amount of this white clay in the lode but it is not known how much was ever raised as a commercial product. Analysis of altered wall-rock (Harestones felsite) from the dumps showed the major alteration product to be kaolinite (Young, 1987).

DEER HILLS

In 1961, a series of trials was made by McKechnie Bros of Widnes on Deer Hills, the fellside to the west of Potts Gill, and showed promising quantities of baryte in lodes beyond the abandoned west end of Old Potts Gill mine. Cross-cuts were driven [NY 310 365; NY 313 365; NY 314 363 ('Dawson's cross-cut')] and a small amount of ore extracted but the lode was poor and work was soon abandoned. Shaw (1970) noted cuprite, an uncommon mineral in the district, from the hanging wall of the main ore shoot. Waste from these cross-cuts contains mostly massive or gossany quartz but small amounts of adamite and an agardite-group mineral have recently been identified from the large dumps at [NY 313 365].

Towards the brow of Deer Hills [NY 3145 3626] are the remains of grassed over dumps from pits or shafts, perhaps sunk on the ENE Deer Hills Quartz vein or its inter-section with the E–W Potts Gill baryte lodes. These dumps contain abundant massive arsenopyrite much altered to compact or microcrystalline scorodite, pharma-cosiderite, and other arsenates.

DRIGGITH–SANDBEDS MINE

The Driggith–Sandbeds vein is the north-eastern extension of the Roughton Gill South lode and was worked from short cross-cuts at the head of Driggith Beck (principally the 12 fathom [NY 324 353] and 30 fathom [NY 327 353] levels), and from longer, deeper, levels at the Sandbeds end of the vein (the 60 fathom [NY 330 359] and 90 fathom [NY 332 362] levels). The two workings connected to form one mine but it has been customary, at least among collectors, to regard them as separate entities. Care must be taken to differentiate between the Sandbeds lead workings (sometimes referred to as 'Old Sandbeds') and the more recent Sandbeds baryte mines

Fig. 27 DRIGGITH MINE: relics of mining, other than the mines themselves, are rare in the Caldbeck Fells; this row of small ore bins (?) stands near the lower levels of the Driggith mine which are situated in the valley in the background.

CHINA CLAY MINE

Originally worked for umber, and known as the Hare Stones Umber mine after the rocky outcrop to the south-east, the China Clay mine [NY 311 347] was opened in 1883 by Messrs Woof & Garth who worked it for one year (Adams, 1988). About 1885 it was investigated by the Cleator Iron Ore Co. who had taken an interest in umber and baryte in the Caldbeck Fells. They built a crushing

(Sandbeds East and West), especially since the 90 fathom adit at Sandbeds gave access to both the Driggith vein and the Sandbeds West baryte vein.

The Driggith–Sandbeds vein averaged about 1.2 m (4 ft) wide with a maximum of 2.4 m; major ore minerals were galena, chalcopyrite, and sphalerite in a gangue of quartz and baryte. There was supposedly some zoning of the deposit with copper in the upper levels and sphalerite in depth (Eastwood, 1921). Parson & White (1829) described the ore as 'hard and steel-grained, and . . . very difficult to smelt, being strongly impregnated with sulphur and antimony. Besides the blue steel-grained lead ore there are green, yellow, red, brown, and white in the same veins; also manganese and the most beautiful yellow, blue and green copper ores . . .'. The oxidized ores were said to be of great value in the higher levels but the ores became progressively more difficult to process in the deeper levels where the intimate association of galena, baryte, and sphalerite caused insurmountable problems for the gravity separation techniques used in the nineteenth century. Difficulties in smelting resulted in the loss of a great deal of the lead from the ore, perhaps as much as 40% if one compares the artificially inflated silver values—up to 60 ozs per ton of lead—derived from the old processes with the later figure of 25 oz extracted by more efficient smelting (Whellan, 1860: 226).

Both Sandbeds and 'Driggate' were noted about 1700 by Pratt (MS) in a survey of Caldbeck mines, but the report ends pessimistically '. . . and tho they did get a lump of the vein the bigdom of a Kible† that was the 4th pt. of it Oars, yet at present there is little or no Oars to be gott.' Nevertheless, Thomas Hillary was cutting a level and shaft here in 1724 and records the carriage of '12 lodes' of ore from 'Driggitt' from September to December (Benson MSS, D/Ben/3116). Nothing further is known of the working until 1790 when the sett, including Carrock End mine, was leased by William Roe and Thomas Smythe who worked Driggith to a depth of 25 fm and erected a smelter by Carrock Beck [NY 351 351] about one kilometre east of the mine. They are reported to have done well from their venture but abandoned the mine sometime before 1810 when it was reopened by Richardson and Lowrey of Carlisle. The latter sold out in 1823 to T. R. G. Braddyll‡ of Conishead Priory, Furness. By now, the mine needed a lower level to extract the ore and Braddyll drove the 60 fm level from the Sandbeds end of the vein [NY 3300 3595] but this long drive left him bankrupt by 1834. The mine continued in work under Barratt & Bennett (1836–1840) and Dickinson & Co. (1840–1849) but did not show

† Kibble (Kible): a mine bucket, from German Kübel, a tub.

‡ The Braddylls may have been involved in the Caldbeck mines once before: In 1568, George Nedham of the Mines Royal negotiated with 'Mr Edward Braddel' the Receiver General of Furness, for charcoal burners (Donald, 1955: 76).

a profit. George Brocklebank and William Jeffrey took up the mine a few years later and, with the installation of new ore-dressing plant and other improvements, returned the mine to a paying concern. They raised 1950 tons of lead and copper ores from 1849 to 1857 (Whellan, 1860). However, they too were beaten by the need for a lower level. The 90 fm Sandbeds level [NY 3315 3615] was begun in 1859 and, thanks to repeated errors of surveying or judgment, took nine years to complete. In the meantime, the company had exhausted its funds and sold out, in 1865, to the West Cumberland Silver Lead Mining Co. They fared no better and went bankrupt in 1874, their problems with ore-dressing and water supply being compounded by a law suit by local farmers complaining about water pollution from the mill. The owners were condemned to pay heavy damages.

Several attempts were made to reopen the mine in the present century. None was successful. Companies found that the complex ores were too difficult to separate or that the old stopes were just too dilapidated and unstable to use. E. F. Goodall raised a few tons of lead, zinc, and baryte in 1905–1907. The mine was tried again in 1926 (J. H. Clay), 1943–1944 (T. & W. T. Shaw), and 1944–1948 (E. Gregory). McKechnie Bros bought out Gregory in 1948 but their attempt to work the mine was short-lived.

The output of the Driggith vein is difficult to establish since the published tonnages were often compounded with those of other mines and the output prior to the establishment of Robert Hunt's Mining Records series in 1845 is rarely recorded. Mannix & Whellan (1847: 460) quote Richardson and Lowrey's output at 200 tons of lead ore annually from 1810 to 1823 giving a total of 2600 tons of ore. However, in a later account, Whellan (1860: 226) states that this output was only maintained for 'a period of five years successively'. Perhaps too much reliance should not be placed on Whellan's figures: at one point Mannix & Whellan (ibid.) state that 'every bing of lead ore yielded one fother of lead' an unlikely result since 1 bing = 8 cwt and 1 fother = 19.5 cwt. The published figures for 1845 to 1907 show that the mine produced at least 3800 tons of lead ore yielding some 2500 tons of lead and 40 000 oz of silver. From 1856 to 1869, 88 tons of copper ore were raised and from 1906 to 1907 a few tons of baryte and zinc ore were recorded.

DRY GILL MINE

This small mine is, mineralogically, one of the most important sites in the U.K., but was never of much economic significance. It exploited an E–W lead vein, possibly an extension of the copper vein at Carrock End mine. The ore was almost entirely phosphatian mimetite, and was associated with manganese oxides in a gangue of hard quartz and baryte. Several hundred tons

Fig. 28 DRY GILL MINE: the strong Dry Gill lode is about 2 m wide where it crosses Dry Gill Beck which is diverted along the footwall of the solid quartz vein. A short distance downstream the beck breaks through the vein and it is here that the Deep, or Pattinson, level of Dry Gill mine commences, its entrance partly obscured in this view by the outcrop. Later levels were driven higher up Dry Gill and it is these workings that have yielded most specimen material this century.

of 'coloured lead ore' were raised in the mine's short working life; some of it sold to the glass-making industry (Ellis, 1851: 174).

The massive quartz 'back' of the Dry Gill vein stands like a wall from the shaly side of the valley but does not appear to have interested the 'old men' who did not value the ore here, probably through difficulty in smelting it. Although mineralogists and collectors were extracting 'campylite' as early as 1830, the first recorded working is that of 1846 when Hugh Lee Pattinson (inventor of the Pattinson process for the desilvering of lead) took out a lease to raise 'ore . . . of the nature of white and yellow ore'. He worked the mine from a level driven directly on the vein (the Deep or Pattinson Level [NY 325 346]) and raised most of the recorded output.

After Pattinson the mine was tried in a small way by F. W. Emerson and C. E. Symonds (1859–1863) and by various lessees of the Roughton Gill mine but little ore was raised. It was abandoned in 1869 and, although the Cleator Iron Ore Co. included Dry Gill in their 1890s search for umber and baryte in the area, nothing further was done (Adams, 1988).

Most of the fine 'campylite' specimens were obtained during the nineteenth century, but in no way exhausted the specimen potential of the deposit. In the last twenty years or so very many specimens have been collected underground, mostly from the levels driven in the higher parts of Dry Gill [NY 322 345] or from the vein outcrop exposed in a collapsed stope above the scree-covered side of the gill. Although the gill is dry, the mine is not; its inhospitable interior is flooded waist deep with perpetually cold water and rotten timbers have been known to collapse suddenly under the weight of stacked 'deads'. It is unfortunate that accidents involving irresponsible individuals in Dry Gill mine have tarnished the local image of mineral collectors and mining historians.

HAY GILL MINE

The Hay Gill sett also included the gills to the north and south (Ingray Gill and Birk Gill), the tributary valleys

Short Grain and Long Grain, and the early workings for lead and copper in Potts Gill although this last property later became a separate mining sett. At the foot of Hay Gill a smelter was built to process ore from the Roughton Gill mines; its remains can still be seen, including the dam in Hay Gill which supplied the water wheel and the collapsed flue on the fellside above.

The Hay Gill copper vein runs NE–SW across the gill just below the confluence of Long and Short Grain [NY 308 360]. There is no documented evidence for a mine until the late eighteenth century when it was worked by one Jos. Scott from 1785 to 1792 (Adams, 1988: 81). The Hay Gill Mining Co. took it up in 1839 and in 1843 a rich copper vein was reported (Watson, 1843: 58) a large specimen from which, described at the time as the richest ever found in the Caldbeck Fells, had been displayed in Carlisle the previous year (Anon, 1842). The outcome of the mining venture is not known but can be gauged from the total recorded output of the Hay Gill sett in the nineteenth century of little more than 20 tons of copper and 5 tons of lead ores. The mine was finally abandoned in 1874 but it is unlikely that much work had been done in the interim.

Hay Gill is reputed to have produced some fine malachite, but significant specimens are not known to the authors. Kingsbury and Hartley found atacamite and cuprite here (both very rare in the district), but the dumps are now mostly barren.

A short level at the foot of Hay Gill [NY 303 361] on a NNW–SSE vein evidently failed to find ore.

INGRAY GILL

Near the head of this shallow gill [NY 307 367] there are two old levels driven north and south of the gill on an almost N–S vein; both are still open but of no great extent. Ingray Gill was included in the Hay Gill mining sett and the levels were probably driven in the nineteenth century. The last records of work here are of the East Cumberland Mining Co. in about 1870. The vein contained lead and copper with arsenopyrite, alteration of the latter leading to the formation of the interesting assemblage of arsenates reported from here by Kingsbury & Hartley (see Appendix I). Inspection of the present dumps shows them to be almost completely barren, none too surprising in the light of Hartley's (1984) description of the waste as 'superficially unpromising.

LONG GRAIN

Mining in this tributary of Hay Gill was mentioned about the beginning of the eighteenth century by Pratt (MS), the working yielding 'verry fine pieces of oars verry near to the Grass' but clearly not in depth. Thomas Hillary refers to working at 'Longgrain' and to supplying 'Utensils for Blasting . . . att West Longrain' in his 'Bargains' book

for 1724 (Benson MSS, D/Ben/3116), but in 1726 he was instructed to 'Give Over the Tryall att Long Grane' (Benson MSS, D/Ben/3119). There is no further mention of the property until the mid-nineteenth century when it formed part of the lease of the Hay Gill sett. The last investigation was by the East Cumberland Mining Co. in 1867 (Adams, 1988). The dumps from two trials can still be seen [NY 313 353; NY 311 357] but no mineralization of interest has been reported.

LOW PIKE

A quartz vein, apparently the continuation of the Silver Gill lode, trends NE–SW across the northern slopes of High Pike and is here known as the Low Pike vein. A short level was driven on it to the east of Potts Gill and several small trials were dug at outcrop on Low Pike. All these workings contained quartz and some low grade baryte (Dunham & Dines, 1945).

In 1986, specimens from one small trial [NY 320 358] brought to the attention of MPC proved to contain the rare copper arsenate, cornwallite. Subsequent examination of the small site has revealed an assemblage of unusual copper and lead arsenate–phosphates including philipsburgite, which also occurs at Old Potts Gill mine.

MEXICO MINE   [see Roughton Gill mine]

NETHER ROW BROW

There are several short drifts, shallow pits, and trenches trending roughly NW–SE across Nether Row Brow from [NY 323 371 to 327 364]. The northernmost trial was driven near the farm of Nether Row where the Nether Row to Potts Gill Baryte mine track makes a hairpin bend; the southern level is close to the Sandbeds to Potts Gill track just north-west of a large glacial erratic known as the 'Dumpy Stone'. Vein material at these sites is similar and they are probably from the same vein.

The minerals found here consist of sparsely disseminated sulphides and sulphosalts in a compact quartz gangue. Of interest to the collector is the variety of rare oxidation products from both sites. However, none of these occurs in much quantity and mostly form as thin crusts and coatings although minute crystals of carminite and pharmacosiderite are not uncommon. The 'Dumpy Stone' level yielded small adamite crystals to Kingsbury and Hartley but none has been found since.

In 1815 a piece of lead ore was found on Nether Row Brow that assayed 600 oz of silver to the ton but the precise origin of this very rich specimen is unknown (Parson & White, 1829).

PODDY GILL

The E–W lead vein seen in Carrock Mine crops out at the foot of Poddy Gill [NY 328 328] and a small trial has been made on it. Wulfenite was reported from here by

Fig. 29 POTTS GILL BARYTE MINE: the aerial ropeway carried dressed baryte just over 1 km from Potts Gill to the road at Nether Row. Since the closure of the mine the site has been cleared and bulldozed leaving virtually nothing but waste rock.

Davidson & Thomson (1951) and later described by Braithwaite, Greenland & Ryback (1963) on specimens collected from the dump. Some 'wulfenite' specimens from this locality have recently proved to be stolzite, and the orange plates of either species grown on green pyromorphite are extremely attractive. In the 1970s Poddy Gill was diverted to by-pass the new settling ponds built for Carrock mine and material from the dump was used to dam the stream's former course.

POTTS GILL

Several mines have been worked here: the Potts Gill Copper mine, Old Potts Gill, and East Potts Gill mines. Shaw (1970) gives a detailed description of the workings of the last two. There are other workings and trials in the area, some of which have become incorporated in the larger mines. The term Potts Gill Baryte mine may refer to either the Old or the East Potts Gill mine, or both. The sett also included Deer Hills (q.v.).

Potts Gill Copper mine

In 1866 the East Cumberland Mining Co. leased the Hay Gill mine sett, which at that time included Potts Gill, and opened (or reopened) this small mine. It exploited a NNW–SSE copper lode from two levels [NY 318 370]

and, although worked vigorously, was not successful. The mine was abandoned in 1871. The workings have collapsed and their extent is unknown. It may well have been from stringers of this vein in the Old Potts Gill mine, that the specimens labelled 'old No. 1 cross-cut' by Kingsbury (see below) originated.

Old Potts Gill mine

Two veins, trending more or less E–W, cross the head of Potts Gill and are known as the North, or Main, vein and the South vein; the former being the richer. The South vein joins the North vein to the west of Potts Gill (see Fig. 4). Baryte is the main mineral present and occurred in the North vein in large lenses up to 3 m across (averaging 0.5 m) separated by barren ground. The veins also contained much broken and altered country rock, quartz, and iron and manganese oxides. Quartz was more abundant in the higher levels whereas to the west, manganese oxides rendered the baryte worthless (Dunham & Dines, 1945: 95–99; Shaw, 1970: 65–67).

The veins were worked at outcrop for lead and copper by the East Cumberland Mining Co. from 1871, although trials may have been made earlier. However, they found little ore and went bankrupt in 1874. A few tons of lead and copper ore are recorded from this period but the figures include all the mines held by the company at that time, i.e. Hay Gill, Potts Gill Copper mine, and other trials in the area. Old Potts Gill mine lay idle for several years until Cleator Moor Iron Co. extracted 400–500 tons of baryte in 1887–1892. Subsequently, there was no interest until the outbreak of war in 1914. Thereafter, the mine was worked successfully, though intermittently, until 1942 when the manganese oxide content became too great and caused the lessees, McKechnie Bros, to abandon the west end. By 1947 all the payable baryte had been removed from above the deepest working (the Endeavour level [NY 319 365]) and, as the ore failed below this level, the mine was then left and the company's efforts transferred to the East Potts Gill mine.

Although large quantities of baryte were extracted, few well crystallized specimens were obtained. The mineralogical reputation of the mine lies with a suite of unusual copper minerals found here by Kingsbury and Hartley in the 1950s (Hartley, 1984). Their specimens came from the old No. 1 cross-cut dumps at the head of the gill [NY 320 362] and included chalcophyllite, conichalcite, devilline, dioptase, serpierite, and tyrolite; an occurrence unique in the district. The origin of these within the mine is not known for certain, but Shaw (1970: 67) notes that 'On the South Lode, just west of the No. 1 Level Crosscut, a small north and south vein came in on the hanging wall side and a little bunch of copper ore was taken out. The bulk of the ore was chalcopyrite and the black oxide, melaconite, some malachite and the rare cornwallite.'

Shaw left some of this material on the dump where it was later investigated by Kingsbury; the site was subsequently buried under waste from the baryte workings (Shaw, in conversation with N. Thomson, *pers. comm.*). Cornwallite has been found by later collectors but the other rarites have not; however, the newly-described species philipsburgite was recently identified on specimens collected from the Potts Gill dumps over twenty years ago. Most of the Potts Gill mine dumps have been bulldozed in recent years in an attempt to improve the landscape, obliterating potentially interesting parts of the site.

East Potts Gill mine

Workings on the eastward extension of the Potts Gill veins began in earnest in 1942 from levels in the east side

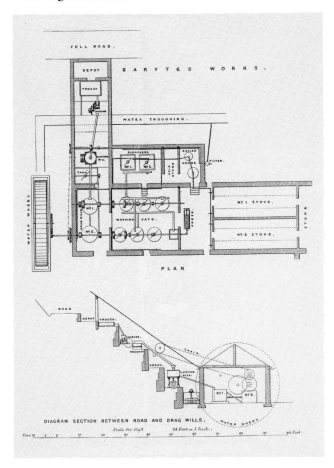

Fig. 30 BARYTE MILL: plan and section (after Addison, 1889–90) of the mill built on the site of the late eighteenth century lead smelter at the foot of Hay Gill. Here, 'the most improved methods' were used by the Cleator Iron Ore Company to grind and purify baryte from Potts Gill. After grinding, using equipment similar to that already devised by the same company for the milling of umber at another Caldbeck working (the 'China Clay mine'), the baryte was purified by boiling in sulphuric acid, washed, toned with 'six to eight table-spoonfuls of ultramarine blue' per 30 cwt of baryte, filtered, and dried. No mention is made in Addison's paper of arrangements for the disposal of the several hundred gallons of muddy acidic effluent created per batch.

of the gill, driven directly on the North and South lodes [NY 320 361]. These were called the John and Thomas levels respectively. A short cross-cut from the former cut a further lode, the New North lode, only 6 m north of the North vein. The majority of the mining was on these two northerly lodes. As the work progressed, further levels were driven lower down Potts Gill and, finally, a long cross-cut (the Tunnel level cross-cut) was driven from the north. The mine continued to be worked by McKechnie Bros, until its closure in 1966, averaging 100 tons of dressed baryte a week. A conspicuous feature of these workings was the aerial ropeway which carried ore over 1.1 km to the road at Nether Row.

By the end of their lives the Potts Gill mines had produced over 90 000 tons of baryte.

RED GILL MINE

An ancient mine, reputedly worked by the Elizabethans and possibly earlier, it exploited a NW–SE lead–copper–zinc vein from several levels in the spur between Swinburn Gill and Red Gill (Fig. 31), about 0.5 km west-north-west of Roughton Gill [NY 295 348]. Levels were also dug in the head of Red Gill and in the opposite bank of Swinburn Gill.

Nothing is known of the Elizabethan workings. The 'Old Dutch' level is attributed to them and the High level and Top level (both in Red Gill proper, but untraceable now) are supposed to have predated them (Shaw, 1970). Workings in Red Gill are mentioned in *c.*1700 (Pratt, MS) and in 1724 Thomas Hillary was working 'Redgill head' and 'West Redgill' (Benson MSS, D/Ben/3116) but thereafter it is not until the nineteenth century that the mine is documented.

In the 1820s it was included in the Roughton Gill sett and may have been worked by that mine's lessees. It is known to have been working in the 1840s and, in 1861, it was leased by the Red Gill Mining Company along with Brae Fell mine and other small trials in the area. A stamp mill was erected in Swinburn Gill; its ruins can be seen by the track to the mine and leats which carried water for power can be traced in the hillside above. The Red Gill workings were extended but the short ore shoots found were not economic and in 1866 the owners decided to concentrate their efforts elsewhere. Total production in this period was about 28 tons of dressed lead ore with peak production of 15 tons in 1862. In addition, 45 tons of dressed copper ore was raised in the ten years to 1871 when the Red Gill Company went into liquidation. From that time there has been no commercial exploitation. Speculators cleaned out the mine in 1882 and 1905 but raised no ore.

Red Gill is famous for its suite of sulphate and sulphate-carbonate minerals; an assemblage that has much in common with that found at Leadhills, Scotland. Linarite, leadhillite, caledonite, and anglesite from Red Gill are

Fig. 31 RED GILL MINE: three run-in entrances to the Red Gill mine trend approximately west-north-west across the spur between Swinburn Gill and Red Gill (in shadow behind the spur). The lowest level seen here is the Deep level and above it is the Old Dutch, or No. 2, level, reputedly the source of the mine's finest linarite specimens. Queitite and mattheddleite have recently been found on the dump to the right of the Old Dutch level but material of specimen quality is now very sparsely distributed in the thoroughly picked-over debris.

Fig. 32 ROUGHTON GILL MINE: the entrance to the 30 fm level cross-cut (on the left of the picture) is mostly run-in in this photograph taken in 1987. The remains of the stone-built retaining walls can still be seen, and part of an old wooden mine rail protrudes from the rubble between. The origins of this cross-cut are unrecorded but, although elsewhere widened by nineteenth century blasting, sections of it are still hand-cut 'coffin' level and show that it must be several hundred years old. Roof falls block progress before the vein is reached.

among the finest ever found in Britain. Two levels are still open: Deep level which runs into the fell just above Swinburn Gill Beck, and the No. 2 or 'Old Dutch' level higher up the slope. Higher still, a small shaft or open stope breaks the surface. The workings themselves are dilapidated and, although a section exists (Adams, 1988: 77) the collapsed and backfilled levels do not correspond to it. Nothing of great importance has been found underground since the nineteenth century. However, the now almost barren dumps have yielded small amounts of macphersonite, mattheddleite, and queitite in recent years.

To the north of Red Gill, there are a number of dumps from small trials in Swinburn Gill, in one of which [NY 297351] an isolated specimen of superb linarite crystals to over 10 mm was found by A. W. G. Kingsbury in 1950. There are also several small dumps in the Dry and Wet Smale Gills (tributaries of Swinburn Gill); they now consist almost entirely of barren quartz or rock 'deads'.

ROUGHTON GILL MINE

This is the largest and most famous mine in the district, with a long history of continuous and occasionally very profitable working. The mining sett includes Roughton Gill, Silver Gill and the Mexico mine, and lies at the head of the Dale Beck valley, the relatively broad reach of which terminates abruptly where the Roughton Gill veins cross it. The veins comprise a series of sub-parallel mineralized fractures trending NE–SW and extend some 5.5 km from Frozen Fell (2 km south-west of Roughton Gill) to Sandbeds mine. The two main veins were known to the miners as the Silver Gill vein and the Roughton Gill South vein. A further vein (the Roughton Gill North vein) runs parallel to and a little to the north of the latter; it was regarded by some as part of the South vein separated merely by large included plates of country rock ('horses'). The vein nomenclature was confused by Eastwood (1921: 31) who referred to the Silver Gill and Roughton Gill lodes respectively as the North vein and the South vein, a usage since continued by many

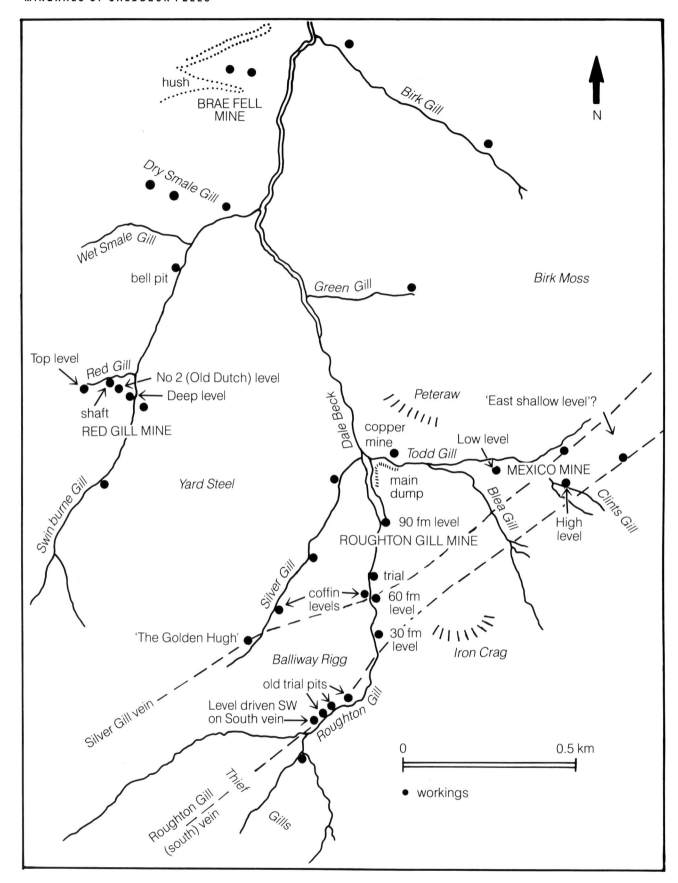

Fig. 33 MAP OF THE ROUGHTON GILL—BRAE FELL AREA.

Fig. 34 ROUGHTON GILL: looking south. On the left is a trial cross-cut to the Silver Gill vein which crops out just upstream. This entrance is often mis-identified as the Roughton Gill mine 60 fm level which actually begins near the larger waterfall to be seen top centre of this picture.

mineralogists and geologists. To enable us to be consistent in our descriptions of both the history and the mineralogy of this vein system we have chosen to adopt the original miners' terms.

The principal ore minerals were galena, chalcopyrite, and sphalerite. The main silver-bearing mineral is tetrahedrite although some silver may occur in solid-solution or as minute sulphosalt inclusions in galena. In the Silver Gill section of the mine the silver content reached 60 oz per ton of ore (Dean, 1852). The secondary minerals, malachite, pyromorphite, and cerussite were also important ores. The lead and copper content of the veins was subject to local enrichment and it may have been in one such ore shoot that an Elizabethan miner obtained copper ore worth £100, a small fortune, in nine weeks work (Collingwood, 1928: 13). The Roughton Gill South vein contained a large orebody referred to by Shaw (1970) as the 'Great Bunch', which extended from the 60 fm level down to the 90 fm level. At times the lode

swelled to 9 m wide; it was worked horizontally for 50 to 125 m. This bunch of ore ensured the prosperity of the mine for many years.

In all, the Roughton Gill lode was worked over 1.2 km from the head of Roughton Gill through to the Mexico mine. The mineralization died out in the extreme west where Skiddaw Slate was the country rock; the Mexico section was never very profitable in spite of promising shoots of cerussite and pyromorphite. The Silver Gill lode was worked almost entirely in Silver Gill, with little being done to the east in the Roughton Gill and Mexico sections. Roughton Gill mine was worked from several levels in this precipitous gill and from levels and shafts under Iron Crag. These were, eventually, continuous with some of the Silver Gill levels, but did not connect with the Mexico section. The full extent of the underground workings is unknown. There are no extant mine plans and, although several of the cross-cuts are accessible for some distance, none gives access to the vein

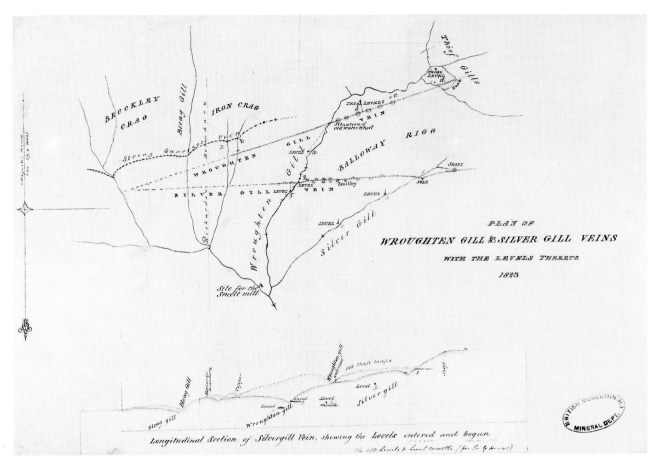

Fig. 35 ROUGHTON GILL AND SILVER GILL MINES 1823: a plan by an unknown hand. The '. . . Section of Silvergill Vein . . .' at the bottom of the plan folds back to reveal a similar section of the 'Wroughten Gill' vein. All the workings shown are still traceable today, though some are almost obscured by scree. In 'Wroughten Gill' the level marked 'a' is the old 30 fm cross-cut; '2' and '5' are trials on the Silver Gill vein—the latter is a superb example of a 'coffin level'. Numbers 1, 3, and 4 in Silver Gill are presumed to be the 'Golden Hugh', the 20, and the 50 fm levels respectively. The two veins do not intersect as shown in this plan (see fig. 4); that the 'old men' thought they did may perhaps explain why so much effort was to be put into developing the Mexico mine, for vein intersections were generally supposed to result in very rich ore deposits.

This plan was found by A. W. G. Kingsbury in 1947 in the back of an old copy of Postlethwaite's *Mines and mining in the Lake District*. It was presented to the BM(NH) in 1958. At least one other copy of this plan is known but does not show all the levels (see Adams, 1988: 71).

workings. It is likely that, following the 'robbing of the pillars' in the last days of mining, the notoriously unstable vein walls have collapsed into the old stopes (see Ward, 1977).

The origins of the mine are unknown but it is certainly one of the oldest in the district. Remains of hand-cut 'coffin' levels may still be seen in the higher workings and may be very old. The Roughton Gill mines are generally assumed to have been the site of the principal Elizabethan workings at Caldbeck but the records are not specific. It may be that the Silver Gill mines were initially more important.

Three main workings can still be seen in Silver Gill, from highest to lowest: the 'Golden Hugh' [NY 2985 3405], driven directly on the outcrop of the Silver Gill vein in the west of the gill; an open 'coffin' level cross-cut in the east bank [NY 2995 3415]; and a run-in and grassed-over level marked by a small dump on the east bank [NY 3005 3430]. These can be roughly correlated, although the depths seem somewhat arbitrary, with levels at 8, 20 and 50 fathoms from the surface described by Dean (1852). Trials were also made on the Silver Gill lode in Roughton Gill: a cross-cut driven south from the east bank [NY 3020 3425]; and a short level parallel to the vein on the downstream side of its outcrop in the steep west bank of the gill [NY 3020 3420] not far below the 60 fm level of Roughton Gill mine. Neither of these two trials is of great extent, but that in the west bank is notable for being one of the finest 'coffin' levels in the Lake District. All these levels are shown on the earliest known map of the workings in 1823 (Fig. 35). In 1988 the remains of a small ore bin, complete with a pile of rich copper–lead–zinc ore, was found buried in scree upstream from the middle level in Silver Gill. The siting here of an ore bin is puzzling and it may be that a further level lies buried nearby.

'Barstow's trench' (see p. 121)

Fig. 36 MEXICO MINE: looking east from the flank of Yard Steel (the west flank of the fellside above Silver Gill). The foot of Balliway Rigg cuts across the bottom of the picture and just above it the small water board pumping house marks the 90 fm horizon of the Roughton Gill mine. In the middle distance 'Barstow's trench' and the dumps from the Mexico mine levels can be seen (see key). 'Barstow's trench' (see p. 121) was the source of much fine pyromorphite in the 1970s but is now largely back-filled.

THE CALDBECK FELLS (CONSOLIDATED) LEAD AND COPPER MINING COMPANY (LIMITED).

Incorporated under the Companies Act, which strictly limits the liability of each shareholder to the amount of his subscription.

Capital £60,000, in 30,000 shares of £2 each, of which upwards of three-fourths are already disposed of.

Deposit 5s. per share on application, and 5s. on allotment.

Future calls not to exceed 5s. per share, and not to be made at less intervals than three months. It is estimated that not more than 20s. per share will be required.

DIRECTORS.

CHAIRMAN—Sir ROBERT BRISCO, Bart., Crofton Hall, Cumberland.
WILLIAM BANKS, Esq., Highmoor House, Wigton, Cumberland.
JOHN R. BINDLEY, Esq., 192, Gresham House, Old Broad-street, E.C.
WILLIAM COWAN, Esq., LL.D., Linburn House, Midcalder, Edinburgh.
THOMAS EYRE FOAKES, Esq., 4, New-square, Lincoln's Inn, W.C., Chairman of the Hammersmith and City Railway, and Director of the Aylesbury and Buckingham Railway.
HERBERT HARDIE, Esq., 34, Church-street, Manchester, Director of the Frontino and Bolivia South American Gold Mining Company (Limited).
FRANCIS RUMMENS, Esq., 5, Queen's-square, Westminster, S.W.
ADAM SCHOALES, Esq., 7, Cleveland-gardens, Hyde-park, W., Director of the Great Wheal Vor Mining Company.

BANKERS—Agra and Masterman's Bank, 35, Nicholas-lane, E.C.

SOLICITORS.

Messss. Calthrop, White, and Buckston, 8, Whitehall-place, Wesminster, S.W.
Messrs. S. and S. G. Saul, Carlisle.

AUDITORS—Messrs. Johnstone, Cooper, Wintle, and Co., 3, Coleman-street-buildings.

BROKERS—James Irving, Esq., Carlisle; Jonathan Drewry, Esq., Newcastle-on-Tyne; Joseph Nicholson, Esq., Whitehaven; Henry Kenyon, Esq, Maryport; R. A. Tyson, Esq., Penrith.

SECRETARY—W. G. Powning, Esq.

OFFICES,—192, GRESHAM HOUSE, OLD BROAD-STREET.

The object of this company is to work more extensively the valuable mineral properties known as the Roughten Gill, Dry Gill, and Carrock-End Mines.

The Roughten Gill Mine is situated in the Caldbeck Fells, about 8 miles from Wigton, and 13 miles from Penrith and Carlisle, in the county of Cumberland. The sett is very large, about 3½ miles long from east to west' and about 2½ miles from north to south. Dry Gill and Carrock-End Mines are a little to the east of the Roughten Gill Mine, and embrace the north flank of Carrock Fells, from 3 to 3½ miles in length.

Both setts have been worked by the present proprietor, but the Roughten Gill has been more extensively developed. The directors have enquired into the returns now made from the latter mine: it appears with the present machinery and the limited force employed, that it is now producing about £2000 per annum nett profit, which may be increased to almost an unlimited extent if greater facilities are made to extract the ores, and additional machinery erected to prepare them for market. The Dry Gill Mine when laid open under the adit is also expected to prove as good as the Roughten Gill, the indications now observed in the shallow workings being extremely encouraging, and presenting every prospect of meeting with large masses of ore in depth.

The locality is very convenient for increasing the water power required for large operations, and there are good roads for the transport of the product to market; and while there are three ports within easy shipping distance, a movement is being made for the construction of a railway, which will materially reduce the costs of carriage, and increase the present facilities of communication.

The company has secured, on advantageous terms, the leases and all the plant, machinery, and effects now on the mines. The machinery and other plant alone are estimated to be of the value of £8000, independently of the levels, cross-cuts, and water-courses—which have been made at a great cost—and are available for large operations. The property is so extensive that portions may be hereafter leased to other parties with advantage to the company.

By the terms of the purchase, the amount to be paid for the leases, plant, &c., above described, is £20,000, of which sum only £10,000 is to be paid in cash, by instalments, the vendors taking the remainder in shares of the company. There being no promotion money, the preliminary expenses will be confined to the amounts necessarily paid.

Seeing the large quantity of ore ground already laid open, and the good prospects of the various lodes, the directors consider that they have every reason to expect a produce sufficient to leave a large and permanent profit on the capital employed, and so satisfied are they of the success of this undertaking, that they and their friends have already agreed to take a large number of shares.

Specimens of the various classes of ore brought from the mines, sections of the workings, copies of several engineers' reports, and Articles of Association, may be inspected, and all further particulars obtained on application at the offices of the compahy.

Notice is hereby given, that NO FURTHER APPLICATIONS for SHARES in this company will be RECEIVED after SATURDAY, the 4th of March.

Feb. 22, 1865. By order, W. G. POWNING, Sec.

Fig. 37 PROSPECTUS: for shares in the Caldbeck Fells (Consolidated) Lead and Copper Mining Company Ltd., published in the *Mining Journal*, 25 February 1865 (page 129). In the following week [*MJ*, 4 March (p. 141)] it was stated that applications considerably exceeded the number of shares to be allocated.

The 'Golden Hugh' is probably the oldest working in Silver Gill; it was mentioned in about 1700 by Pratt (MS) and was crudely mapped, along with a lower level, as 'The great lead silver mine of Golden [H]ugh and Silver Gill' in 1710 (Walker, MS). The 'coffin' levels mentioned above are also ancient but both have been widened in places by nineteenth century blasting. In 1724 Thomas Hillary was employing several men to work Golden Hugh and Silver Gill and to drive a drift in 'what they call Yalld Stele', probably Yard Steel between Silver Gill and Swinburn Gill (Leconfield MSS, D/Lec/219). That year there seems to have been a celebration, for Hillary records 2 shillings spent on 'Drink to the Workmen that Cut into Golden Hugh's Vein'. In 1726 he was ordered to hasten the work there and to sink a shaft upon the vein but the outcome is not known (Benson MSS, D/Ben/3117; 3119).

The early miners in Silver Gill are reputed to have removed a considerable quantity of argentiferous lead ore; indeed, legend has it that 'a family once lived in a hut, and coined silver money from the produce of the old vein called Silver Gill, till they were discovered and obliged to abscond' (Parson & White, 1829). However, by about 1700 the Silver Gill lode was reported to have been worked clean through Balliway Rigg and 'great triall made . . . and by all appearances but a small quantity of oars gotten' (Pratt, MS). The lower levels were driven forward in the 1850s (Dean, 1852) but little ore was found, and the lode seems to have been abandoned for a time. It was taken up again from the Roughton Gill mine 90 fm level in the 1870s but proved almost valueless.

Of Roughton Gill itself, there is no mention until a smelter was built there in 1794 (Postlethwaite, 1913) but the mine must be older than this. The earliest workings were probably those at outcrop on the Roughton Gill South vein in higher Roughton Gill [NY 330 338 to NY 302 339]. During the eighteenth century the principal working is thought to have been from the 30 fm level [NY 302 341] a cross-cut to the Roughton Gill vein. It was stoped almost to the surface under Iron Crag and worked to the east and west for several hundred metres. By the 1830s it was worked out and a new adit, the 60 fm cross-cut, was begun in Roughton Gill [NY 302 342].

Between 1838 and 1845, 3229 tons of lead ore and 150 tons of copper ore were extracted (Mannix & Whellan, 1847). Roughton Gill vein was worked to the south-west of the cross-cut for over 500 m and ran through a rich pocket of gossany ore containing large quantities of pyromorphite, malachite, and cerussite. Beyond this, the lode consisted mainly of galena and chalcopyrite in a gangue of calcite (Eastwood, 1921), the 'Great Bunch' mentioned above. The mine was abandoned in 1845 when the owners lease ran out and the landowners demanded an excessively high rent for renewal. The mine was still a valuable property, however, and for the next twenty years was to make rich men out of several leaseholders.

In 1849, the lease was taken up by the Roughtengill [*sic*] Silver, Lead and Copper Mining Co. who erected a new smelter at the foot of Hay Gill* and began driving the 90 fm cross-cut adit [NY 3025 3440] and the Mexico mine levels (Low level [NY 3055 3450]; Intermediate level [NY 3065 3455]; High level [NY 3075 3445]). The 'Great Bunch' was still productive: it was described in a company prospectus in 1852 as 'a very fine lode of immense size, composed chiefly of friable and compact quartz, fluccan [clay] and gossan, thickly impregnated with phosphate of lead, of which about 20 tons were broken . . . from two small pitches in the back of the level' (Dean, 1852). Peak production, in 1851, was 659 tons of dressed lead, falling to 200 tons a year in 1853–1854 then averaging 400 tons a year for the next ten years. Lessees in this period were James Dixon and Samuel

* The line of the smelter flue can still be traced on the fellside above the site and the remains of the mill pond dam still partially block Hay Gill beck. Water was also brought in wooden launder boxes from Dale Beck at the foot of Birk Gill; the route taken is clearly visible just above the road. By 1865 the smelter had been abandoned and converted into a line of miner's cottages. These were derelict in 1889–1890 when the site was converted into a baryte dressing plant by Percy Addison for the Cleator Iron Ore Co. (Addison, 1889–1890). In 1894–1895 the plant was broken up and sold.

Merryweather (1855–1863), and John and Jesse Tustin (1863–1865) all of whom made fortunes. It appears, however, that these companies did little development work, concentrating on removing the rich and easily won ores. In 1865, the newly formed Caldbeck Fells (Consolidated) Lead and Copper Mining Company took over with the share prospectus (Fig. 37) proclaiming 'Seeing the large quantity of ore ground already laid open, and the good prospects of the various lodes, the directors consider that they have every reason to expect a produce sufficient to leave a large and permanent profit on the capital employed.' This company also purchased the sett to the east incorporating Dry Gill and Carrock End. The directors took the unprecedented step of inviting a party, including several eminent Cornish mining engineers, to view and comment on the property. It was unanimously agreed that the mine was potentially one of the richest in the country and only required competent management to become a very profitable venture. The 'gossan of the extraordinary lodes' of Roughton Gill mine contained 'thousands of tons of

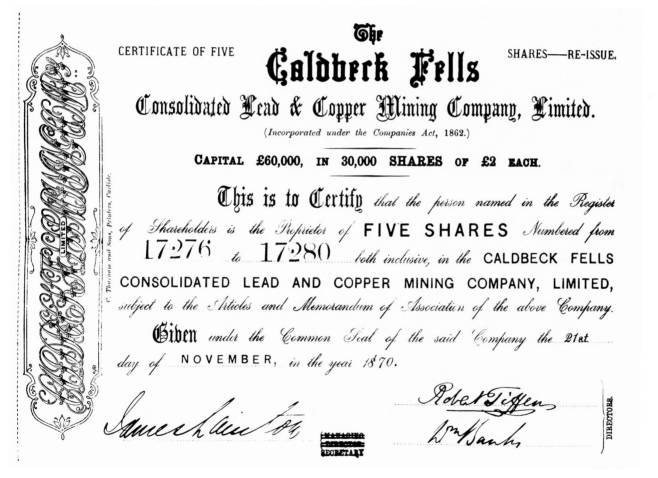

Fig. 38 SHARE CERTIFICATE: of the Caldbeck Fells Consolidated Lead and Copper Mining Company. By 1870 the Caldbeck Fells Consolidated Lead and Copper Mining Company's shares were not a good investment, in fact it is unlikely that they ever were. Falling metal prices and a shortage of ore in their Roughton Gill workings were taking their toll. Far from taking a profit, shareholders were called upon to make further payments, and, dogged by accusations of incompetence and double-dealing, the company was to go bankrupt by 1876. D. R. Hacker Collection.

Fig. 39 ROUGHTON GILL MINE: a fragment of a grindstone and the ashlar foundations of a building are almost all that remains of the once extensive ore-dressing plant at Roughton Gill mine. The last mill on this site was that used by the Cleator Iron Ore Company to dress umber from the Hare Stones Umber mine (the China Clay mine). Everything of value was dismantled and sold on the closure of the Company's Caldbeck operations in 1894. Last to go was the overshot water wheel, previously used for power at Red Gill mine; it was eventually broken up for scrap.

phosphates and carbonates of lead, from the top of the mountain even to its base, a depth of about 90 fathoms', and suggested to all that fabulously rich primary ore (galena) underlay the 90 fm adit level. This potential was never realized. In a distant echo of the Mines Royal's disastrous enterprise, the company spent thousands of pounds driving levels at Mexico mine (also known as Crown Point), sinking an engine shaft to dewater the proposed workings below the 90 fm adit level, and constructing ever more costly ore dressing equipment, but never showed a penny profit. The Mexico mine was a complete failure and was abandoned about 1868. Work on the new engine shaft ('Lainton's Shaft') was frequently held up by lack of funds or manpower. In 1872–1873 most of the workforce left for more remunerative work in the expanding iron mines and collieries of Cumberland and Lancashire. Moreover, the company was beset by

managerial squabbles and incompetence and the mine machinery was regularly halted by lack of water through drought or frost. The only reasonable run of ore they had was almost lost when, through careless mining, tons of rock fell on the underground pumping wheel in Junction Shaft. The regular reports and angry correspondence in the *Mining Journal* from 1865 to 1878 show that, yet again, failure was inevitable. That they lasted so long is some measure of their hope and faith, but in February 1878 the bankrupt company was wound up, bringing to an end several hundred years of metal mining. Subsequently, the crumbling mine and its dumps were briefly worked over for umber and baryte, but by 1894 it was all over.

Carlisle Urban District Council bought the mine in 1913 for use as a water supply and their small pumping house remains the only marker for the buried 90 fm level portal. Even the mine dumps have been greatly eroded— a great flood in 1895 reputedly carried away half of them—and waste material is spread the length of Dale Beck. Collectors cannot hope to match the magnificent specimens brought out during the nineteenth century working, but still dig into the dumps that remain in the hope of unearthing specimens of pyromorphite, mimetite, hemimorphite and plumbogummite, for which the locality is renowned.

SANDBEDS MINE   [see Driggith mine]

SANDBEDS EAST AND WEST MINES
These two mines worked an E−W baryte lode. The outcrop at Sandbeds East was found in 1927 but was not developed until 1946 when a level was driven from near the old 90 fm level of the Driggith–Sandbeds mine [NY 333 361]. At first, some rich ore was worked, but the lode was generally poor and did not improve in depth. Shaw (1970: 72) states that the 100 fm level was largely driven through unaltered rock 'which showed that the working was at the base of the barytes zone', and that the yield from the lode was very poor.

Sandbeds West, discovered in 1956 by driving a cross-cut to the projected extension of the Sandbeds East lode, worked ore which, although very variable, was remarkably rich in places. Some 35 000 tons of dressed baryte was extracted, equivalent to a solid rib of baryte 60 cm thick over the entire stoped area. It was the richest baryte mine of the Potts Gill–Sandbeds group (the 'Caldbeck Mines') and was eventually opened out on 6 levels from 30 to 90 fm below ground. The last level was driven from within the old Driggith–Sandbeds 90 fm adit. Further details are given by Shaw (1970: 70–74) who was directly involved in the management of these mines.

No notable specimens came from either mine.

SHORT GRAIN
Of the several small mines and trials recorded in this tributary of Hay Gill (see Adams, 1988: 79) only one has proved to be of mineralogical interest. This level, Short Grain North [NY 3130 3585], was driven northwards on the NNW−SSE Deer Hills quartz lode. The mine was last worked in 1870 and, since 1937, the date on the pumping house, the workings have been sealed and used as a water supply.

Recent examination of the small dump of mostly rock 'deads', quartz and baryte, has shown that some cavities in the baryte contain minute amounts of the rare super-gene minerals susannite and mattheddleite.

SILVER GILL MINE   [see Roughton Gill mine]

TODD GILL
On the north side of Todd Gill, opposite the main dumps of the Roughton Gill mine, is a small collapsed trial on a copper vein [NY 3035 3455]. This may be the working referred to by Pratt (MS) in about 1700: 'On the south side of Petra [Peteraw, the fell between Birk Gill and Todd Gill] there is a copper vein driven about 12 yds into the hill, which they tell us was good copper & pretty quantity at the beginning, but of little consequence when it was left of working.' Thomas Hillary was working a vein in 'Toodgill' or 'Toddgill' in 1724 but gives no information to identify the site (Benson MSS, D/Ben/3116).

Other than some sphalerite and traces of copper minerals, the present small dump is barren. Adams' (1988: 72) reference to gold from this site probably confuses Kingsbury's record of gold from the nearby Mexico mine Low level [NY 3055 3450] driven in Todd Gill in the nineteenth century.

WET SWINE GILL
In 1981, a previously unrecorded antimony-bearing vein was discovered about half way up the gill [NY 3144 3215] by J. D. Ingham and the mineralogy was published by Fortey et al. in 1984. A few years later, the small exposure had been all but collected out. Of the antimony sulphosalts, which occur here with arseno-pyrite and other sulphides in a quartz gangue, fülöppite is the most sought after. However, it occurs only sparingly and many specimens have been sold so labelled, deliberately or not, when the specimen contains mainly stibnite.

COLLECTORS

… through whose exertions many rare and beautiful minerals have been introduced into the cabinets of amateur collectors, which otherwise would probably have rested for ages in their dark security unknown to the eye of science.

(Sowerby, 1850: 14, on Bryce Wright).

The Caldbeck Fells mines were not only unimportant commercially in the late seventeenth and for much of the eighteenth centuries but they also appear to have been largely ignored by scientists and collectors in the then nascent field of mineralogy. It has been frustrating whilst researching this period—and even the early years of the nineteenth century—to note how many eminent scientists passed the Caldbeck Fells by on their way to the richer lead mines of Alston Moor or to the valuable and historic 'Wadd' (graphite) mine in Borrowdale in search of scientific and technical knowledge. Other visitors to the Lake District at this time, from the gentleman scholar to the writers who formed the hub of a growing tourist industry, also neglected the northern fells in favour of the central lakes and mountains (see Nicholson, 1955).

By the mid-nineteenth century the lead mines of the Caldbeck Fells were at their zenith both as ore and specimen producers. However, the area seems to have lacked a coterie of mineral dealers and collectors to parallel that developed in Cornwall at the turn of the century (see Embrey & Symes, 1987: 61–78), due partly, perhaps, to a decline in amateur collecting in fashionable society. Nevertheless, a few collectors and dealers acquired Caldbeck Fells' specimens with considerable enthusiasm.

The early twentieth century saw the final days of lead and copper mining in the Caldbeck Fells and decline in many other U.K. mining fields. Mineral collecting entered a correspondingly quiescent period. However, in the latter part of this century there has been a remarkable resurgence of interest in mineralogy both as science and hobby. In Great Britain the Caldbeck Fells were, and remain, an important element in this revival. We attempt here to sketch those persons and collections that have made important contributions to our understanding of the mineralogy of the area, and to trace the history of the discovery of major species and to note the present whereabouts of significant specimens and collections in Great Britain. For a more general view of the history of mineralogy and collections in Great Britain the reader is referred to the works by Smith (1969, 1978), Embrey (1977a), Cleevely (1983), and Embrey & Symes (1987).

It is of no surprise to find that the earliest documented specimens of Caldbeck Fells' minerals are those in the cabinet of the great English collector Dr John Woodward (1665–1728). Woodward was one of the first to collect geological specimens for their scientific interest rather than as mere curiosities, although it was said by a contemporary, Sir John Clerk, that Woodward himself was 'the greatest Curiosity on earth, being a vain, foolish and affected man' (Eyles 1965: 870). He began his collection about 1696 and either personally, or through friends and agents, collected minerals, rocks, slags, fossils and cut stones from Great Britain and overseas (Eyles, 1965; Porter, 1979). On his death his collection was bequeathed to Cambridge University where it may now be seen in the Sedgwick Museum in its original and elegant cabinets. Woodward's own catalogues, published in two volumes in 1728 and 1729, could hardly be improved upon today for their meticulous recording of the origins and characteristics of the specimens. Unfortunately, his specimens from the Caldbeck Fells would not excite the taste of the modern collector: they include fragments of galena ('formerly work'd for silver by the Hochstetters'), chalcopyrite, granular pyromorphite and a heavy slag 'taken off the surface of the lead, smelted out of Caudbeck-ore'. Of this last, Woodward observed: 'I never saw the like in other lead-works: but 'tis constant here. Observing it to be very ponderous, I suspected there was metal in it, and making trial I got a considerable proportion of lead out of a piece of this sort' (Woodward, 1729: specimen A q.9).

Fig. 40 MIMETITE: Dry Gill mine. A selection of nineteenth century 'campylites' from the BM(NH) collections, dominated by the huge specimen (20 × 25 × 15 cm) donated by Hugh Lee Pattinson, the lessee of the mine, to the Museum of Practical Geology (BM 1985, MI15426). Ranged in front of it are, from left to right: a variegated specimen of dark brown mimetite with a partial green overgrowth of the same mineral (BM 24338) bought by the BM from Bryce Wright in 1849 and two specimens from the Russell Collection BM 1964, R8171 and BM 1964, R8134. The former was acquired by Russell from the collection of George Penrose of Truro and had previously belonged to D. Bain of Keynsham. Specimen BM 1964, R8134 is partially coated with 'psilomelane' and was originally collected by Pattinson.

Although the past importance and potential of the Caldbeck mines are mentioned throughout the eighteenth century in books on the history or natural history of Cumberland, little mention is made anywhere of the actual mineral products. One of the earliest natural histories is *An essay towards a natural history of Cumberland and Westmorland* (1709) by Thomas Robinson, Rector of Ousby, near Penrith. Robinson was widely read in geology and related matters and wrote several books on the subject. He was an enthusiastic, if incompetent, promoter of mining and smelting in Cumberland, sometimes to the detriment of his church. Both he and his superior, William Nicolson, Bishop of Carlisle, provided specimens of local ores to John Woodward. In 1696 he leased the coal mine at Bolton, north of Caldbeck, from the Duke of Somerset and in 1697 began promoting the re-opening of the old Mines Royal property at Goldscope, near Keswick. By 1714 he had been arrested no fewer than six times for debts incurred in these projects. A complaint had also been made concerning his interference in the Caldbeck mines but his influence here was slight as the workings were not on Somerset's land at the time. None of his projects was successful (Grant, 1985).

A rare eighteenth century account of Caldbeck minerals is that of an anonymous visitor who wrote in 1747:

> most of their lapilli are a fluor of the stalactite kind, or a sparry talc resembling white flint variegated with hexagonal crystalline spars, whose points will cut glass like the adamant, but immediately lose that property from their fragile quality. Others are impregnated with the marcasite of lead, but so blended with an arsenical sulphur that they evaporate in the process of separation, and others are of the copperas kind ... indeed in *Brandlegill Beck* [Brandy Gill] and the Northern descents, copper has formerly been dug, but the mines are long since worn out; hereabouts the *lapis calaminaris* is also found.
>
> (Anon, 1747: 523)

The map which accompanies this account (Fig. 2, p. 8) suggests the author did not venture much further into the Fells than Mosedale; the minerals he mentions possibly including quartz, galena, and arsenopyrite from the veins in Brandy Gill. It is tempting to interpret the 'lapis calaminaris'—an old term for zinc ore—as hemimorphite from Roughton Gill since the only other zinc mineral common in the district is sphalerite whose value as an ore was not appreciated until John Champion proved its use in 1758.

Towards the end of the century, the Caldbeck lead mines were being worked sufficiently vigorously to justify the construction of smelters for Roughton Gill and Driggith in 1794, but the lead minerals themselves were then, apparently, of little interest. The Brandy Gill

tungsten veins, however, were regarded with great excitement. James Sowerby included an illustration of an unprepossessing, but mineralogically important, specimen of molybdenite from Caldbeck in volume 3 of his monumental *British Mineralogy* (1809). Apatite from the same source appeared in volume 5 (1817: 279) 'in a vein of Quartz ... accompanied by hexahedral laminae of Mica, Mispickle, Pyrites, and that rare British mineral Sulphuret of Molybdenum.' Adam Sedgwick's comments on the working of the Brandy Gill veins by mineral collectors in the 1820s have been referred to earlier (p. 13). Small scheelite crystals collected by him from this locality are in the collection of Cambridge University. Henry Heuland (1778–1856), one of the most influential and well-connected dealers of the early nineteenth century, may have been one of those alluded to by Sedgwick. In 1820 Heuland sold a collection of minerals, that contained several fine scheelite crystals (Fig. 102a,b), apatite and molybdenite (one with 'acide molybdique jaune'—most likely ferrimolybdite), to Charles Hampden Turner of Godalming, Surrey. The collection, based on one started by Heuland's uncle Jacob Forster, was catalogued for Heuland by Armand Lévy (1837) and was later acquired by Henry Ludlam (see below).

In Edinburgh, the wealthy collector Thomas Allan (1777–1833) acquired fine scheelite specimens from the Caldbeck Fells. The catalogue of his collection contains meticulous crystal drawings of these specimens (Fig. 41) by his son Robert (1806–1863), the well known author of several important mineralogy texts including the fourth edition of Phillips' *Elementary introduction to the knowledge of mineralogy* in 1837 (Embrey, 1977a).

Away from the Brandy Gill tungsten veins, mimetite appears to have been the next important mineralogical discovery. The earliest dated 'campylites' from Dry Gill in the BM(NH) were acquired by Thomas Allan in 1830–1831 but it was not until 1837 that Robert Allan (*in* Phillips, 1837: 364) gave an account of 'arseniate of lead ... aggregated in opake, orange-yellow coloured individuals, which consist each of three hexagonal prisms curved towards their terminations in a manner often beautifully symmetrical.' No more specific locality than 'Caldbeck Fell' is given. Likewise, the 'honey-yellow botryoidal' mineral analysed by Thomas Thomson (1773–1852), Professor of Chemistry at Glasgow, was not precisely localized. Thomson's specimen was bought from an unnamed Cumberland mineral dealer as 'vanadiate of lead' but declared by Thomson (1839) to be 'diarseniate of lead ... a new mineral species'. It was undoubtedly mimetite. After his death Thomson's collection (or a part of it) was acquired by the Department of Mines, Victoria, Australia, where it was catalogued by W. Vazie Simons, a London surgeon (Simons, 1866). This catalogue mentions a variety of species from 'Carrickfell' or 'Caldbeckfells' including a 'Campellite—

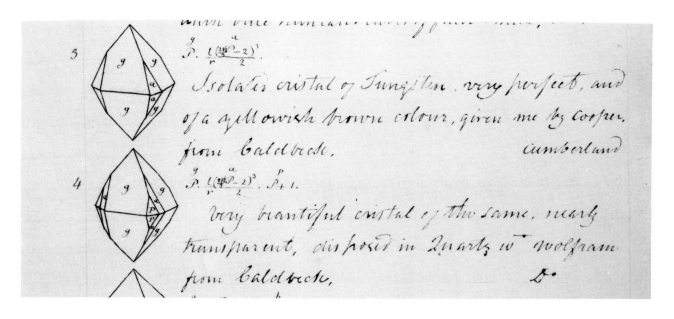

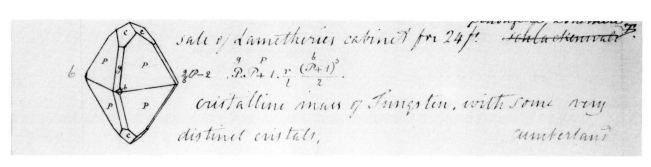

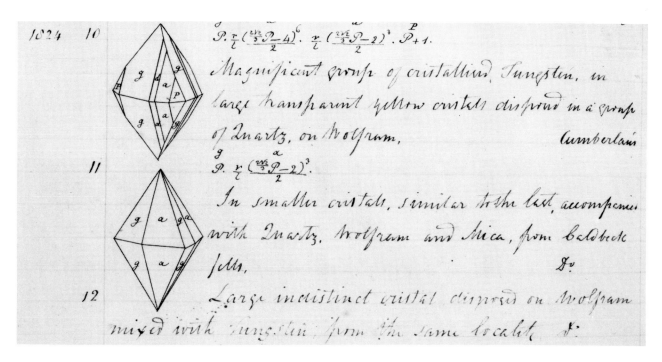

Fig. 41 ALLAN–GREG CATALOGUE: entries for scheelite ('Crystallized Tungsten') made by Thomas Allan in the catalogue to the Allan–Greg Collection, Vol I: 249–250.

Fig. 42 MIMETITE: Dry Gill mine. A remarkable crystal (one of two on quartz) 'so symmetrical that it has all the appearance of a vegetable production'. Presented to Thomas Allan by his son-in-law, D. Smith, in 1831. Allan–Greg Collection, BM(NH) (AG 60).

diarseniate of lead'. The collection was later moved to the Industrial and Technological Museum but is now housed in the Museum of Victoria, Melbourne. Unfortunately, searches of the latter's collections have, so far, failed to locate Thomson's 'campellite' and the specimen may well have been mislaid during one of the collection transfers (W. D. Birch, *pers. comm.*). In 1841 Johann Breithaupt published a formal description of 'Kampylite' (= phosphatian mimetite) from Baden, Germany and from the improbable locality of 'Alston More [*sic*], Cumberland' (*op. cit.*: 293); an error for Dry Gill, Cumberland that was repeated by many later authors (including some British mineralogists) and that still persists in old collections (e.g. Burchard & Bode, 1986: 190). The majority of nineteenth century specimens were obtained during Hugh Lee Pattinson's lease of the deposit in the 1850s. In 1851 Pattinson displayed Dry Gill 'campylite' specimens ('rarely found in such large masses') at the Great Exhibi-

tion of Science and Industry held in the aptly named Crystal Palace in London. Visitors to this prestigious event were also treated to a 'collection of minerals ... including 2000 specimens, arranged and cemented together by Mr Isaac Robinson of Nenthead'. This lavish exhibit, probably in the form of the 'spar boxes' or 'grottoes' popular at the time, featured specimens from several north of England mines including many from the Caldbeck Fells. Malachite, chalcopyrite, mimetite, pyromorphite, 'oxide of manganese', 'blue carbonate of zinc' [probably hemimorphite] etc. were contributed by the owners and agents of Dry Gill and Roughton Gill mines (Ellis, 1851: 167–168, 174). The fate of this undoubtedly spectacular exhibit is unknown but one of Pattinson's 'large masses' of campylite may be the extraordinary specimen later donated by him to the Geological Museum (Fig. 40) and probably the largest Dry Gill mimetite known.

When Greg & Lettsom published their *Manual of the mineralogy of Great Britain and Ireland* in 1858, the majority of the classic collector species from the Caldbeck Fells were known and the area was well established as a source of fine minerals. Robert Philips Greg and William Garrow Lettsom both maintained extensive private collections. That of Greg was based on the Thomas and Robert Allan collection (see above) which had been bought by Greg's father in 1835 for £1300. R. P. Greg spent some £800 in developing it into 'by far the finest private collection in the country' (Smith, 1907). It was sold to the British Museum in 1860. The detailed three volume manuscript catalogue to the Allan–Greg collection lists many Caldbeck specimens including some twenty 'campylites' from Dry Gill (e.g. Fig. 42); several specimens of scheelite, pyromorphite, hemimorphite, malachite (Fig. 74), apatite, linarite etc. One of the linarite specimens is the finest known from Red Gill and is one of the most remarkable examples in the world (Fig. 71). There is no independent catalogue of W. G. Lettsom's collection. It was sold to William Nevill when Lettsom— a career diplomat—left England for Mexico in the 1850s. Nevill's own catalogue (published in 1872) lists dozens of fine Caldbeck specimens; the collection was acquired by Henry Ludlam in 1877 (see below). One species notable for its absence in Greg & Lettsom (1858) is plumbogummite, although several specimens exist in the Allan–Greg collection. They, like many other authors and collectors, mistook it for hemimorphite, smithsonite or chalcedony (see p. 116).

Many of Greg's specimens were obtained from the renowned collector-dealer Bryce (or Brice) McMurdo Wright (1814–1874), a native of Hesket Newmarket, near Caldbeck. He dealt from a variety of premises in Liverpool (*c.*1843–1857) and London (from *c.*1858), providing specimens to many museums and collectors. Wright's endeavours are mentioned several times by

Greg & Lettsom (1858) who also relied on him for 'a very complete list of Cumberland localities' (*op. cit.*: vii). He was responsible for many mineralogical discoveries, especially in the Lake District and Derbyshire, the most important of which was the (then new) lead fluorochloride, matlockite (Greg, 1851). He was active in other natural sciences also, particularly palaeontology and conchology (Anon, 1875) and, although other 'new' species of shells found by him have been reduced to the synonymy, 'Wright's Spiny Oyster' (*Spondylus wrightianus*, Crosse, 1872) still bears his name.

An account of a mineral collecting expedition in the Caldbeck Fells is given by Wright in a chapter of Henry Sowerby's *Popular Mineralogy* of 1850 (see also Cooper,

1988). This details a trip made in the summer of 1847 when Wright acted as a guide to 'Mr C* . . . well known in the mineralogical world' on a two-day collecting trip to Roughton Gill, Dry Gill, Driggith, Sandbeds and other unspecified sites. Underground in Roughton Gill they found 'fine crystallized *Arseniate of Lead* in its native place, adhering to the roof of the mine . . . and procured some capital specimens' (Sowerby, 1850: 19). They were lucky too at Dry Gill, where 'excellent specimens of the *Arseniophosphate of Lead*, in very fine and perfect crystals' were obtained from the vein outcrop. But, although the trip was successful, Wright is careful to describe the

* Perhaps W. G. Lettsom, with whom Wright was *'engaged to go to Cumberland'* in 1847 (letter from Wright, Dept. of Mineralogy, BM(NH)).

Fig. 43 BRYCE McMURDO WRIGHT: in 1873 Prof. Richard Owen of the British Museum described a new species of fossil bird, *Odontopteryx toliapicus*, from a specimen provided by Bryce Wright snr. The well-known Victorian illustrator and satirist Ernest Griset (1843–1907) depicted this discovery in a pair of cartoons. In the first (shown here) the eccentric but brilliant Owen is shown identifying at first sight the fossil skull, offered by Wright, as a new species. Griset's caption reads: 'Owen. ''Hullo!! Bryce-Wright—What a new discovery! Why!! It's a dentigerous bird!! I'll find it a *simple* name say 'Odontopteryx Toliapicus' ''.' In the second picture (reproduced by Lambourne, 1979: 17, pl. 1), Owen shows Wright a model of *Odontopteryx* reconstructed from this fragmentary evidence. The truth is more mundane: it is likely that the fossil, embedded in a concretion, was bought in a job lot of supposed fossil fish or reptile nodules and was not recognised as anything particularly interesting until it was extracted from the matrix at a later date. But whatever their historical or scientific accuracy, these pictures are our only portrayals of Wright; seemingly a very sprightly 59-year-old (if pictured as in 1873), conservatively, but fashionably, dressed, with an ostentatious taste in buttonholes. He died the following year of 'disease of the heart'.

attendant dangers and the necessity of a good guide: 'stupendous and dangerous precipices' abound—Mr C. nearly falling over one on the way to Dry Gill mine 'which lay between two stupendously high mountains' (*ibid.*: 21). Wright's overwrought descriptions seem ridiculous now but to the early Victorian readers they were probably what they expected, or hoped, to find, and Wright was obviously jealous of his position as collector and guide. There was plenty of competition for the latter post: the writer Charles Mackay (1846: 128–129) describes 'half a dozen professional guides . . . who all thrust their cards into our hands, and made profuse offers of their services' waiting at the inn where he was staying in Keswick. Several boasted of a knowledge of minerals and one Joseph Brown styled himself 'an auctioneer . . . guide, boatman and mineralogist, and dealer in lead pencils', the latter derived from the Borrowdale mine.

After his death in 1874 Wright's private mineral collection was sold, specimens being bought by the British Museum and by Henry Ludlam. His son, Bryce M. Wright jnr. (1850–1895), carried on the business, styling himself 'Bryce-Wright' in later years. He contributed a chapter on mineralogy to H. L. Jenkinson's popular *Practical guide to the English Lake District* of 1875 (the same chapter was retained in subsequent editions). Although he seems to have been a very active and well-connected dealer, and a man of wide knowledge and interests, there is an air of sharp practice associated with his name. Complaints of high prices and misrepresentation are common in MSS comments by Lazarus Fletcher, Keeper of Minerals at the British Museum, on letters from Bryce-Wright in the Department of Mineralogy, BM(NH).

Bryce-Wright went bankrupt in 1888 (Cleevely, 1983), but was dealing from a new address the following year. The business died with him in 1895.

In 1875 J. G. Goodchild (1844–1906), of the Geological Survey, discovered wulfenite in the Caldbeck Fells. His published descriptions do not give a precise locality; it may have been Brandy Gill Lead mine or Poddy Gill. He wrote an update of the minerals of Cumberland in three parts (1882, 1884, 1885) but made no further new finds. He moved to Edinburgh in 1887 and eventually took charge of the Heddle collection at the Royal Scottish Museum. He was editor of Heddle's classic *Mineralogy of Scotland* (1901).

The superb collection of Henry Ludlam (1822–1880) was bequeathed to the Geological Museum in London on his death. Widely regarded as 'the most complete and probably the finest collection of minerals ever made by a private collector' (Davies, 1881) it included the collections of C. H. Turner and W. Nevill mentioned above. A description of these specimens formed part of F. W. Rudler's work on the mineralogy of Great Britain and Ireland published in 1905. Amongst the rich suite of

Caldbeck minerals in Ludlam's collection are fine specimens of apatite (Fig. 50) scheelite, plumbogummite and hemimorphite, together with many pyromorphite and mimetite specimens from Roughton Gill and Dry Gill.

The first paper to be devoted entirely to the Caldbeck Fells mineral deposits is that by F. H. Day (1928), which concentrates more on the mining history than the mineral species and concludes, pessimistically 'on the whole the days of fruitful hunting in the Caldbeck Fells have gone by for the mineralogist'. He was, in retrospect, quite wrong but his observation perhaps gives some indication of the ease with which earlier collectors found fine specimens. Even in the 1940s good specimens of the species for which the Fells are renowned could still be found on the dumps with relative ease: the eminent British collector, R. J. King, recalls that at that time a collector could pick and choose his specimens and

Fig. 44 MIMETITE ON PLUMBOGUMMITE: Roughton Gill mine, 55 mm high. A beautiful specimen of greenish yellow phosphatian mimetite crystals on pale blue plumbogummite. It was collected in 1890 by J. G. Goodchild and later bequeathed by his son, W. Goodchild, to R. J. King. King Collection, NMW (NMW83.41G.M7822; K762/658.)

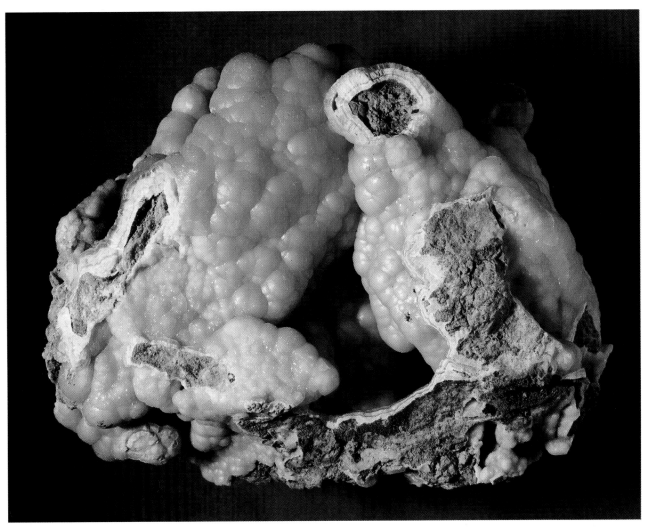

Fig. 45 HEMIMORPHITE: Roughton Gill mine, 130 × 100 mm. A fine large cabinet specimen of hemimorphite of typical colour encrusting a rock breccia. Roughton Gill is well known for this classic material but many specimens were mistaken for smithsonite in the nineteenth century and may often be seen so labelled in old collections. This piece formed part of the collection of John Pears Walton (1838–1915) acquired by Sir Arthur Russell in 1924. It came to the BM(NH) in 1964 as part of the Russell bequest (BM 1964, R9616).

return the following year to find his rejects still in the same place! King's early trips to the Caldbeck Fells were in the company of W. Goodchild, doctor at Threlkeld Sanatorium near Keswick and son of J. G. Goodchild (see above). Specimens from the Goodchilds' collections (e.g. Fig. 44) were later bequeathed to King whose own splendid collection now forms the backbone of the collection of the National Museum of Wales in Cardiff (e.g. Figs 86, 90–93).

Arthur Russell (1878–1964) published his rediscovery of J. G. Goodchild's wulfenite locality in 1936. Although he is best known for his collecting in Cornwall, Russell's collection, preserved intact in the British Museum (Natural History), contains many excellent specimens from the Caldbeck Fells including several rare species obtained from Arthur W. G. Kingsbury (see below).

In 1951 William F. Davidson and Norman Thomson published details of their vigorous collecting in Cumberland and Westmorland. Davidson's interest in the Caldbeck Fells area was principally commercial; he provided specimens to museums, collectors, and dealers around the world and, on retiring from mineral dealing, sold his personal collection to Scott Williams of the U.S.A. Thomson, a lecturer in geology and chemistry at Carlisle under F. H. Day, is now retired but maintains an active interest in the minerals and mining history of Cumbria.

Davidson and Thomson made thorough searches of the Caldbeck Fells and employed several out-of-work miners to help their efforts. They turned over dumps at Roughton Gill, Red Gill and elsewhere and dug out Red Gill and Brandy Gill Lead mines but found nothing underground of the quality they wanted. Davidson updated the earlier paper in 1957 but much of the data in this short paper was taken from the publications of two of the most

Fig. 46 PYROMORPHITE: Mexico mine. Excellent translucent greenish-yellow prisms to 12 mm, of near end-member composition, from an exposure of the Roughton Gill (South) lode near the High level of the Mexico mine. The same cavity also yielded an arsenatian variety in crusts of emerald green globular aggregates (see Fig. 96). J. G. Wilson Collection.

important researchers in the area: Arthur W. G. Kingsbury of Oxford University Museum and Jack Hartley of Leeds University.

Arthur Kingsbury (1906–1968) began collecting in the northern Lake District in 1938. His first exciting discovery in the Caldbeck Fells came in 1947 when he found bayldonite—at that time known only from Tsumeb, SW Africa (Namibia) and Penberthy Croft, Cornwall—on the dumps of Brandy Gill Lead mine where he had gone in search of the wulfenite reported by Russell (1936). The bayldonite was confirmed by Heinrich Neumann, a Norwegian working at Leeds University, whom Kingsbury had met on a field trip in Cornwall arranged by Kingbury and Russell for the 1948 International Geological Congress. Kingsbury returned to Caldbeck with Neumann in 1949 and collected further specimens of bayldonite from Brandy Gill, Driggith and Sandbeds. At Brandy Gill he also found stolzite—the first confirmed British occurrence. In 1950 Neumann re-turned to Norway and suggested that his colleague Jack Hartley, also at Leeds, should continue the work (Kingsbury, MS 3). Kingsbury and Hartley made a careful study of the minerals of the Caldbeck Fells and discovered many rare minerals, some of which were new to Britain, such as adamite, carminite, cosalite, cyanotrichite, dioptase, stolzite, and lindgrenite. These discoveries they announced in a series of articles in the *Mineralogical Magazine* from 1955 to 1960, at about which time their collaboration ceased. Hartley wrote a summary and update shortly before his retirement in 1984 listing many previously unpublished finds. Representative specimens are preserved in the Kingsbury Collection at the British Museum (Natural History) together with copious notes and drafts of unpublished articles. Many of the rarest Caldbeck species are known only from this collection. Kingsbury also donated specimens from Caldbeck to the Oxford University Museum. A suite of specimens from Hartley is in the Geology Department, Leeds University.

From the late 1960s the hobby of mineral collecting has gained wide popularity in Great Britain. The American collector J. H. Marshall visited Caldbeck in 1970 and 1972 and, although commenting that field collecting here was 'still in its infant stage' was surprised in 1972 to find how much material had been removed in the intervening two years (Marshall, 1973). Since then, the major localities in the Caldbeck Fells have been visited by countless amateur and professional collectors, dealers, and scientists.

There have been some notable specimens found in recent years, particularly mimetite and plumbogummite from Dry Gill mine, pyromorphite from the Roughton Gill South vein, and wolframite and scheelite from the recent workings at Carrock mine. Such finds are the exception, but as the supply of cabinet quality specimens has dwindled so the sophistication and ingenuity of collectors in the field has risen. Careful microscopic examination of specimens has extended the known range of many rare species and increased the number of British species with hedyphane, fülöppite, philipsburgite and queitite being found in recent years, largely due to the activities of amateur collectors.

Unfortunately, over-collecting and the unethical, and occasionally illegal, exploitation of certain vein exposures by dealers has led to some resentment in the mineralogical community and to friction with the Lake District Special Planning Board (LDSPB), the planning authority for the land within the Lake District National Park and owners of those parts of the Fells within the Caldbeck parish boundary. The policy of the LDSPB may be summarized as follows:

a vehicular access is prohibited.

b underground collecting or exploration is prohibited.

c surface collecting is allowed with restraint: the removal of large quantities of material is prohibited,

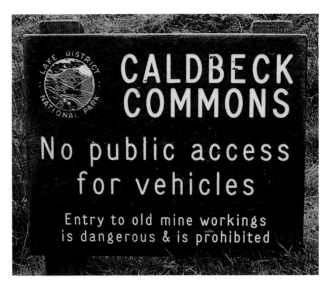

such excavations as are made should be backfilled when collecting is over.

d collecting is restricted to the old dumps.

e commercial exploitation is prohibited.

For those interested in seeing fine specimens from the Caldbeck Fells, the collections of the British Museum (Natural History) are without parallel. Of the other museum collections not already mentioned there are excellent suites of specimens in the Oxford University Museum*; Tullie House Museum, Carlisle (appropriately Tullie House was built by a descendent of the Höchstetter family — see Collingwood, 1910); Keswick Museum and Art Gallery; and the Department of Earth Sciences, Cambridge University.

* Includes a fine selection of nineteenth century mimetite and pyromorphite specimens acquired from Sir Henry Enfield Roscoe (1833–1915) in 1906 and an interesting suite of modern material from the M. W. Thomas Collection purchased in 1984.

THE MINERALS

The Caldbeck Fells contain a greater variety of mineral species than any other area of comparable size in Great Britain. About 175 valid species have been reported from the metalliferous veins; a further 40 are known from the country rocks. This represents more than two-thirds of the total number of species listed by Young (1987) for the whole of the Lake District and adjacent areas.

Of the vein minerals, over 65 were contributed by Kingsbury & Hartley and more than 30 of their finds remain unique to them. In the twenty years since Kingsbury's death the list has increased by about 30 species, nearly half of which were first found by amateur collectors. Although the area is yet to be distinguished by a locality of type status there are about a dozen species for which it is the second or third world occurrence, or both, and over 30 that were, when first recorded, new to Great Britain.

In the descriptive catalogue below, we have generally restricted ourselves to the vein minerals and their alteration products, although some species usually regarded as 'rock forming' have been included where their origin within a deposit is debatable or ambiguous. As partial compensation for this bias, we include a list of minerals from the country rocks as Appendix 2.

To compile the catalogue we have collated many different sources of information. References from the literature given in the bibliography have been endorsed where possible by examination of the specimens, partly to confirm identifications and partly to expand the published descriptions. No attempt has been made to give a complete citation of the literature for each species; a fuller listing is given in the *species by locality* lists in Appendix 1. More detailed locality information is given in the chapter on the mines. Many public and private collections have been examined for specimen material and documentary information (see the acknowledgements). In addition the authors have drawn on their own long-established field experience of the area as ore mineralogist (CJS) and collector (MPC). The sources of information are cited in the text, whether a literature reference, a collection, a manuscript (MS) or *pers*(onal) *comm*(unication). A citation of a private collection implies an examination and usually a characterization by, or for, the authors. Where relevant, the analytical facility used in the determination (*det.*) is given, with the method(s) used: XRD—X-ray powder diffraction; IR—infra-red spectrophotometry; EPMA—electron probe micro-analysis. Some of the organization names are abbreviated: BGS—British Geological Survey; BM(NH)—British Museum (Natural History); OUM—Oxford University Museum; NMW—National Museum of Wales, Cardiff; UMIST—University of Manchester Institute of Science and Technology.

ADAMITE $Zn_2(AsO_4)OH$

Very rare, and, until recently, represented only by specimens in the Kingsbury Collection BM(NH). The Sandbeds occurrence, the first in Britain, was noted in 1951 (Kingsbury & Hartley, MS) and is presumably that referred to as 'Cumberland' by Spencer (1958) on the authority of Kingsbury. This, and other Kingsbury localities (Nether Row Brow and Old Potts Gill mine), were not otherwise published until 1984 (Hartley).

Deer Hills Baryte mine Very small quantities of a minutely globular emerald green mineral were recently found on the dump from the cross-cut at [NY 3130 3655] associated with agardite-mixite and aurichalcite. The green mineral gave an X-ray powder pattern near to cuprian adamite (M. P. Cooper Collection; *det.* BM(NH): XRD).

Driggith mine A cuprian variety was identified at the BM(NH) (XRD) on a specimen from the D. R. Middleton Collection. The adamite forms small pale to dark green zoned prismatic to bladed crystals (< 0.2 mm) on gossany matrix (Fig. 48).

Fig. 47 PYROMORPHITE: Roughton Gill mine, 140 mm high. One of the finest pyromorphite specimens known from Roughton Gill, this exceptional, solid, mass of large crystals (20 mm) was collected c. 1840–50. The partly composite structure and slight colour zoning are characteristic of Roughton Gill pyromorphite crystals, but specimens of this quality are very rare. R. Sutcliffe Collection.

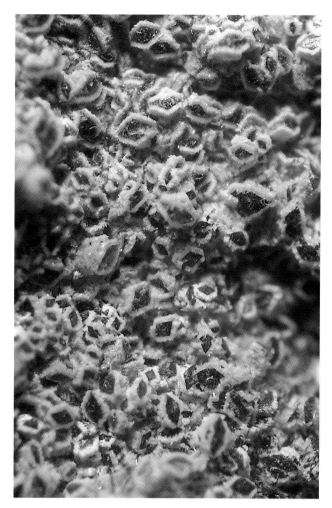

Fig. 48 ADAMITE: Driggith mine. Minute (0.2 mm) dark and light green zoned crystals of cuprian adamite encrusting quartz from the Driggith mine main dump. D. R. Middleton Collection.

Nether Row Brow Radiating sheaves, to 3 mm, of green crystals in gossan from the 'Dumpy Stone' level.

Old Potts Gill mine Globular green adamite occurs with serpierite or malachite on specimens from the 'old No. 1 cross cut'.

Sandbeds mine The first British occurrence; discovered on the 'old middle level' dumps in 1950 where it occurs as small (< 3 mm) sheaves of colourless to pale greenish crystals on gossany quartz. Forms shown are $\{101\}$, $\{110\}$, $\{210\}$ and $\{010\}$ with, more rarely, $\{120\}$ and $\{121\}$ (Kingsbury & Hartley, MS). Recently, a cuprian variety was identified (BM(NH):XRD) on a small specimen in the C. M. Leppington Coll. forming thin, minutely drusy, green crusts on quartz; a habit entirely different from Kingsbury's material.

AGARDITE $(REE,Ca)Cu_6(AsO_4)_3(OH)_6 \cdot 3H_2O$

Coincidentally, specimens of agardite-group minerals from two new Caldbeck localities were identified on the

same day in 1988 at the BM(NH). The finely fibrous structure and small quantities of material present preclude characterization beyond 'agardite-like': both give XRD patterns of agardite-mixite; EPMA was used to determine rare earth elements and bismuth.

Brandy Gill Lead mine Identified on a small specimen from the upper west level submitted to MPC by W. van den Berg. EPMA shows the presence of Ce, La, and Nd; Bi was not detected. Small grain size prevented quantitative results. The mineral forms minute sprays of pale green needles with mimetite on iron-stained quartz. Agardite-mixite has subsequently been identified (BM(NH): XRD) on a specimen from the C. M. Leppington Collection (*pers. comm.*).

Deer Hills Baryte mine Specimens collected by B. Young from the dump of a cross-cut to the Deer Hills baryte lode [NY 3130 3655] show minute pale green sprays (< 0.7 mm) on quartz. In addition to Ce, La, and Nd the fibrous crystals contained some Bi.

More recently found as minute pale blue fibrous crystals with a mineral near cuprian adamite and aurichalcite (M. P. Cooper Collection; *det.* BM(NH): XRD).

AIKINITE $PbCuBiS_3$

Carrock mine As minute crystals in quartz stringers in greisen; the first British locality (previous references to 'aikinite' in Britain concern wolframite pseudomorphs after scheelite from Wheal Maudlin, Cornwall) (Kingsbury & Hartley, 1956*b*).

ALLOPHANE AMORPHOUS ALUMINIUM SILICATE HYDRATE

Driggith mine Recorded from the 12fm level dumps (Hartley, 1984).

Old Potts Gill mine Noted from the No. 1 level dumps by Kingsbury (MS 1).

ALUNITE $KAl_3(SO_4)_2(OH)_6$

Grainsgill A ferrian variety as powdery coatings with jarosite on quartz (Kingsbury & Hartley, 1958).

ANGLESITE $PbSO_4$

Not common, although known from all the lead mines and from several trials. The best specimens have come from Red Gill and Roughton Gill. Principal localities are:

Brae Fell mine Greg & Lettsom (1858) note its occurrence here, but specimens are rarely represented in collections. Most specimens are not well crystallized but the King Collection (NMW) contains a remarkable intergrown mass of cream to black, bladed, anglesite crystal sections to 25 mm (smaller crystals are terminated) associated with granular cerussite, bright yellow micro-crystalline pyromorphite and relic galena.

Brandy Gill Lead mine Associated with the wulfenite (Goodchild, 1875) that was shown by Russell (1936) to have originated here; listed by Hartley (1984).

Driggith mine In small crystals from the Driggith levels and from the Driggith–Sandbeds outcrop workings (Hartley, 1984). Steep bipyramidal crystals to 20 mm were found at the latter location in 1951 (Kingsbury Collection, BM(NH)); Davidson & Thomson (1951: 141) record 'numerous vugs of small, brilliant crystals … around decomposing galena' revealed during exploratory work in 1950.

Dry Gill 'with campylite' Young (1987: 12).

Mexico mine Recorded as a then-recent find by Greg & Lettsom (1858: 394)

Old Potts Gill mine Listed by Hartley (1984).

Red Gill mine Although more common here than at any other locality in the area, anglesite is not plentiful; however, specimens from this locality are by far the best to be found in the Caldbeck Fells. The small bladed crystals are often water-clear and lustrous and contrast beautifully with associated linarite or caledonite. Larger crystals, up to 25 mm, have been found but generally span cavities in the veinstone. Habits vary from elongated blades to rhombic tablets, the latter easily confused with baryte.

Roughton Gill Crystals to 25 mm were found in the nineteenth century workings (BM(NH)) but very little has been found since the mine closed. Specimens in old collections are often dull and opaque and rarely approach the quality of Red Gill crystals.

Sandbeds mine Listed by Hartley (1984).

Short Grain Small crystals in altered galena from the old level at the source of the beck [NY 316 358]. (King Collection, NMW).

Silver Gill From the 'Golden Hugh' as small transparent tablets with a rhombic outline; occasionally seen altered to leadhillite (D. Middleton Collection). As small colourless prisms in altered sulphides with linarite etc. from an old ore pile at [NY 2995 3415].

ANKERITE   Ca(Fe,Mn,Mg)(CO$_3$)$_2$

Brandy Gill Lead mine Recorded by Claringbull (1951); Davidson & Thomson (1951).

Carrock mine As a late infilling in the tungsten veins and in considerable amounts in the 'ankerite veins' (mineralized faults diverging north-westwards from the Emerson vein). Smythe & Dunham (1947) published an analysis of 'ankerite' from the Harding vein, but with only 7.5 wt% FeO this represents a ferroan dolomite.

Dry Smale Gill On 'the highest tip' Shaw (1970: 60).

Old Potts Gill mine 'light and dark coloured varieties' Shaw (1970: 65).

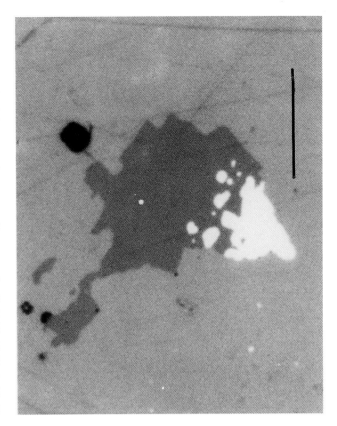

Fig. 49 ANTIMONY: Driggith mine. A reflected light photomicrograph illustrating inclusions of native antimony (white) with bournonite (dark grey) in galena (pale grey). Scale bar is 15 μm.

ANTIMONY   Sb

Driggith mine Minute grains, generally less than 1 μm and rarely larger than 5 μm, are associated with bournonite inclusions in galena (Stanley & Vaughan, 1981).

Wet Swine Gill In the 'antimony vein' as grains up to 20 μm in quartz (Fortey *et al.*, 1984). The same authors (*op. cit.*: 61) also observed '… minute inclusions of a possible Sb-As alloy … in a berthierite prism'.

ANTLERITE   Cu$_3$(SO$_4$)(OH)$_4$

Very rare; very few specimens in collections.

Old Potts Gill mine Found as bright emerald green powdery aggregates in malachite by Kingsbury & Hartley (MS; Hartley, 1984) and on quartz veinstuff by W. F. Davidson (BM(NH)).

Sandbeds Reported associated with bayldonite by Young (1987) on the basis of a specimen in the King Collection, NMW. An XRD investigation of this specimen (NMW 83.41G.M8484) for the authors (by J. Horák NMW) has shown that both of the compact, dark and light green, minerals composing it are malachite.

APATITE GROUP   Ca$_5$(PO$_4$)$_3$(F, OH)

Widespread as an accessory mineral in the Carrock Fell

Fig. 50 APATITE: Carrock mine. Three large greenish crystals (the largest 32 × 18 mm) on iron-stained 'gilbertite' mica and quartz. The crystal protruding from the matrix on the left-hand side of the photograph has been detached from another part of the specimen and glued in its present, more prominent, position. A very similar faked specimen (of almost identical material) is in the King Collection (NMW) suggesting a contemporary trade in reconstructed specimens. The specimen here must have been collected before 1880. Ludlam Collection, BM(NH) (BM 1985, Lud 16135).

Igneous Complex (Harker, 1894, 1895), but good specimens are known only from the Carrock tungsten veins.

Carrock mine The early workings of the Carrock tungsten veins were a source of fine apatite specimens. The occurrence was noted as early as 1817 (as 'asparagus stone') by Borie. A previous record of beryl from 'Caldew beck' (Lysons & Lysons, 1816) was probably of apatite from Grainsgill. Carrock apatite quickly became a collector's item (e.g. Lévy, 1837) and was well established by the time Greg & Lettsom (1858) erroneously recorded the colour as 'celandine green' rather than celadon green.

Crystals up to 30 mm occur on an iron-stained muscovite and quartz matrix and appear to have been most common on the selvedges of the veins (Fortey, 1978). Colourless and yellow crystals have also been found and a blue prism is in the Ludlam Collection, BM(NH). This latter crystal does not fluoresce; the green crystals fluoresce orange-yellow in short-wave UV light. Blue apatite crystals embedded in quartz with pyrite have recently been found in the old No. 1 level (north) on the Harding vein (D. Hacker, *pers. comm.*, 1988). Crystals in which the green colour passes into pink at the termination were described by Wright (1875) and Rudler (1905), but a search of the Ludlam Collection has failed to reveal such specimens.

Smaller crystals may be near gem quality, but the largest are usually flawed and of patchy colour. Commonly, they lie flat on the matrix: projecting crystals attached by a pinacoid should be investigated for glueing, especially if quartz or muscovite scars show on the prism faces (Fig. 50).

The only published analysis of apatite from Carrock mine is that of Finlayson (1910) which shows it to be a fluorapatite.

Recent workings on the Harding vein revealed some small crystals of good colour but much inferior to the old-time specimens, of which good examples are rare in collections.

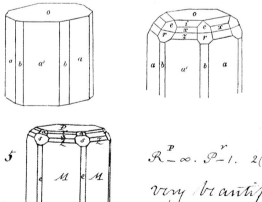

Fig. 51 APATITE: an entry from the Allan–Greg catalogue (Vol. 1: 85) and (above) Greg & Lettsom's published drawings of apatite from 'the foot of Brandy Gill' (1858: 76).

ARAGONITE
CaCO₃

ARAGONITE — $CaCO_3$

Brandy Gill Common in the 'ankerite vein' as small, tapering, white to colourless crystals in small cavities in ferroan dolomite. First noted by Goodchild (1884).

Roughton Gill Tapering prisms were reported by Goodchild (1884) but are rare.

ARSENIOSIDERITE — $Ca_3Fe_4^{3+}(AsO_4)_4(OH)_6.3H_2O$

First recorded from Britain by Kingsbury & Hartley (1957a) as minute brown scales or fibrous aggregates from four localities in the Caldbeck Fells. Except at Ingray Gill it is probably derived from the alteration of scorodite.

Brandy Gill Lead mine In the vein outcrop.

Carrock mine As drusy, slightly botryoidal aggregates coating quartz and arsenopyrite.

Ingray Gill With scorodite, pharmacosiderite, and erythrite and 'almost certainly derived from alteration of the erythrite' (Kingsbury & Hartley, 1957a: 500).

Nether Row Brow Arseniosiderite has been found with scorodite, beudantite, and carminite in material from both the Nether Row Farm level (Kingsbury & Hartley, 1957a; Hartley, 1984) and the 'Dumpy Stone' level (Kingsbury & Hartley, 1960).

ARSENOPYRITE — $FeAsS$

Found chiefly in the south of the district, especially in veins close to the Skiddaw Granite, but also in scattered occurrences in the north as at Ingray Gill and Nether Row Brow.

Brandy Gill Lead mine Massive (Davidson & Thomson, 1951). Earlier reports of arsenopyrite in Brandy Gill (e.g. Greg & Lettsom, 1858; Goodchild, 1882) probably relate to the present site of Carrock mine.

Carrock mine Abundant in the tungsten veins, particularly the Smith and Wilson veins, with wolframite, scheelite, and other sulphides, in crystals to several centimetres across. Idiomorphic crystals are common (up to 45 mm), but usually partly overgrown by later minerals. Where the enclosing matrix is calcite excellent groups of lustrous striated arsenopyrite crystals have been exposed by dissolving the calcite in acid (R. W. Barstow, G. Wilson, *pers. comms.*).

Deer Hills Dumps from old workings near the junction of the Deer Hills Quartz vein with the Potts Gill baryte veins [NY 3145 3626] contain massive arsenopyrite much altered to granular scorodite, pharmacosiderite etc.

Driggith As 'corroded inclusions in chalcopyrite and galena' (Stanley & Vaughan, 1981: 258).

Ingray Gill Recorded by Hartley (1984) from the northern level.

Nether Row Brow As small masses in quartz from

Fig. 52 ARSENOPYRITE: Carrock mine. A pair of well formed crystals (25 mm) with typical deep striations and ragged terminations, recently collected from the adit level on the east branch of the Smith vein. Several good matrix specimens were also found in the same calcite-filled vugh and all were etched out of the enclosing carbonate with dilute acid. J. G. Wilson Collection.

both the Nether Row Farm and 'Dumpy Stone' levels (Kingsbury & Hartley, 1957a; Hartley, 1984).

Old Potts Gill mine Found in small amounts on the dump from the old No. 1 level (Kingsbury & Hartley, 1960). Shaw (1970: 67) records 'a small "lead" vein' in the Endeavour level containing arsenopyrite, 'marmatite', and 'a very little galena'.

Potts Gill mine [East] 'a small stringer carrying crystallized mispickel' was found in 1950 in a cross-cut between 'Potts Gill Mine' and 'Sandbeds Mine' (Davidson & Thomson, 1951: 153).

Wet Swine Gill Uncommon in the 'antimony vein' as euhedral tabular crystals to 60 μm thick; the cores are enriched in antimony (< 7 wt% Sb) (Fortey *et al.*, 1984).

ATACAMITE — $Cu_2Cl(OH)_3$

Hay Gill Copper mine Atacamite was reported from Hay Gill by Kingsbury & Hartley (1956c: 350) who commented that it 'closely resembles and might easily be mistaken for malachite'.

Old Potts Gill mine Kingsbury & Hartley found atacamite here in 1950; their published note on the occurrence (1956c: 349) gave the locality as 'a small copper vein near Potts Gill' but unpublished MSS in the BM(NH) make it clear that the specimens originated from dumps of the 'Old No. 1 level', a source of many rare species (see also Hartley, 1984). The atacamite forms aggregates of indistinct crystals either with malachite and iron oxides or alone on a compact reddish matrix. This latter material is very similar to a specimen in the BM(NH) labelled 'Roughton Gill' (see below) and was compared directly with it by Kingsbury & Hartley (MS) who concluded that 'it would hardly seem possible for them all not to have come from the same provenance'.

Roughton Gill In 1950, Bannister, Hay & Claringbull reported that of all the British 'atacamites' in the BM(NH) only one, from Roughton Gill, had been confirmed as that species whereas the remainder (from Cornwall) had been shown to be the dimorph paratacamite. The Roughton Gill specimen had been obtained from a Mr D. Lowry in 1860. Kingsbury & Hartley (MS; 1956c) doubted this occurrence since the specimen was so similar to material collected by them from Potts Gill (q.v.) and they could find no trace of atacamite at Roughton Gill.

AURICHALCITE $(Zn,Cu)_5(CO_3)_2(OH)_6$

Occurs in several localities as micaceous to froth-like silky masses, as aggregates of thin crystals, or as fans of thin blades. With the exception of Deer Hills Baryte mine, aurichalcite is associated with malachite, cerussite, hemimorphite etc. Other, ill-defined, zinc-copper carbonates occur as post-mining formations on dump material from the same localities (Kingsbury & Hartley, MS).

Deer Hills Baryte mine In small amounts as pale turquoise blue scales and masses with (cuprian?) adamite and agardite-mixite from the cross-cut dump at [NY 3130 3655] (M. P. Cooper Collection, *det.* BM(NH): XRD).

Driggith In vein material from the 12 fm and 30 fm level dumps (Kingsbury & Hartley, MS; Hartley, 1984).

Old Potts Gill mine From the 'old No. 2 [No. 1?] cross-cut' (Kingsbury & Hartley, MS; Hartley, 1984).

Roughton Gill Found here about 1852 by Bryce Wright (Allan–Greg Collection Catalogue, BM(NH)) and reported by Greg & Lettsom in 1858. This has been the most prolific locality (Davidson & Thomson, 1951) and it is likely that most specimens labelled simply 'Caldbeck Fells' originated here. Acicular tufted caledonite has been confused with aurichalcite in the past (Fig. 107, p. 129).

Sandbeds From the 'top level dumps' (Kingsbury & Hartley, MS; Hartley, 1984).

AZURITE $Cu_3(CO_3)_2(OH)_2$

Very rare in the district despite the claim that 'the Caldbeck mines are famous for the variety of rare secondary ore minerals ... notably ... chessylite, cornwallite and melaconite at Potts Ghyll' (Dunham *et al.*, 1978: 274). Most specimens suspected of being azurite turn out to be linarite.

Carrock mine With gold and malachite etc. on metamorphosed Skiddaw slate from the No. 1 level (north) on the Harding vein (Kingsbury Collection, BM(NH); Kingsbury, MS2).

Driggith 'a small amount of azurite' was recorded by Thimmaiah (1956); azurite was also found by Stanley & Vaughan (1981).

Dry Gill mine Recorded from the 'lower day level' (Kingsbury & Hartley, 1960) or 'bottom level' (Hartley, 1984) with beudantite, baryte and 'psilomelane'.

Old Potts Gill mine A small specimen in the Kingsbury Collection, BM(NH) shows small azurite crystals embedded in matted cyanotrichite fibres. Listed from here by Hartley (1984).

Roughton Gill mine From the 30 fm and 90 fm level dumps (Hartley, 1984). A specimen in the King Collection (NMW), obtained from an old collection by W. F. Davidson, and reputed to come from Thief Gills [i.e. probably the ancient outcrop workings in higher Roughton Gill] in 1912 is, if authentic, easily the best azurite from the area. It shows a striated crystal 15 mm in diameter with fibrous malachite on 'copper pitch'.

Sandbed mine From the 'top level dumps' (Hartley, 1984).

BARYTE $BaSO_4$

A common mineral in the Caldbeck Fells but good crystals of appreciable size are rare. Small crystals may easily be mistaken for anglesite, or even leadhillite. Moulds of quartz after tabular baryte ('hacked quartz') are common.

Brae Fell mine (Hartley, 1984).

Brandy Gill Lead mine (Hartley, 1984).

Carrock mine Recorded by Dewey & Dines (1923). A specimen in the M. W. Thomas Collection (OUM) shows cockscomb baryte blades (< 15 mm) in a cavity in iron-stained massive baryte.

Driggith mine Massive baryte occurred here in some quantity and was worked from both the Driggith and Sandbeds levels (Shaw, 1970).

Dry Gill mine First recorded by Greg & Lettsom (1858), baryte occurs here with mimetite and 'psilomelane'. Tabular crystals are not uncommon and may reach 50 mm or more on edge, but are generally dull and stained with manganese oxides (Fig. 53, p. 81). Deep scars, presumably from baryte plates, may sometimes be seen in mimetite crystals.

Ingray Gill (Hartley, 1984).

Low Pike As solid masses to 30 cm and as small, complex, water-clear crystals on cornwallite, from an old trial on the Low Pike vein [NY 320 358] (Fig. 64, p. 92).

Nether Row Brow From the 'Dumpy Stone' level (Hartley, 1984).

Potts Gill Baryte mines Thousands of tons of massive baryte were mined from the complex workings in Potts Gill but very little specimen material was found. Davidson

Fig. 53 BARYTE: Dry Gill mine. A 35 × 33 mm crystal with 'campylite'. Despite the large amount of baryte in the Caldbeck Fells' veins, specimen-quality material is neither common nor spectacular; however, the opaque, manganese-stained individuals from Dry Gill make interesting location pieces. D. Hacker Collection (86–77).

& Thomson (1951: 140) record 'only one "lough" [vugh] containing crystals has been found ...' they are 'pale blue, curved, tabular, about half an inch long ... on psilomelane'. Unremarkable white cockscomb aggregates have been found in the Endeavour level of Old Potts Gill mine (King Collection, NMW).

Red Gill mine Cleavable massive white or pinkish baryte is plentiful on the dumps. Eastwood (1921: 40) suggested 'it appears to belong to the southern N.W. and S.E. vein'.

Roughton Gill In its declining years, Roughton Gill mine, and the dumps, were worked for baryte but little specimen material is recorded. Small crystals with malachite were mentioned by Greg & Lettsom (1858).

Sandbeds Baryte was extracted from the Driggith lode via the Sandbeds level. The main working here, however, was on the E–W baryte veins which yielded much massive baryte. Shaw (1970: 65) recorded 'a form of stalagmitic barytes ... in the 90 fm level workings of Sandbeds West mine which contained 57.53% $BaSO_4$ and 33.80% SiO_2'.

Short Grain As solid masses and as small indistinct tabular crystals with pyromorphite from the northern trial. Other trial workings, now mostly obliterated, were made for baryte in Short Grain.

Wet Smale Gill Shaw (1970).

BAYLDONITE $PbCu_3(AsO_4)_2(OH)_2 . H_2O$

Brandy Gill Lead mine Kingsbury found bayldonite here in 1947 on specimens collected on the dumps from the upper west level (Kingsbury & Hartley, MS; Kingsbury, MS 3). The associated minerals were malachite, pyromorphite, mimetite, and (as shown later by Kingsbury & Hartley, 1956a) mottramite, on quartz. Bayldonite occurs as thin, minutely botryoidal crusts up to 120 × 80 mm. Pseudomorphs of bayldonite after mimetite are common.

Davidson & Thomson (1951) claimed that duftite was more common than bayldonite at Brandy Gill but Kingsbury & Hartley (MS) disputed this and commented, moreover, that some specimens of 'duftite' they had examined had been mislabelled and were, in fact, bayldonite. Both minerals occur at Brandy Gill as pseudomorphs after mimetite and as green crusts on matrix, and there is no simple way to distinguish them.

Carrock mine Traces of bayldonite were found in material 'from an old cross-cut at, or near, the junction of the east–west lead veins with the Emerson vein at the foot of Brandy Gill' (Kingsbury & Hartley, MS; Hartley, 1984: 36).

Driggith mine Found in 1949 by Kingsbury & H. Neumann on the dumps from the 12, 30 and 60 fm levels, and *in situ* in open-cast workings between Driggith and Sandbeds where it was more abundant. Associated minerals include malachite, cerussite, 'psilomelane', mimetite, linarite, and baryte (Kingsbury & Hartley, MS; Kingsbury, MS 3; Hartley, 1984).

East Potts Gill mine Identified on specimens from the Blockley lode (*det.* BM(NH): XRD, N. Thomson, *pers. comm.*)

Low Pike Bayldonite has recently been identified on specimens from an old trial on the Low Pike vein [NY 320 358] where it forms thin, light green crusts with a greasy lustre on quartz and occurs as pseudomorphs after mimetite with cornwallite, beudantite etc. (*det.* UMIST: IR).

Old Potts Gill mine 'found on several specimens forming botryoidal aggregates in quartz, associated with baryte and pseudomalachite or cornwallite' from the 'old No. 2 [No. 1?] cross-cut' (Kingsbury & Hartley, MS; Hartley, 1984).

Poddy Gill 'traces' from the E–W lead vein (Kingsbury & Hartley, MS; Hartley, 1984).

Sandbeds mine Kingsbury & Neumann found several specimens of bayldonite on their first visit here in 1949 on the top level dumps, where it occurs alone, or with a trace of malachite, on quartz (Kingsbury & Hartley, MS; Kingsbury, MS 3). Further specimens were found by Davidson & Thomson (1951).

BEAVERITE $Pb(Cu, Fe^{3+}, Al)_3(SO_4)_2(OH)_6$

Widespread as bright yellow powdery coatings resulting from the alteration of galena, it is associated with anglesite, cerussite, brochantite etc. The alteration series, carminite → beudantite → beaverite → plumbojarosite, in whole or in part, can be seen in many specimens (Kingsbury & Hartley, 1957e).

Brandy Gill Lead mine Found here in 1949 by Kingsbury; the first British locality. It occurs as light yellow to greenish yellow powdery masses in part pseudomorphous after galena. Darker, less powdery, material may have altered from beudantite with which it is commonly associated (Kingsbury & Hartley, MS; 1957e).

Carrock mine From 'material collected around an old cross-cut at, or near, the junction of the east–west lead veins with the Emerson vein at the foot of Brandy Gill' (Hartley, 1984: 36).

Driggith mine Powdery aggregates on cerussite and altered galena at the vein outcrop (Kingsbury & Hartley, MS; 1957e).

Ingray Gill As light yellow coatings on decomposing galena on dump material from the northern level (Kingsbury & Hartley, 1957e).

Nether Row Brow With beudantite and plumbojarosite from the Nether Row Farm level, also with beudantite etc. from the 'Dumpy Stone' level (Kingsbury & Hartley, 1957e).

Old Potts Gill mine From the dumps of the 'old No. 1 cross-cut', the most interesting occurrence of the species in the district: beaverite was found as 'light canary-yellow powdery aggregates with small brilliant crystals of brochantite ... and as small (0.5mm) brilliant, well-formed yellow rhombohedra in the same matrix. This appears to be the first reported occurrence of beaverite in this habit' (Kingsbury & Hartley, 1957e: 702).

Roughton Gill Occurs with jarosite and chrysocolla in quartz from the outcrop of the Roughton Gill South vein on the flank of Balliway Rigg (Kingsbury & Hartley, 1957e).

BERAUNITE $Fe^{2+}Fe_5^{3+}(PO_4)_4(OH)_5 \cdot 4H_2O$

Burdell Gill Listed by Hartley (1984). Young (1987) was wrong to suggest that Hartley's record was a misprint for braunite (J. Hartley, *pers. comm.*).

BERTHIERITE $FeSb_2S_4$

Wet Swine Gill In the 'antimony vein' as crystals to 2 mm with other sulphosalts embedded in quartz (Fortey *et al.*, 1984).

Fig. 54 BEUDANTITE: Arm o'Grain. Beudantite is a common mineral in the Caldbeck Fells and shows great variability of appearance. These minute (0.2 mm) colour-zoned pseudocubic crystals were thought to be pharmacosiderite until X-ray analysis revealed their true identity. D. R. Middleton Collection (10–9).

BERYL $Be_3Al_2Si_6O_{18}$

Carrock mine As small poor crystals in 'gilbertite' in specimens in the Kingsbury & Russell Collections, BM(NH), collected by the former who noted 'from north-west branch (= south drive on the Harding vein) of the new low-level cross-cut to the Harding vein—the vein in which beryl occurs is apparently an early member of the suite; also in iron-stained mica on dump' (Kingsbury, MS1). The reference of Lysons & Lysons (1816: cx) to beryl from 'Caldew-beck ... found by the Rev. Mr Mandall' probably refers to apatite (q.v.).

BEUDANTITE $PbFe_3^{3+}(AsO_4)(SO_4)(OH)_6$

Widespread in small amounts, as drusy masses or small well formed crystals. Specimens from the Caldbeck Fells were first identified as beudantite in 1949 (Kingsbury & Hartley, MS).

Arm o' Grain A small vein outcrop in this tributary of Grainsgill has yielded two different habits of the species (D. R. Middleton Collection) as small, dark brown, acute rhombohedra and as minute (0.3 mm) pale brown, transparent, pseudo-cubic crystals with darker brown cores, at first mistaken for oxidized pharmacosiderite (*det.* BM(NH): XRD).

Brandy Gill Lead mine Relatively common in the outcrops of the vein; it was first mentioned by Kingsbury & Hartley (1957*e*) as a precursor of beaverite. In 1960, these authors described granular beudantite as yellow, greenish yellow, to brown, crusts, often pseudomorphous after carminite, on the sides of the vein and in the granophyre wall rock. In addition, small acute rhombohedra and zoned hexagonal plates (to 2 mm) were found in the vein quartz. The latter habit shows 'a large basal plane and narrow faces of two rhombohedra or of the hexagonal prism or of all three and this appears to be the first recorded occurrence of this euhedral platy habit' (Kingsbury & Hartley, 1960: 428). They also noted 'a hollow hexagonal epimorph . . . (probably after mimetite) of which one end consisted of carminite, the middle portion of beudantite, and the other end of beaverite'. Beudantite also occurs as aggregates of extremely small, transparent, olive green crystals on float quartz from the head of Brandy Gill to the north of the mine (D. R. Middleton Collection, *det.* BM(NH): XRD); and as rare minute (< 0.2 mm) sharp rhombohedral crystals and brownish yellow crusts pseudomorphous after carminite and mimetite from a vein outcrop in the dry tributary valley to the east [NY 3240 3385] (M. P. Cooper Collection, *det.* UMIST: IR).

Burdell Gill Occurs in three forms on specimens collected (by D. R. Middleton) from dumps of the old workings near the head of the gill. Beudantite forms somewhat sheafy aggregates of acute rhombohedral crystals to 2 mm, partially embedded in massive beudantite on quartz; and minute (< 1 mm) brownish crystals of pseudo-octahedral aspect resulting from the equal development of the pinacoid and a rhombohedron. On this latter habit the rhombohedron faces are lustrous whilst the pinacoids are dull; these characters show that the habit is not an isometric octahedron (*det.* BM(NH): XRD).

Carrock mine 'as brown, powdery aggregates in gossany material from near the intersection of an east–west "lead-vein" with the north–south Emerson vein' (Kingsbury & Hartley, 1960: 427).

Deer Hills Identified on a specimen from an old working on the Deer Hills Quartz vein [NY 3145 3626] where it is associated with carminite and scorodite (*det.* BM(NH): XRD, N. Thomson, *pers. comm.*)

Driggith mine In small amounts with carminite, mimetite, cerussite, beaverite and plumbojarosite; also as yellow-brown to brown powdery aggregates on altered galena 'from the outcrop of the main vein' (Kingsbury & Hartley, 1960; 428: see also 1957*e*).

Dry Gill mine Found 'in material from the middle cross-cut about half-way up the gill' [NY 3205 3450], as greenish-yellow powdery aggregates associated with olivenite, and in material from the lower day-level [NY 325 346] as yellow crystalline and brown fine-grained aggregates, with baryte, azurite, and 'psilomelane'. (Kingsbury & Hartley, 1960: 428).

Ingray Gill Minute yellow rhombohedra with carminite, scorodite, and pharmacosiderite, and powdery and crystalline coatings on galena were recorded by Kingsbury & Hartley (1957*e*).

Low Pike On one recently collected specimen, beudantite occurs as minute, golden yellow, slightly iridescent rhombohedra on iron-stained quartz with mimetite, bayldonite, and cornwallite from an old trial on the Low Pike vein above Potts Gill [NY 320 358] (M. P. Cooper Collection, *det.* BM(NH): XRD). Also as a minutely crystalline yellow crust (B. Young, *pers. comm.*, *det.* BGS: XRD).

Nether Row Brow From the 'Dumpy Stone' level as yellowish green to brown microcrystalline crusts with residual carminite, scorodite and beaverite; and from the Nether Row Farm level as small yellow acute rhombohedra with scorodite, arseniosiderite and carminite, and as yellow to greenish brown powdery to microcrystalline aggregates with mimetite, mottramite, scorodite, pharmacosiderite, plumbojarosite, and beaverite (Kingsbury & Hartley, MS; 1957*e*; 1960). Beudantite is still common, in small quantities, at both localities.

Old Potts Gill mine With carminite, scorodite and pharmacosiderite as yellow-brown acute rhombohedra and as powdery yellow to yellow-brown coatings on altered galena from the 'old No. 1 cross-cut' (Kingsbury & Hartley, 1960: 429).

Roughton Gill Found in the outcrop of the Roughton Gill South vein on the side of Balliway Rigg in higher Roughton Gill as powdery, yellow- to greenish brown aggregates with decomposing galena, cerussite, chrysocolla, jarosite and plumbojarosite and as yellow rhombohedra with carminite and mimetite in quartz (Kingsbury & Hartley, MS; 1958; 1960).

BINDHEIMITE $Pb_2Sb_2O_6(O,OH)$

Driggith mine From the 30 fm level dumps (Kingsbury MS1). J. Hartley (*pers. comm.*, 1987) confirmed the find as 'yellow earthy . . . in cavities in quartz with malachite'.

Mexico mine As a yellow powder with pyromorphite, cerussite, and wulfenite in cavities in quartz from the Low level dump in Todd Gill (M. P. Cooper Collection, *det.* Leicester Univ.: XRD).

Roughton Gill From the flank of Balliway Rigg in higher Roughton Gill (Hartley, 1984). Kingsbury (MS1) claimed the occurrence as 'new to GB'. Also from the 90 fm level dumps as a yellow powder in cavities in quartz (M. P. Cooper Collection, *det.* BM(NH): XRD).

Wet Swine Gill Common in the 'antimony vein' as yellowish earthy crusts derived from stibnite or other antimony minerals (Fortey *et al.*, 1984).

BISMITE Bi_2O_3

Carrock mine The 'bismuth ochre' reported from 'Brandy Gill' as an associate of bismuth (Goodchild, 1882: 104) may have been bismite or bismutite. Bismite has been recorded from Carrock mine 'in minute amounts' as a yellowish white alteration of bismuthinite (Davidson and Thomson, 1951); and from the dumps of an old level 'at, or near, the junction of the east–west lead veins with the Emerson vein at the foot of Brandy Gill' (Hartley, 1984).

BISMUTH Bi

Carrock mine Occurs here in small cleavable masses with bismuthinite and bismuth tellurides in quartz. The occurrence was referred to as 'Caldbeck Fells' (Greg & Lettsom, 1858), 'Brandy Gill' (Hall, 1868), and 'Carrock Fells' (Kendall, 1884). According to Hitchen (1934), bismuth minerals were most common in the 'west band of the Harding vein'. Shaw (1970: 51–52) mentions 'bismuth' in float quartz from the 'Dry Gill side' of Carrock Fell, also 'fine specimens of bismuth' from the Emerson vein.

BISMUTHINITE Bi_2S_3

Carrock mine As acicular crystals to 25 mm and as small masses with typical fibrous-lamellar cleavage in association with bismuth, jošeite, ingodite, molybdenite etc. in quartz. Phillips (1837) first noted the occurrence. In its finely fibrous form it is difficult to distinguish from acicular sulphosalts such as cosalite, jamesonite and boulangerite and was described vividly by Davidson & Thomson (1951: 142) as 'tufts of delicate hair-like crystals which easily become detached from the matrix and blow away in the wind'.

BISMUTITE $Bi_2(CO_3)O_2$

Carrock mine Recorded by Hitchen (1934) and listed from the 'main dump' by Hartley (1984). The 'bismuth ochre' of Goodchild (1882: 104) may have been bismutite or bismite.

BORNITE Cu_5FeS_4

Carrock mine With 'mispickel, pyrite, chalcopyrite ... and chalcocite' in 'complex ore' (Davidson & Thomson, 1951: 143).

Driggith mine Replacing chalcopyrite (Thimmaiah, 1956); also mentioned from 'Driggith–Sandbeds' by Eastwood (1921).

Old Potts Gill mine 'traces' from the 'old No. 1 cross-cut dumps' (Kingsbury, MS 1); listed by Hartley (1984).

Roughton Gill Massive specimen in Keswick Museum (Young, 1987).

BOULANGERITE $Pb_5Sb_4S_{11}$

Carrock mine 'as dark grey minute acicular crystals or fibres, tufts or wool-like aggregates, or small fibrous patches' very similar to zinckenite and jamesonite which also occur here. Associated with pyrite, arsenopyrite, chalcopyrite, and galena (Kingsbury & Hartley, 1956*b*: 298).

Nether Row Brow Small fibres in quartz on samples collected from the Nether Row Farm level by B. Young in 1987 (*det.* BM(NH): XRD).

BOURNONITE $PbCuSbS_3$

Driggith mine 'in three forms: (i) as relatively large grains ($< 100\,\mu m$) commonly enclosed in argentian tetrahedrite; (ii) along cleavages in galena, with chalcopyrite and minor tetrahedrite, possibly the result of post-cleavage remobilization; (iii) as intergrowths in galena, either as platelets or rods, usually no more than a few microns in width and clearly oriented along structural planes of the galena, or as rounded blebs ($< 5–10\,\mu m$) arranged in irregular curved strings, possibly along galena grain boundaries. Irregular grains of bournonite ($20–30\,\mu m$) also occur either associated with native antimony or as somewhat smaller grains at chalcopyrite/galena grain boundaries' (Stanley & Vaughan, 1981: 258–259).

Nether Row Brow As small grains in sugary quartz from the Nether Row Farm level, collected by B. Young in 1987. (*det.* BM(NH) and BGS: XRD).

Roughton Gill Recorded as 'intergrown with galena' from higher Roughton Gill in the 'crop workings etc. along the back of the south lode on the S.E. flank of Balliway Rigg' (Kingsbury, MS1).

BRAUNITE $Mn^{2+}Mn_6^{3+}SiO_{12}$

Burdell Gill Listed in error for beraunite in Young (1987).

BREITHAUPTITE $NiSb$

Old Potts Gill mine Specimens in the Kingsbury Collection, BM(NH) show breithauptite with galena and sphalerite in calcite. Kingsbury (MS 1) suggests the specimens came from the 'old No. 1 cross-cut dumps', however, the occurrence was not known to his one-time colleague, J. Hartley (*pers. comm.*, 1987).

'BREWSTERITE'

Roughton Gill mine The 'brewsterite' recorded by Hall (1868) as an associate of tenorite and chalcopyrite is unlikely to be the zeolitic brewsterite (of Brooke) as assumed by Young (1987). It is more likely to be the 'brewsterite' listed by Branston (1910) and Postlethwaite

(1913) as 'protoxide of copper'. Although the latter is a synonym for cuprite, the name brewsterite in this context does not appear in any standard mineralogy or synonymy known to the authors and the precise definition of the term appears to be lost.

BROCHANTITE $Cu_4(SO_4)(OH)_6$

The Victorian mineral dealer Bryce Wright claimed the first Cumbrian discovery of this species (Wright *in* Jenkinson, 1875). It is widespread in the Caldbeck Fells, but is nowhere common. It is also found occasionally as a post-mining formation on weathered dump material.

Brandy Gill Lead mine From the 'upper western dump' (Kingsbury & Hartley, MS; Hartley, 1984).

Driggith mine From the 12 fm and 30 fm levels (Kingsbury & Hartley, MS; Hartley, 1984). Specimens in the Kingsbury Collection, BM(NH) and in the Hartley Collection (Leeds University) show small (< 2 mm) striated brochantite crystals on microcrystalline linarite. Also found as a powder (Davidson & Thomson, 1951).

Hay Gill mine (Kingsbury & Hartley, MS; Hartley, 1984).

Low Pike A rare associate of cornwallite, malachite etc. from an old trial on the Low Pike vein [NY 320 358] (*det.* Leeds Univ.: XRD; D. I. Green, *pers. comm.*)

Mexico mine Kingsbury & Hartley (MS) list brochantite from 'Todd Gill'; Kingsbury (MS1) gives the locality as 'just east of Roughton Gill lead works. Old cross-cut at the foot of the gill, driven on the North vein' i.e. probably the Mexico mine Low level.

Old Potts Gill mine In a matrix of 'gossany quartz, intergrown with red, earthy, or hard compact haematitic matter, malachite and baryte [with] small kernels of chalcopyrite, and chalcocite' from the 'old No. 2 [No. 1 ?] cross-cut' (Kingsbury & Hartley, MS). The matrix and the form of the 'well-crystallized' brochantite upon it, was 'absolutely indistinguishable from ... specimens labelled from Roughton Gill, Caldbeck Fells or Brandy Gill to be seen in collections'. Also found as small brilliant crystals with powdery yellow beaverite (Kingsbury & Hartley, 1957*e*).

Red Gill Brochantite is now very rare at this locality although excellent specimens may be seen in old collections. It was Davidson & Thomson's (1951) experience that caledonite was some fifty times more common than brochantite here. Even less common are pseudomorphs of brochantite, or of brochantite with anglesite, after bladed crystals of linarite (Fig. 55).

Roughton Gill Greg & Lettsom (1858: 327) described brochantite from Roughton Gill: 'lately in small but very perfect and brilliant crystals ... on a white quartzose rock, associated with fibrous malachite'. Specimens fitting this description may still be found on the extensive dumps

Fig. 55 BROCHANTITE: Red Gill mine. A rare pseudomorph after linarite crystals (to 1.5 mm) with minor cerussite on quartz. Collected from the Old Dutch level dumps in 1949. J. Hartley Collection, Dept. of Geology, Leeds University.

below the 90 fm level. An occasional associated species is tsumebite (q.v.).

Some specimens in old collections have a matrix similar to that of specimens collected from Potts Gill (see above).

Also reported from workings in higher Roughton Gill (Davidson & Thomson, 1951).

Sandbeds mine (Kingsbury & Hartley, MS; Hartley, 1984) Also from the Driggith–Sandbeds outcrop workings (Hartley, 1984).

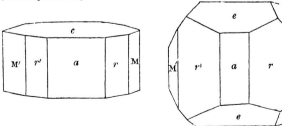

Fig. 56 BROCHANTITE: from Roughton Gill. Crystal drawing after Greg & Lettsom (1858: 326).

Silver Gill As minute rounded scales (< 1 mm); and as fibrous sprays apparently altering from langite (D. I. Green *pers. comm.*; *det.* Leeds Univ.: XRD).

CACOXENITE $Fe_9^{3+}(PO_4)_4(OH)_{15}.18H_2O$

Burdell Gill (Hartley, 1984). This appears to be the first published British occurrence of the species, although long-known from localities in Cornwall. Specimens in the Kingsbury Collection, BM(NH), show yellow fibres of cacoxenite on a 'limonitic' matrix.

CALCITE $CaCO_3$

Generally uncommon in the area, but locally abundant in some veins.

Carrock mine Abundant in the Harding and Smith veins, and mostly massive; uncommon as crude scalenohedra or as steeply rhombohedral crystals with low rhombohedral termination. Pale pink equant crystals with this latter habit (< 20 mm across) were found in the last workings on the Smith vein. The largest crystal known to the authors is a 50×50 mm 'nailhead' crystal collected during mining operations in 1985 (N. Thomson Collection).

Driggith mine (Thimmaiah, 1956; Stanley, 1979).

Dry Gill (Hartley, 1984).

Hay Gill mine (Hartley, 1984). Kingsbury (MS1) referred to calcite from Hay Gill in 'obtuse rhombohedra': specimens in the Kingsbury Collection, BM(NH), show almost tabular crystals of this habit (< 15 mm) and are labelled as from 'Deer Hills . . . at the top of Hay Gill'.

Ingray Gill As sprays of slender prismatic (or very steeply rhombohedral) colourless crystals on altered rock in the south level (N. Thomson, *pers. comm.*, 1987).

Old Potts Gill mine (Hartley, 1984).

Red Gill mine Small deeply etched lenticular crystals occur rarely on drusy quartz from a small dump by Swinburn Gill a few metres south of the Red Gill deep level. The No. 2 level dump also contains moulds of scalenohedral crystals in compact quartz that may represent earlier calcite.

Roughton Gill Not uncommon on the 90 fm level dumps but mostly massive. 'Nail head crystals' were recorded by Davidson & Thomson (1951). Large amounts of calcite formed the principal gangue mineral in the 'Great Bunch' in the South vein (Dewey & Eastwood, 1925). Calcite containing 'traces of strontium' was noted by Melmore (1920: 268). Scalenohedral moulds in compact quartz from the 90 fm level dump may be pseudomorphs after calcite.

CALEDONITE $Pb_5Cu_2(CO_3)(SO_4)_3(OH)_6$

This rare and beautiful species is one of the most sought-

Fig. 57 CALEDONITE: Red Gill mine. Beautiful gem-like crystals to 1.5 mm on quartz, collected in 1975. The variation in colour seen in the largest crystal is due to changes in orientation: the crystal is slightly curved from fracturing and healing. R. E. Starkey Collection (MO450-03).

after from the Caldbeck Fells. Red Gill was the second occurrence of the species, the type locality being Leadhills, Scotland, and its discovery seems to have been made shortly before the publication of Greg & Lettsom (1858). Good crystals have been found in several other localities, but in much smaller quantity than at Red Gill.

Brae Fell mine As small crystals and masses with linarite from the mine dumps and from waste material at the foot of the 'hush' to the north of the lower dump. Listed by Hartley (1984).

Brandy Gill Lead mine From the upper west level dumps (Hartley, 1984); specimens in the Kingsbury Collection, BM(NH), show 1–2 mm crystals with linarite.

Driggith mine From the 30 fm level dumps, with linarite (Kingsbury Collection, BM(NH)).

Red Gill mine Small specimens may still, with luck, be found on the dumps. Crystals are often bright and transparent; they may reach 5 mm in length but are usually smaller. Habit varies from short to long prismatic (Greg & Lettsom, 1858; Hessenberg, 1870), tabular, or bladed. The colour varies in shades of greenish blue but is never the clearer blue of Leadhills specimens. Caledonite occurs in cavities in a quartz-sulphide matrix either alone or accompanied by linarite, anglesite or leadhillite. It is also a typical associate of rare minerals such as mattheddleite (Fig. 76), susannite, macphersonite, and queitite.

The crystal structure of caledonite was determined by Giacovazzo, Menchetti & Scordari (1973) on a Red Gill specimen.

Roughton Gill mine Its existence here was implied by Wright (*in* Sowerby) in 1850; and it was listed (possibly in error for Red Gill) by Bristow (1861). Caledonite is much less common here than at Red Gill. It is found, principally, in the old workings on the South vein in higher Roughton Gill where it occurs with leadhillite, susannite, lanarkite, mattheddleite, and, very rarely, scotlandite. An unusually rich specimen in the Ludlam Collection (BM(NH)) has fibrous caledonite—originally labelled 'aurichalcite'—as a velvet-like encrustation on quartz with susannite (*det.* BM(NH): XRD). The locality is given merely as Roughton Gill (cf. Fig. 107, p. 129).

Sandbeds mine From the 'top level' dumps (Hartley, 1984); also as 'tiny crystals' (Davidson & Thomson, 1951). Specimens in the Kingsbury Collection, BM(NH), show

Fig. 59 CARMINITE: Brandy Gill Lead vein. Minutely drusy carminite and beudantite forming a partial epimorph after a 3 mm mimetite prism from a small and sparsely mineralised outcrop in the dry gully on the east of Brandy Gill. M. P. Cooper Collection (8868).

sharp crystals to 2 mm in quartz.

Short Grain From the northern trial, but rarely, as minute prismatic gem-like crystals on quartz (D. I. Green Collection); or as fibrous encrustations of recent (post-mining) formation in cavities in massive baryte (*det.* Leeds Univ.: XRD; D. I. Green, *pers. comm.*).

Silver Gill From the 'Golden Hugh' as radiating bunches of minute, acicular, crystals on decomposing sulphides. Probably of post-mining formation.

CARMINITE $PbFe_2^{3+}(AsO_4)_2(OH)_2$

Kingsbury & Hartley (MS; 1957*e*; 1960) found carminite in several Caldbeck Fells localities where it occurs as small acicular crystals, but more commonly as thin, drusy encrustations, or spots and stains resembling dried blood. It alters to beudantite.

Brandy Gill Lead mine Associated with beudantite, mimetite, and beaverite; much of the beudantite seems to be altered from, or pseudomorphous after, carminite

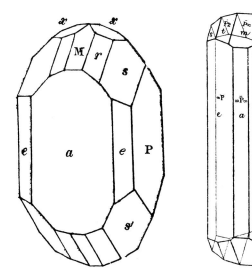

Fig. 58 CALEDONITE: from Red Gill. Crystal drawings after Greg & Lettsom (1858: 403) and Hessenberg (1870).

(Kingsbury & Hartley, 1957e; 1960). Vein exposures near the mine, on the east side of Brandy Gill and in the dry tributary valley to the east [NY 3240 3335] have also yielded a few fairly rich specimens of carminite as minute crystals and drusy crusts on quartz with beudantite (D. R. Middleton and M. P. Cooper Collections, *det.* UMIST: IR) (Fig. 59, p. 87).

Deer Hills In small amounts as encrustations with beudantite and scorodite from an old dump at, or near, the junction of the Deer Hills Quartz lode and the Potts Gill baryte lode [NY 3145 3626] (*det.* BM(NH): XRD, N. Thomson, *pers. comm.*).

Driggith mine Carmine to brownish red crystalline aggregates occur in quartz, with beudantite, mimetite, and cerussite from 'the outcrop of the main vein' (Kingsbury & Hartley, 1960: 428; also MS).

Dry Gill mine Kingsbury & Hartley (1960) claimed that some of the beudantite they found here appeared to have been derived from carminite but they found no traces of the latter.

Ingray Gill From the northern level as 'tufts of minute prisms in cavities in saccharoidal quartz, associated with beudantite in minute yellow rhombohedra, scorodite, and pharmacosiderite'. (Kingsbury & Hartley, 1960: 430).

Nether Row Brow From the 'Dumpy Stone' level as 'small residual patches with considerable amounts of . . . beudantite, together with red-brown scorodite, beaverite, and "limonitic" matter' (Kingsbury & Hartley, 1960: 429). Also from the Nether Row Farm level with beudantite, scorodite, and arseniosiderite; specimens may still be collected from this locality, as minute crystals or thin crusts on vein quartz.

Old Potts Gill mine As 'tufts of minute, brick-red, tapering acicular crystals associated with . . . beudantite, scorodite, and pharmacosiderite, in a gossany quartz-goethite matrix', from dump material outside the 'old No. 1 cross-cut' (Kingsbury & Hartley, 1960: 429).

Roughton Gill In the outcrop of the South vein on the flank of Balliway Rigg in higher Roughton Gill as 'drusy botryoidal aggregates and tufts of minute prisms in cavities in quartz, with yellow rhombohedra of beudantite, some of them attached to the surface of the carminite, and small, colourless, tapering prisms of mimetite' (Kingsbury & Hartley, 1960; 430).

Sandbeds mine With beudantite, cerussite and other minerals from an exposure 'near Sandbeds mine' (J. G. Wilson, *pers. comm.*, 1988).

CARPHOLITE $MnAl_2Si_2O_6(OH)_4$

Carrock mine As unusually pale, almost cream yellow, 'thin, fibrous-radiating aggregates in joints in white

vein-quartz . . . almost certainly from the Emerson vein' (Kingsbury & Hartley, 1957c: 502). Specimens in the Kingsbury Collection (BM(NH)) match this description.

CASSITERITE SnO_2

Carrock mine A few small crystal sections, embedded in quartz and mica, were found by Kingsbury in 1953 from the Harding vein 'new low-level cross-cut, south drive' and are represented by specimens in the Russell and Kingsbury Collections, BM(NH). In addition the King Collection (NMW) contains a good grey-brown incomplete geniculate twin, originally labelled scheelite, which, if authentic, is undoubtedly the best Carrock specimen extant. It may have been found during the 1940s working and was obtained by King from the H. F. Harwood collection (R. J. King, *pers. comm.*).

The 'ores of tin, both of a resinous and nearly black colour' in a matrix 'nearly as hard as tempered steel', reported by Parson & White (1829) from 'a vein at Brandy Gill near the Caldew' no doubt refer to scheelite and wolframite.

CERUSSITE $PbCO_3$

Cerussite is common in the Caldbeck Fells but is rarely found as very remarkable specimens. Large quantities of, apparently, massive material were extracted from the Mexico mine, and small crystals occur in many other mines and trials.

Brae Fell mine First mentioned, without description, by Greg & Lettsom (1858: 391) from 'Bray Fell'. Crystals are generally insignificant but an attractive combination of silky, white, acicular crystals (< 10 mm) with small green pyromorphite crystals was found on the low level dump (Kingsbury Collection, BM(NH)).

Crystals (< 20 mm) occur with bright canary yellow pyromorphite on the top level dumps.

Brandy Gill Goodchild (1884: 193) found 'stellate macles, like six-rayed stars' in the interiors of corroded galena crystals from 'Brandy Gill' and Davidson & Thomson (1951) found cerussite with galena and pyromorphite on a dump 'at the foot of the gill'. An occurrence in Brandy Gill Lead mine was listed by Hartley (1984). Here, quartz and pyromorphite-mimetite are both found as hollow epimorphs after small sixling twins of cerussite.

Carrock mine From an 'old cross-cut at, or near, the junction of the east–west lead veins with the Emerson vein at the foot of Brandy Gill (Hartley, 1984: 36).

Carrock End mine (Hartley, 1984).

Driggith mine Mentioned from 'Driggath' by Greg & Lettsom (1858: 391). Most specimens are unremarkable. Small greenish crystals (enclosing malachite?) occur with pyromorphite on quartz (OUM).

Dry Gill (Hartley, 1984).

Fig. 60 CERUSSITE: Red Gill mine, Old Dutch level. A small (2.5 mm), but perfect, twin of cerussite perched on goethite pseudomorphs after ?anglesite on quartz. D. R. Middleton Collection (15–19).

Ingray Gill (Hartley, 1984).

Mexico mine Described as 'crystallized and acicular' by Greg & Lettsom (1858: 391). A mining report of 1865 (Shaw archive, Carlisle, D/Sh/1/9) describes the 60 fm level 'driven 15 fm [27 m] all in ore worth up to [2 tons] per fm all carbonate'.

Nether Row Brow 'a little cerussite' was found in association with beaverite, beudantite, and mottramite from the Nether Row Farm level (Kingsbury & Hartley, 1956a: 292).

Poddy Gill From a dump at the foot of the gill with pyromorphite (Davidson & Thomson, 1951; Hartley, 1984).

Red Gill (Greg & Lettsom, 1858). Common in small crystals of various habits; particularly attractive when coated with a thin skin of malachite. Goethite and chrysocolla epimorphs of cerussite also occur.

Roughton Gill Good specimens were obtained when the mine was working, particularly sprays of white crystals (< 10 mm) scattered in dense mats of acicular malachite (q.v.). Some specimens in the BM(NH), collected by Bryce Wright in 1865, show tabular crystals from 10–20 mm with an almost metallic lustre. Pyromorphite epimorphs after acicular cerussite (< 30 mm) also occur (King Collection, NMW; Carlisle Museum). Similar specimens were found in higher Roughton Gill ('Thief Gills') by Davidson & Thomson (1951).

Sandbeds mine From the 'top level' (Hartley, 1984).

Silver Gill (Greg & Lettsom, 1858). Found in the 'Golden Hugh' as small attractive striated prisms with acicular malachite in small cavities in quartz.

CHALCANTHITE $CuSO_4 . 5H_2O$

Driggith mine Specimens labelled chalcanthite, showing thin bluish crusts on quartz-sulphide matrix, are preserved in the Kingsbury Collection, (BM(NH)). Kingsbury (MS3) comments on the occurrence: 'x-ray photo has since shown it to be an "unidentified" sulphate'. The persistence of chalcanthite in an area of such high rainfall is doubtful.

CHALCOPHYLLITE $Cu_{18}Al_2(AsO_4)_3(SO_4)_3(OH)_{27} . 33H_2O$

Old Potts Gill mine (Hartley, 1984). Specimens from the 'old No. 1 cross-cut dumps' are preserved in the Kingsbury Collection, BM(NH), and show typical small hexagonal milky green crystals encrusting small pieces of matrix.

CHALCOPYRITE $CuFeS_2$

Common throughout the district with the notable exception of Dry Gill. The principal ore of copper at Carrock End, Hay Gill, Potts Gill Copper, Red Gill and Roughton Gill mines. Almost always massive. Principal localities are: *Brae Fell mine, Brandy Gill Lead mine, Carrock End mine, Carrock mine, Driggith mine, Hay Gill mine, Ingray Gill, Low Pike, Mexico mine, Nether Row Brow, Old Potts Gill mine, Potts Gill Copper mine, Red Gill mine, Roughton Gill mine, Sandbeds mine, Short Grain, Silver Gill.* See Appendix 1 for references.

CHALCOSINE Cu_2S

Brandy Gill Lead mine (Hartley, 1984).

Carrock mine With arsenopyrite, pyrite, chalcopyrite and bornite in 'complex ore' (Davidson & Thomson, 1951). The paragenesis of chalcosine here is discussed in detail by Thimmaiah (1956).

Driggith mine Replaces bornite (Thimmaiah, 1956). Noted from the 12 fm and 30 fm level dumps by Hartley (1984).

Potts Gill With chalcopyrite, altering to brochantite and malachite (Kingsbury & Hartley, MS); (also, Hartley, 1984).

Red Gill (Kendall, 1884).

Roughton Gill (Kendall, 1884).

CHENEVIXITE $Cu_2Fe_2^{3+}(AsO_4)_2(OH)_4 \cdot H_2O$

Brandy Gill Lead mine From an outcrop of the vein in the west bank of the gill (Hartley, 1984).

Fig. 61 CHRYSOCOLLA: Red Gill mine. Epimorphs after spherical aggregates of malachite (to 3 mm) and acicular cerussite. Collected from the Old Dutch level dumps in 1987. M. P. Cooper Collection (8740).

CHLORARGYRITE AgCl

Driggith mine In the vein outcrop workings (Hartley, 1984); 'traces' according to Kingsbury (MS 1).

CHRYSOCOLLA $(Cu, Al)_2H_2Si_2O_5(OH)_4 \cdot nH_2O$

Widespread and fairly common.

Brae Fell mine (Hartley, 1984).

Brandy Gill Lead mine (Hartley, 1984).

Carrock End mine (Greg & Lettsom, 1858; Davidson & Thomson, 1951; Hartley, 1984).

Carrock mine (Davidson & Thomson, 1951; Hartley, 1984).

Driggith (Davidson & Thomson, 1951; Hartley, 1984).

Dry Smale Gill (Shaw, 1970).

Hay Gill (Hartley, 1984).

Ingray Gill (Hartley, 1984).

Potts Gill (Davidson & Thomson, 1951; Shaw, 1970).

Red Gill (Greg & Lettsom, 1858; Davidson & Thomson, 1951). Occurs as pseudomorphs after radiating sprays of malachite and as epimorphs after acicular cerussite.

Roughton Gill (Greg & Lettsom, 1858; Rudler, 1905; Davidson & Thomson, 1951). Miers (1897) describes a chrysocolla pseudomorph, apparently after siderite rhombohedra.

Sandbeds mine (Hartley, 1984).

Silver Gill (Hartley, 1984).

CINNABAR HgS

Caldbeck Fells 'Some time last year [1880–1881] a notice went the round of our local newspapers to the effect that cinnabar ... had been discovered somewhere or other out Caldbeck Fells way' (Goodchild, 1882: 105). Goodchild doubted the occurrence.

Mercury has been detected in ppm in the Wet Swine Gill 'antimony vein' (Fortey *et al.*, 1984).

COLUMBITE $(Mn, Fe^{2+})(Nb, Ta)_2O_6$

Carrock mine Forms minute grains (exceptionally up to 180 μm, but mostly < 30 μm) in arsenopyrite, scheelite and carbonate minerals replacing wolframite. Manganocolumbite is the dominant end-member at Carrock (Beddoe-Stephens & Fortey, 1981).

CONICHALCITE $CaCu(AsO_4)(OH)$

Brandy Gill Lead mine Specimens labelled conichalcite are preserved in the Russell and Kingsbury Collections, BM(NH), but Kingsbury seems later to have considered the mineral to be a calcian duftite ('calcioduftite') although the X-ray powder pattern was 'close to (but by no means identical with) that of conichalcite' (Kingsbury &

Fig. 62 CORKITE: Mexico mine. Pseudocubic dark brown crystal (1 mm) on minutely botryoidal goethite on gossany quartz. Found in 1976 in scree above the High level; probably originating in the outcrop of the Roughton Gill (South) vein. D. R. Middleton Collection.

Hartley, MS). Conichalcite has been found intimately associated with bayldonite forming a dark green crystalline crust on quartz (*det.* BM(NH): XRD, B. Young, *pers. comm.*).

Driggith–Sandbeds outcrop workings Found *in situ* by Kingsbury & Hartley (MS) in 'one of the old open-cast workings' in a form 'similar to that at Potts Gill mine' with iron-stained sugary quartz and 'psilomelane'. Listed by Hartley (1984). 'With wulfenite, pyromorphite, mimetite and anglesite (BM(NH))' (Young, 1987: 39).

Old Potts Gill mine From the 'old No. 2 [No. 1 ?] cross-cut' as 'small, characteristic bright grass-green globules and botryoidal aggregates in cavities in iron-stained quartz: in one case it is associated with olivenite' (Kingsbury & Hartley, MS). Specimens matching this description are preserved in the Kingsbury Collection, BM(NH).

CONNELLITE $Cu_{19}Cl_4(SO_4)(OH)_{32} \cdot 3H_2O$

Old Potts Gill mine Listed from the 'No. 1 cross-cut dumps' (Kingsbury, MS 1).

COPPER Cu

Driggith mine (Stanley & Vaughan, 1981)

CORKITE $PbFe_3^{3+}(PO_4)(SO_4)(OH)_6$

Mexico mine From debris near the High level, on a few specimens collected in 1976 as dark brown to almost black, pseudo-cubic (or pseudo-cuboctahedral) crystals to 1.5 mm across, scattered on lustrous black goethite in cavities in gossany quartz, associated with small amounts of later, green, pyromorphite (D. R. Middleton, *pers.*

comm.; *det.* BM(NH): XRD). A further specimen was later confirmed as corkite by XRD and semi-quantitative analysis at the Royal Museum of Scotland (M. Wirth, *pers. comm.*).

CORNUBITE $Cu_5(AsO_4)_2(OH)_4$

Old Potts Gill mine During the characterization of cornubite as a new species (Claringbull *et al.*, 1959: 2) two specimens from Potts Gill were examined. They were both collected by Kingsbury and showed 'light and dark green botryoidal cornubite, with on the latter specimen a bluish skin of cornwallite'. Although visually different, the two cornubite varieties yielded identical X-ray powder photographs, the data for which was tabulated by Claringbull *et al.* (*op. cit.*).

CORNWALLITE $Cu_5(AsO_4)_2(OH)_4 \cdot H_2O$

Low Pike First identified by us on a few specimens collected by D. R. Middleton, cornwallite is fairly common in small amounts on dump material from an old trial on the Low Pike vein above Potts Gill [NY 320 358]. It forms thin, drusy, crusts of a bright turquoise colour in fractures in vein quartz with mimetite, bayldonite, philipsburgite, beudantite, and baryte (*det.* BM(NH): XRD). A similar, but darker green mineral has been identified as a phosphatian variety (M. P. Cooper Collection, *det.* UMIST: IR).

Old Potts Gill mine 'numerous specimens' were collected from the 'old No. 1 cross-cut' by Kingsbury & Hartley (MS), where it occurred as sub-botryoidal encrustations on quartz. With cornubite (q.v.) (Claringbull *et al.*, 1959). Noted also by Shaw (1970) and Hartley (1984).

Sandbeds mine Specimen in the King Collection (NMW) (Young, 1987).

Fig. 63 CORNWALLITE: Low Pike. Drusy microcrystalline crust on quartz, SEM photo, scale bar 20 μm. M. Rothwell Collection.

Fig. 64 CORNWALLITE: Low Pike. Drusy microcrystalline crust on quartz with later water-clear baryte crystals to 2 mm. D. R. Middleton Collection.

CORONADITE $Pb(Mn^{4+}, Mn^{2+})_8O_{16}$

Dry Gill mine Found here with massive quartz, 'psilomelane' and mimetite ('campylite'); it occurs in two forms: 'a silver-white, inclining to steel-grey, metallic mineral when fresh, tarnishing to a dull black. The habit varies from massive to fibrous, the fibres being especially well-developed when the mineral is botryoidal, not only as radiating fibres within the body of the globules, but as minute acicular crystals on their surface giving the appearance of a black velvet. As a dull black, fibrous, botryoidal mineral, indistinguishable from psilomelane in the hand specimen'. The first British record (Hartley, 1959: 344).

CORUNDUM Al_2O_3

Carrock Fell 'Lately found, in opaque bluish-grey hexagonal crystals, in nacrite [= muscovite], by Mr. Bruce [*sic*] Wright, at Carrock Fells' (Greg & Lettsom, 1858: 235). A specimen in the BM(NH), BM 89460, collected *c*.1855, fits the above description and, apart from the presence of corundum, appears typical of specimens from the Grainsgill greisen. No record of a subsequent find exists.

COSALITE $Pb_2Bi_2S_5$

Carrock mine The first British occurrence of cosalite (Kingsbury & Hartley, 1956*b*). Also noted by Thimmaiah (1956). According to Kingsbury & Hartley (1956*b*: 297): 'It occurs in small quartz stringers, otherwise barren, in the greisen, or in the greisen itself where it may be accompanied by, but is not always closely associated with, traces of arsenopyrite, pyrite and chalcopyrite; in the greisen it usually forms minute tufts, rarely exceeding 3–4 mm, of capillary fibres in cavities, while in the quartz stringers it is found in the same habit and also in fibres up to $1\frac{1}{2}$ cm in length as well as in small compact fibrous patches. Many of the tufts are loose in the cavities and fall out when the matrix is broken; in some cases, single fibres or groups are included in nearly clear quartz surrounding the cavities. The compact fibrous material is generally steel-grey, but the more separate fibres are nearly all very dark grey and often show a bluish or yellowish tarnish.' In the quartz stringers it may be accompanied by aikinite; in the greisen it occurs alone. Kingsbury & Hartley (*ibid*) point out that cosalite is the most abundant of the sulphosalts found by them at Carrock: on this basis many otherwise unidentified specimens of capillary sulphosalts from Carrock are labelled cosalite.

Recently identified (by CJS) in polished section, in association with bismuthinite, krupkaite, and bismuth tellurides.

Fig. 65 COSALITE: Carrock mine. Capillary crystals (5 mm) on quartz. Cosalite is the commonest of the hair-like sulphosalts at Carrock but is difficult to distinguish visually from other species of similar habit. R. E. Starkey Collection (0671-01).

COVELLINE CuS

As replacements of other sulphides, covelline occurs in small quantities in several localities.

Brandy Gill Lead mine (Hartley, 1984).

Carrock mine replacing chalcopyrite (Thimmaiah, 1956).

Driggith mine replacing bornite (Thimmaiah, 1956); and galena (Stanley & Vaughan, 1981). Listed from the Driggith–Sandbeds outcrop workings by Hartley (1984).

Old Potts Gill mine from the old No. 1 level dumps (Kingsbury, MS 1).

Roughton Gill From the South vein outcrop workings in higher Roughton Gill (Hartley, 1984).

Silver Gill 'outside the lowest level at 1500 ft [450 m]' (Hartley, 1984).

CROCOITE PbCrO$_4$

Doubt surrounds the claimed occurrences of crocoite in the Caldbeck Fells.

Brandy Gill A specimen, formerly part of the R. C. Walsh Collection, now in the King Collection (NMW) is said to have originated in the Brandy Gill area. It is almost certainly incorrectly provenanced (R. J. King, *pers. comm.*).

Poddy Gill A specimen in the Kingsbury Collection, BM(NH), with a crudely crystalline orange encrustation with green pyromorphite on a massive galena and quartz matrix was investigated during the present study. It has an associated label: 'pyromorphite with ?mimetite and ?wulfenite on galena and quartz. Shaft on east/west vein near foot of Poddy Gill, Carrock Fell ... 1951' in Kingsbury's handwriting. The orange mineral was shown by XRD to be crocoite. The result is an enigma: Kingsbury was too experienced a mineralogist to have missed the obvious possibility of crocoite; in spite of the locality having been heavily collected over the years for wulfenite and pyromorphite, the authors are not aware of other crocoite specimens from here, and the occurrence requires confirmation.

Roughton Gill 'Chromate of Lead, or Crocoisite' from Roughton Gill was recorded by Branston (1910: 18) on the basis of a specimen in Carlisle Museum. This specimen has been examined by several mineralogists and all agree that it is typical of crocoite from Beresov, Siberia, and is incorrectly provenanced.

CUBANITE CuFe$_2$S$_3$

Carrock mine Ewart, 1957; Hartley, 1984.

CUPRITE Cu$_2$O

Although Hutchinson (1794: Vol. 1, 44) refers to Caldbeck only under the heading cuprite ('Red Copper Ore — minera cupri calciformis, pura et indurata, colore rubra, Cronstedt') in his list of copper minerals from Cumberland, cuprite is a very rare mineral in the district and has been reported from the cited localities in only small amounts.

Brae Fell mine In small amounts with chrysocolla (M. Leppington Collection, *det.* M. Rothwell: EPMA).

Brandy Gill Lead mine (Hartley, 1984).

Carrock End mine (Hartley, 1984).

Deer Hills From the baryte workings to the east of Potts Gill Baryte mine (Shaw, 1970).

Driggith mine From the Driggith–Sandbeds outcrop workings (Kingsbury Collection, BM(NH)).

Hay Gill mine (Hartley, 1984).

Mexico mine 'red oxide' (Shaw, 1970).

Old Potts Gill mine As small red poorly crystalline masses with malachite etc. (Kingsbury Collection, BM(NH); Hartley, 1984).

Red Gill mine Listed by Berg (1985).

Roughton Gill See 'brewsterite'.

Silver Gill As thin strings in masses of altered sulphides from an old ore pile at [NY 2995 3415] (*det.* M. Rothwell: EPMA, *pers. comm,*).

CYANOTRICHITE Cu$_4$Al$_2$(SO$_4$)(OH)$_{12}$.2H$_2$O

Old Potts Gill mine As a felted mass of pale blue fibres with small azurite crystals, ?jarosite, and malachite on a small specimen from the "old No. 1 cross-cut dumps" (Kingsbury Collection, BM(NH)). Listed by Hartley (1984).

DESCLOIZITE PbZn(VO$_4$)(OH)

Brandy Gill mine On the dump from the east level, as aggregates of small greenish brown, brown, or reddish brown crystals with vanadinite. Found only by Kingsbury and Hartley (1956a), who comment that it is much rarer than mottramite.

Old Potts Gill mine With duftite on a specimen from the foot of an air shaft on Deer Hills (*det.* BM(NH): XRD, N. Thomson, *pers. comm.*)

DEVILLINE CaCu$_4$(SO$_4$)$_2$(OH)$_6$.3H$_2$O

Occurs as poorly defined crystalline crusts on veinstone; possibly a post-mining formation.

Brandy Gill Lead mine The only record is that of Berg (1985) who cannot now substantiate the record by specimen or reference (*pers. comm.*, 1988). Requires confirmation.

Driggith mine From the 30 fm level (Hartley, 1984).

Sandbeds mine From the top level dumps (Hartley, 1984).

DIGENITE Cu_9S_5

Red Gill As a blue-black powder, collected in an unsuccessful search for tenorite (Davidson & Thomson, 1951).

DIOPTASE $CuSiO_2(OH)_2$

Old Potts Gill mine (Hartley, 1984) The first British record of dioptase. Specimens in the Kingsbury Collection, BM(NH), collected in 1953 from the 'old No. 1 cross-cut' dumps show attractive prismatic crystals (< a millimetre or so) on small pieces of matrix.

DJURLEITE $Cu_{1.94}S$

Driggith mine In small amounts replacing galena (Stanley & Vaughan, 1981).

DOLOMITE $(Ca,Mg)CO_3$

Carrock mine Cream to brown, massive, ferroan dolomite is common as a late-stage mineral in the tungsten veins and forms much of the 'ankerite veins' which split off westwards from the Emerson vein. Uncommon as crystals. An analysis of a specimen from the Harding vein was given by Smythe & Dunham (1947) who called the mineral 'ankerite' but the analysis shows the iron content to be too low for this species.

Old Potts Gill mine (Hartley, 1984).

Roughton Gill Abundant as a massive brown to dark brown mineral (Day, 1928; Davidson & Thomson, 1951).

Sandbeds West Baryte mine Abundant in the 60 fm level: '. . . some of the dolomite was of the very dark variety which carries approximately 12% of manganese' (Shaw, 1970: 73).

DUFRENITE $Fe^{2+}Fe^{3+}(PO_4)_3(OH)_5 \cdot 2H_2O$

Burdell Gill (Hartley, 1984).

DUFTITE $PbCu(AsO_4)(OH)$

Brandy Gill Lead mine The first British locality; recorded by Claringbull (1951) who identified the species on a specimen collected by W. F. Davidson: 'thin botryoidal coatings of duftite varying in colour from pale emerald-green to deep moss-green in association with mimetite, pyromorphite, stolzite, cerussite, malachite, ankerite, and linarite on a quartzose matrix containing galena and chalcopyrite.' (Claringbull, 1951: 610). Davidson & Thomson (1951: 142) also reported the occurrence and commented 'bayldonite is also reported . . . [here] . . . but we collected a large number of green botryoidal specimens . . . and the latest report from the British Museum is that all the Brandy Gill material is duftite'. Kingsbury & Hartley (MS) refuted this, claiming that bayldonite was more common and, moreover, that material they had

collected that resembled, but was not identical with, duftite was actually an intermediate between duftite and conichalcite. They coined the term 'calcio-duftite' for this mineral on the basis of the intermediate nature of the X-ray powder spacings, and a qualitative (spectrographic) analysis that showed significant calcium. Claringbull (*ibid*) also mentioned the affinity of the X-ray pattern of Brandy Gill duftite with conichalcite and commented on the variation of refractive index within individual spherules of the mineral which, he suggested, resulted from a corresponding variation in composition with the core being richer in lead than the outer areas.

Most duftite from Brandy Gill appears to be β-duftite as defined by Guillemin (1956: 70) who re-examined Claringbull's (1951) X-ray data. Infra-red absorption spectrophotometry readily distinguishes α- and β-duftite and also shows the predominance of the latter at this locality (R. S. W. Braithwaite, *pers. comm.*). However, a few specimens recently examined appear to be α-duftite which, at Brandy Gill, forms small globular masses on quartz (M. P. Cooper Collection, *det.* P. J. Dunn, Smithsonian Institution: XRD) or minute crystals with agardite-mixite (*det.* BM(NH): XRD, C. M. Leppington, *pers. comm.*).

A specimen investigated during the present study (Hartley Collection, Leeds Univ.) gave an IR absorption spectrum related to duftite and conichalcite (R. S. W. Braithwaite, *pers. comm.*, 1986). The mineral encrusts, and appears to be altering from, phosphatian mimetite. Other specimens gave IR spectra close to duftite, but could not be identified by XRD. Work continues on these minerals.

Driggith mine In small amounts with 'malachite, cerussite, chrysocolla, pyromorphite and other secondary minerals in material that apparently comes from a small copper-bearing vein near [Driggith] beck on the west side, a little way below the 30 fm level. Old records and information obtained from the mine manager, Mr W. H. P. Parkinson, suggest that this vein had been tried at one time but that the level was now collapsed and buried under debris from later workings' (Kingsbury & Hartley, MS). (Hartley, 1984).

Low Pike Very rarely, as a yellow crust with bayldonite from a small trial on the Low Pike vein [NY 320358] (*det.* BGS: XRD, B. Young, *pers. comm.*).

Old Potts Gill mine With descloizite on a specimen from the foot of an air shaft on Deer Hills (*det.* BM(NH): XRD, N. Thomson, *pers. comm.*).

ELYITE $Pb_4Cu(SO_4)(OH)_8$

Red Gill As a pale purple coating on galena in a specimen collected by P. Briscoe from waste near the old stamps at the Red Gill–Swinburn Gill confluence (*det.* BM(NH): XRD). Probably dump-formed (Briscoe, 1986).

ERYTHRITE
$Co_3(AsO_4)_2 . 8H_2O$

Ingray Gill From the northern level as bladed purple crystals 2–3 mm long, in cavities in sugary quartz alone, or with pharmacosiderite, scorodite and arseniosiderite (Kingsbury & Hartley, 1957e; Kingsbury Collection, BM(NH)). Pink globular erythrite, perhaps of post-mining formation, has also been found on one specimen from the same dump (N. Thomson, *pers. comm.*, 1987).

Roughton Gill As pink encrustations on quartz and calcite from the 90 fm level dumps (Young, 1987). Probably formed on the dumps.

FERRIMOLYBDITE
$Fe_2^{3+}(MoO_4)_3 . 8H_2O$

Carrock mine Yellow, fibrous to powdery alteration products of molybdenite have been known for a considerable time from these veins. Sowerby (1817: Note 9 to the Systematic Index) recorded 'Oxyde of Molybdenum occurs with the handsome specimens of Sulphuret of Molybdenum ... found lately at Caldbeck Fell ...'. Lévy (1837) included 'acide molybdique jaune' in his catalogue; and Greg & Lettsom (1858) and Hitchen (1934) recorded 'molybdine' and 'molybdite' respectively. Greg & Lettsom's reference was quoted as synonymous with ferrimolybdite by Palache, Berman & Frondel (1951). Ferrimolybdite was listed by Hartley (1984).

FLUORITE
CaF_2

Carrock mine Rare; first reported by Rastall (1942: 342) who 'found three or four crystals of green fluorite on a joint face of the Grainsgill greisen'. Small mauve specks and purple crystals were found by Davidson & Thomson (1951), and pale blue-green euhedral cubes were found in a vein breccia from the E–W lead–zinc crosscourse by Stanley (1979). In 1987, sharp octahedral crystals of green to purple zoned fluorite (< 6 mm) were found in cavities in quartz with calcite and iridescent pyrite from recent workings on the Smith vein. White microcline crystals are a later partial encrustation on some of these specimens. The fluorite octahedra have green cores with later purple and colourless zones, and covered areas to about 40×20 mm (D. R. Hacker Collection). On the opposite side of the same level, pale green unzoned octahedra have subsequently been found (D. I. Green, *pers. comm.*).

FÜLÖPPITE
$Pb_3Sb_8S_{15}$

Wet Swine Gill Some dark grey metallic patches of fibrous crystals accompanying stibnite in the 'antimony vein' were identified 'with some confidence' as fülöppite by Fortey *et al.* (1984) on the basis of their X-ray powder patterns. However, the authors could not identify the species in polished sections. Specimens of the typical sulphide-sulphosalt assemblage from this locality are commonly labelled fülöppite, but may consist largely of stibnite.

Fig. 66 FLUORITE: Carrock mine. A 6 mm pale purple octahedron with a pale green core (the latter impossible to capture on colour film) on calcite from an isolated pocket in the adit level on the west branch of the Smith vein. Fluorite is very rare in the Lake District and the few specimens from this find are among the best known. On some pieces the fluorite was partly overgrown with small milk white microcline crystals. D. R. Hacker Collection (87-29).

GALENA
PbS

The commonest ore of lead, present in most of the mines. As it is mostly massive, there are few specimens in collections, although one of the earliest known mineral specimens from this district is of 'lead-ore, glossy and shining, formerly work'd for silver by the Hochstetters' (Woodward Collection, Cambridge Univ.; see Woodward, 1729: specimen n. 109). For citations to the localities listed below, see Appendix 1.

Brae Fell mine

Brandy Gill 'The old records give galena crystals from this locality' (Davidson & Thomson, 1951: 142). Unfortunately, neither the locality nor the old records can now be identified with certainty.

Brandy Gill Lead mine Drusy quartz epimorphs after a cubic mineral (to 15 mm on edge) occur in a vein exposure on the flank of Brandy Gill above the east level of the lead mine. The hollow 'boxes' are coated with small yellow-green mimetite crystals associated with rare stolzite tablets. The epimorphs probably represent original galena crystals. No euhedral galena crystals have been reported but the massive sulphide is common.

Carrock mine Mainly associated with the E–W lead–zinc veins. Finlayson (1910) records 'well crystallized' galena from Carrock mine.

Carrock End mine

Driggith mine Inclusions in galena from the Driggith vein are discussed by Stanley & Vaughan (1981).

Dry Gill mine Uncommon.

Ingray Gill

Mexico mine

Old Potts Gill mine

Poddy Gill From an old working on an E–W lead–zinc vein.

Red Gill mine Closely associated with chalcopyrite.

Roughton Gill The only notable galena specimen seen in this study is purported to come from here: it is a Bryce M. Wright specimen, in the Russell Collection, BM(NH), and comprises an almost solid mass of cube-octahedra to 9 mm with 'hacked quartz'.

Sandbeds mine

Short Grain As small inclusions in massive baryte from the northern trial.

Silver Gill From the level at *c.*450 m (1500 ft) and from the head of the gill, the so-called 'Golden Hugh'.

Swinburn Gill Mostly massive; small cube-octahedra altered almost entirely to cerussite, linarite etc. occur in dump specimens on the east bank opposite the Red Gill mine.

GOETHITE   FeO(OH)

Common in many veins as thin fibrous crusts and masses; as a constituent of 'limonite' and 'umber'. Notable specimens have not been recorded.

Brandy Gill Lead mine

Burdell Gill

Driggith mine

Harestones Umber mine (also known as the 'China Clay mine'.)

Mexico mine Black, botryoidal, goethite forms the matrix for corkite (q.v.). The lustrous surface is criss-crossed by minutely globular goethite which has grown along minute cracks like strings of tiny beads (D. R. Middleton Collection).

Old Potts Gill mine

Roughton Gill Goethite, 'limonite', and umber, the last once worked (Eastwood, 1921).

Sandbeds mine

GOLD   Au

Very rare. Gold 'disseminated in small specks' on lead ore was recorded by Calvert (1853: 106) from an unspecified locality in the Caldbeck Fells and has been reported from several localities since. In most cases these occurrences are known only from specimens collected by Kingsbury and described in an unpublished manuscript *Notes on the occurrence of gold in the Lake District by AWGK* (Kingsbury, MS 2). Specimens are preserved in the BM(NH) and in the OUM. The gold values of stream sediments in the district (usually less than 0.15 ppm) were investigated by Appleton & Wadge (1976).

Carrock mine The presence of gold in 'bismuth telluride' at Carrock mine was noted by Dewey & Dines (1923). Kingsbury (*op. cit.*) found gold here in three separate occurrences:

In 1950 he collected gold *in situ* in the No. 1 level on the Harding vein 'right at the point of intersection' of the Harding vein and an E–W lead vein. At this point, he writes: 'it was seen that some of the "schist" wall-rock [i.e. metamorphosed Skiddaw Slate] was partially coated and impregnated with green and blue copper minerals, including malachite, azurite, possibly linarite and probably some brochantite. It is not easy to examine material with only the light of a mining-lamp and when it is wet and dirty, so as much as possible was removed and looked at subsequently. In some of this material, minute sprigs and flakes of gold are present, partly in the foliae of the "schist" and partly disseminated through the secondary copper minerals.'

In 1953 'five very small specks of gold were found in parts of a narrow quartz-vein broken out from a block of greisen ... which had been taken out of a new low-level cross-cut [the No. 2 or Canadian cross-cut] ... The small vein in which the gold occurred carried a little pyrite, small amounts of galena and arsenopyrite and traces of chalcopyrite in a quartz-matrix which here and there contained traces of ankeritic or dolomitic carbonates. The gold is intimately associated with or partly embedded in galena with which a little arsenopyrite is associated'. Kingsbury concluded that this vein material was associated with E–W cross-courses.

In 1956 gold was found in quartz vein-material that had been washed from the Carrock dumps during torrential rain a few years previously. 'In one specimen specks of gold are visible in dark brown goethite, suggesting derivation from pyrite; on the others no sign of sulphides is present ...' (Kingsbury, *op. cit.*).

R. J. King (*pers. comm.*) found a small sprig of gold on

goethite-encrusted quartz *in situ* in the Harding vein working; and small specimens of gold in quartz, or with 'josëite', have been found on the dumps (R. S. W. Braithwaite, *pers. comm.*). Reported from the Emerson vein by Shaw (1970).

Ingray Gill 'two tiny specimens of native gold have been found in cavities in slightly iron-stained, saccharoidal quartz' in dump material from the northern level (Kingsbury, *op. cit.*).

Mexico mine From the low level dumps in Todd Gill 'small sprigs and specks of gold ... have ... been found in ... oxidised vein material, associated with malachite and decomposed chalcopyrite' (Kingsbury, *op. cit.*).

Red Gill 'a few specks of gold have been found in iron-stained quartz, with some decomposed chalcopyrite and malachite, in material derived from the lowest cross-cut' [i.e. the Deep level] (Kingsbury, *op. cit.*).

A possible Red Gill gold, originally labelled 'Cumberland', was discussed by Sweet (1960): it comprises minute grains and crystals of gold in a quartz gossan with caledonite, linarite, cerussite, and hemimorphite.

Roughton Gill mine 'in some ... carbonate veinstone collected near the entrance to the 90-fathom cross-cut, a tiny sprig of native gold has been found. It occurs in calcite which is stained reddish by iron and greenish by malachite and other copper-minerals; in addition to malachite, a little chalcocite and what is probably brochantite are also present and the gold occurs in intimate association with chalcocite and secondary alteration-products.' (Kingsbury, *op. cit.*).

Swinburn Gill From 'an old bell-pit ... sunk on a N.W.–S.E. vein' at the foot of Wet Smale Gill [NY 297 351] tiny sprigs of gold were found in malachite or in iron-stained quartz associated with decomposing chalcopyrite and malachite (Kingsbury, *op. cit.*). These specimens (BM(NH)) are among the richest found in the district.

'GRÜNLINGITE'

Carrock mine A supposed new bismuth telluride described by Muthmann and Schröder (1897) but discredited by Peacock (1941). Many specimens labelled 'grünlingite' are in old collections: most are probably mixtures of josëite-A, bismuthinite, ingodite (Peacock, 1941; Zav'yalov & Begizov, 1981*a*, *b*) and possibly also josëite-B (q.v.).

GYPSUM   CaSO$_4$.2H$_2$O

Carrock mine As a 'White crystalline crust on quartz from the No. 3 level' (Young, 1987: 55).

HEDLEYITE   Bi$_7$Te$_3$

Carrock mine Associated with native bismuth, bismuthinite and josëite-B with chalcopyrite, arsenopyrite, and

Fig. 67 HEDYPHANE: Brandy Gill Lead mine. Creamy globular masses and radiating crystals (to 2 mm) on quartz with later duftite. Just a few specimens have been found at this, the only, British locality. R. E. Starkey Collection (1176-01).

molybdenite in greisen on specimens in the BM(NH). Hedleyite forms grains up to 200 μm (*det.* CJS, BM(NH): EPMA).

HEDYPHANE   (Ca,Pb)$_5$(AsO$_4$)$_3$Cl

Brandy Gill Lead mine As club-shaped aggregates of creamy prismatic crystals to 2 mm with duftite on quartz on a few specimens found *in situ* in the top west level in 1985 (*det.* BM(NH): XRD; R. Starkey, *pers. comm.*, 1985). The first British record.

HEMATITE   Fe$_2$O$_3$

Widespread as thin films and powdery masses.

Brandy Gill Lead mine (Hartley, 1984).

Carrock mine (Hartley, 1984).

Potts Gill Copper and Baryte mines (Hartley, 1984).

Roughton Gill mine (Davidson & Thomson, 1951).

Sandbeds mine (Hartley, 1984).

Fig. 68 HEMIMORPHITE: Roughton Gill mine, 50 mm across. An exceptional white to sky blue banded crust on quartz. The crystallized surface is most unusual. It was bought by the BM, as 'cupreous smithsonite', from the collection of R. Campbell in 1862 (BM 34401).

HEMIMORPHITE $Zn_4Si_2O_7(OH)_2.H_2O$

One of the species for which the Caldbeck Fells are famous: very many beautiful sky blue botryoidal hemimorphite specimens were collected from the Roughton Gill mine to adorn collections the world over. Occurrences at other Caldbeck mines are sporadic and, generally, insignificant.

Balliway Rigg Minute crystals and crusts with rosasite from dumps of an old working on the Silver Gill vein [NY 301 342] (M. P. Cooper Collection).

Brae Fell mine As a thin, minutely drusy, white coating on small quartz crystals (M. P. Cooper Collection, *det.* UMIST: IR).

Driggith mine From the 12 fm and 30 fm level dumps (Hartley, 1984).

Ingray Gill Listed from the nothern trial by Hartley (1984).

Red Gill Rarely; in small colourless crystals and globular aggregates (*det.* BM(NH): XRD). Associated with linarite, caledonite and gold in a specimen described by Sweet (1960) as probably from Red Gill.

Roughton Gill A classic locality for this mineral where it once occurred in large quantities (cf. Fig. 45, p. 71). Specimens as much as 30 cm across were recovered in the nineteenth century, showing beautiful pale to sky blue crusts (up to 3 cm thick) cementing a vein breccia. It is possible that the 'lapis calaminaris' mentioned in an early note (Anon, 1747) referred to this species. ['lapis calaminaris' did not refer to any one zinc mineral. In 1747, the implication was of an oxidized ore, usually smithsonite or hemimorphite. Sphalerite was not used as an ore until John Champion demonstrated a technique for smelting it in 1758 (Hamilton, 1926)]. Roughton Gill hemimorphite was well known by the time of Greg & Lettsom (1858). It was occasionally mistaken for smithsonite and specimens, especially the paler varieties, are sometimes seen so labelled.

The surface of the botryoidal hemimorphite is usually

smooth, less often drusy; the colour varies from sky blue to blue-grey and green. Hemimorphite in this form usually occurs alone, rarely with a scattering of embedded pyromorphite crystals. Radiating masses and sprays of small, colourless to pale blue euhedral crystals of hemimorphite are also found and in this form it is commonly associated with later globular rosasite.

Fine specimens of the botryoidal variety could still be found on the 90 fm level dumps in the 1940s but are very rare today. It has been found recently, in small amounts, *in situ* in an outcrop of the South vein in higher Roughton Gill (J. G. Wilson, *pers. comm.*).

Sandbeds mine Specimens in the Kingsbury Collection, BM(NH), show colourless crystals from the 'middle level' dumps and good, pale aquamarine blue blades to 7 mm from the 'top level' dumps. The occurrences were listed by Hartley (1984). Davidson & Thomson (1951: 140) also mention 'fine pale blue ... (rare)' hemimorphite from Sandbeds mine.

Silver Gill From the 'lowest level at 1500 ft [450 m]'. (Hartley, 1984).

HIDALGOITE $PbAl_3(SO_4)(AsO_4)(OH)_6$

Roughton Gill mine Supposedly a component of 'plumbogummite' (Förtsch 1967). However, the analysis of plumbogummite by Hartley (1900)—used by Förtsch—shows no sulphate and only trace amounts of arsenic.

HINSDALITE $(Pb,Sr)Al_3(PO_4)(SO_4)(OH)_6$

Old Potts Gill mine Grey massive with baryte from the 'old No. 1 cross-cut' dumps, collected in 1953 (Kingsbury Collection, BM(NH)). Kingsbury (MS 1) also notes: 'new to G.B.'. Listed by Hartley (1984).

Roughton Gill mine Förtsch (1967) suggested that hinsdalite was a constituent of 'plumbogummite' with hidalgoite (q.v.)

HISINGERITE $Fe_2^{3+}Si_2O_5(OH)_4 \cdot 2H_2O$

Brandy Gill Lead mine Listed from the upper west level dump (Hartley, 1984).

HÜBNERITE (see WOLFRAMITE)

HYDROCERUSSITE $Pb_3(CO_3)_2(OH)_2$

Widespread but uncommon. The known localities were all discovered by Kingsbury and Hartley, and most are described in their unpublished MS of 1951. The hydrocerussite occurred as 'compact, white, cleavable masses, some up to 2 or 3 cm across, or, less commonly, as minute, colourless, hexagonal plates and as rough, snow-white crystals or aggregates in quartz. It is usually closely associated with cerussite, pyromorphite, leadhillite, linarite, chrysocolla, galena and baryte, from

which latter mineral, it might not always be easy to distinguish it.' These and subsequent finds were listed by Hartley (1984), and specimens are preserved in the Kingsbury Collection, BM(NH), and Hartley Collection, Leeds Univ. Their localities are:

Brae Fell mine

Carrock mine From the E–W lead vein at the foot of Brandy Gill.

Driggith mine 12 fm and 30 fm level dumps.

Poddy Gill From the lead vein at the foot of the gill as minute pearly plates in quartz. (Kingsbury Collection, BM(NH); Hartley, 1984).

Red Gill mine Upper and middle levels. Also recently identified (BM(NH): XRD) as minute lenticular crystals with mattheddleite, susannite, silver etc. (M. Wirth, *pers. comm.*).

Roughton Gill mine From the 30 fm level dumps (Kingsbury & Hartley, MS); from the 60 fm and 90 fm level dumps (Hartley, 1984). Also as small, very pale blue masses in quartz with leadhillite, chrysocolla and small pyromorphite pseudomorphs after cerussite from 'Thief Gills (northern)' [probably the outcrop workings in higher Roughton Gill] (Hartley Collection. Leeds Univ., *det.* UMIST: IR).

Sandbeds mine 'top level' dumps.

Swinburn Gill From the 'old bell-pit' at the foot of Wet Smale Gill [NY 297 351] (Kingsbury & Hartley, 1951) and from an old trial in the east bank just south of Red Gill mine (Hartley, 1984).

HYDROZINCITE $Zn_5(CO_3)_2(OH)_6$

Old Potts Gill mine Listed by Kingsbury (MS 1) but not known to his one-time colleague J. Hartley (*pers. comm.*).

Sandbeds mine 'Pale blue crystalline crusts (BM(NH))' Young (1987: 63).

INGODITE Bi_2TeS

Carrock mine The species was first characterized during a study of 'grünlingite' from Brandy Gill [almost certainly the present site of Carrock mine] and Ingoda in central Transbaikal. It occurs associated with josëite-A and bismuthinite (Zav'ylov & Begizov, 1981*a,b*). It has also been identified on specimens from Carrock mine in the BM(NH). Probably the 'Mineral CF' of Clarke (1974).

JAMESONITE $Pb_4FeSb_6S_{14}$

Caldew Valley In a small quartz vein exposed by the side of the track below Coomb Height, just north-east of Wet Swine Gill [NY 3210 3215] (Fortey *et al.*, 1984).

Carrock mine '... in small amounts ... as dark grey minute acicular crystals or fibres, tufts or wool-like aggregates, or small fibrous patches'; in the hand specimen virtually impossible to distinguish from the boulangerite and zinckenite also occurring here (Kingsbury & Hartley, 1956b: 298).

Nether Row Brow Identified by P. H. A. Nancarrow of the BGS (*det*. XRD) as dark grey fibrous masses in cavities in quartz from the dump of the Nether Row Farm level (B. Young, *pers. comm.*).

Wet Swine Gill 'forms straight or curved capillary crystals between 60 and 250 μm in length with diamond-shaped cross-sections 2 to 20 μm in width. These hair-like crystals occur in groups grown in coarse quartz . . .' (Fortey *et al.*, 1984: 60).

JAROSITE $KFe_3^{3+}(SO_4)_2(OH)_6$

Surprisingly, considering its abundance, not recorded as a British species until 1958 when Kingsbury and Hartley reported it from several Caldbeck Fells localities as aggregates of very small, glistening yellow or golden-brown to brown crystals or compact masses.

Brandy Gill Lead mine 'in the outcrop of an east–west lead–copper vein near the head of the gill on the western side'; also on the dump from the eastern level (Kingsbury & Hartley, 1958: 813). From the top western dump (Hartley, 1984).

Burdell Gill As compact masses and as rhombohedral crystals to 2 mm on goethite and saccharoidal quartz. 'The crystals resemble brownish pharmacosiderite also occurring here' (Kingsbury & Hartley, 1958: 813).

Carrock mine On vein quartz, with ferrian alunite, from 'the "granitic" suite of veins' (Kingsbury & Hartley, 1958: 813).

Driggith–Sandbeds outcrop workings (Hartley, 1984).

Ingray Gill From the northern trial (Kingsbury & Hartley, 1958).

Nether Row Brow From both the Nether Row Farm and the 'Dumpy Stone' levels (Kingsbury & Hartley, 1958).

Old Potts Gill mine Associated with 'various secondary arsenates' from the dumps of the 'old No. 1 cross-cut' level (Kingsbury & Hartley, 1958: 814).

Roughton Gill '. . . with beaverite, beudantite, and chrysocolla in chalcedonic quartz, in the outcrop of the south vein along the flank of Balliway Rigg' in higher Roughton Gill (Kingsbury & Hartley, 1958: 814).

JOSÉITE–A Bi_4TeS_2

Carrock mine The bismuth tellurides at Carrock mine have presented a considerable problem to mineralogists for well over a hundred years.

Tetradymite was assumed to be the dominant phase by Greg & Lettsom (1858: 381) but they had to admit that 'The Cumberland telluric bismuth would appear to differ much in composition from other tetradymites'. They

recorded its occurrence with bismuth, bismuthinite, and molybdenite and gave as distinguishing characteristics its brilliant metallic lustre (on fresh surfaces), laminar cleavage, and flexibility.

Specimens were reanalysed and redefined by Muthmann & Schröder (1898) who regarded it as a new species which they named 'grünlingite'. In 1938 Garrido and Feo examined a number of dubious bismuth sulphotellurides and claimed that among them 'grünlingite' and oruetite were identical to each other, but different from joséite—itself of doubtful status. Joséite was redefined by Peacock (1941) who split it into two species—joséite-A (also known simply as 'joséite') and joséite-B—and demonstrated the identity of 'grünlingite' and oruetite with the former. There the matter rested for some time, but collectors continued to label specimens from Carrock mine tetradymite, 'grünlingite', or joséite.

Electron microprobe analysis of the Carrock mine tellurides led to the discovery of the new mineral ingodite (Zav'yalov & Begizov, 1981a, b). They confirmed the presence of joséite-A, and reported that specimens labelled grünlingite' from Brandy Gill and Ingoda (Russia) were mixtures of joséite-A and bismuthinite.

Specimens in the BM(NH), recently examined by CJS using optical and electron microprobe techniques, show that those labelled tetradymite contain mostly ingodite and joséite-B, while those labelled "grünlingite" contain joséite-A, joséite-B, bismuthinite and minor ingodite. A more detailed description is in preparation.

JOSÉITE–B Bi_4Te_2S

Carrock mine (see above).

KERMESITE Sb_2S_2O

Wet Swine Gill Possibly as 'tenuous red films' on quartz with primary antimony minerals (Fortey *et al.*, 1984). Requires confirmation.

KIPUSHITE $(Cu, Zn)_5Zn(PO_4)_2(OH)_6 . H_2O$

Low Pike An old trial on the Low Pike vein above Potts Gill [NY 320358] yielded small amounts of minutely crystalline philipsburgite (q.v.) containing considerable phosphate substituting for arsenate. The IR spectra of some samples (M. P. Cooper Collection) suggested that the substitution proportion might be sufficient to render the mineral kipushite (Braithwaite & Ryback, 1988). However, specimens analysed by XRD (BM(NH)) are closer to philipsburgite and a well crystallized sample, from the D. Hacker Collection, analysed semi-quantitatively by EPMA shows a somewhat higher arsenate : phosphate ratio than type philipsburgite. (*det*. Leicester Univ.).

KRUPKAITE $CuPbBi_3S_6$

Carrock mine Electron microprobe analyses (by CJS) of a

mineral replacing bismuthinite in a telluride-rich specimen (BM(NH)) give a formula consistent with that of krupkaite. Grains are minute (30–60 μm).

LANARKITE   Pb$_2$(SO$_4$)O

Very rare; known mainly from specimens collected by Kingsbury and Hartley in 1950 (Kingsbury Collection, BM(NH)). Their localities were not published until 1984 (Hartley).

Brae Fell mine 'three small specimens . . . (one from the upper level and two from the lower) have proved to be lanarkite . . . in the form of small, bladed or fibrous aggregates, colourless to greyish white and . . . not distinctly crystallized: it is associated with cerussite, hydrocerussite and a little yellow pyromorphite' (Kingsbury & Hartley, MS). Specimens in the Kingsbury Collection, BM(NH), fit this description; one, from the lower dump,

Fig. 69 LANARKITE: Roughton Gill (South) vein. White feathery blades to 5 mm fill cavities in altered galena from an outcrop in higher Roughton Gill near the confluence of the Thief Gills. The occurrence is very localized and only a few specimens are known. D. I. Green Collection.

contains in addition to leadhillite, excellent crystals of mattheddleite. A further Kingsbury specimen in the Russell Collection, BM(NH), from the same dump exhibits transparent, terminated (but mostly broken) prisms to about 15 mm.

The record by Young (1987) of lanarkite with leadhillite from Brae Fell in the NMW Collection is an error (R. E. Bevins, *pers. comm.*).

Red Gill mine Identified during this study in sprays of minute pale blue tapering bladed crystals on altered galena (D. Middleton; J. Wolters Collections, *det.* Leeds Univ. & BM(NH): XRD). Very rare.

Roughton Gill As pale sea-green blades and radiating sprays of crystal sections to 20 mm with leadhillite, from the outcrop workings on the South vein in higher Roughton Gill (Kingsbury Collection, BM(NH)). Recently found *in situ* in the same area forming thin grey laths to 2 mm with mattheddleite, leadhillite, caledonite, and scotlandite in pods of altered galena (D. I. Green *in prep.*).

LANGITE   Cu$_4$(SO$_4$)(OH)$_6$.2H$_2$O

In addition to the langite localities below, unconfirmed copper sulphate minerals resembling langite occur at several localities as post-mining formations.

Brae Fell mine On one specimen as minute crystalline aggregates (C. M. Leppington Collection; *det.* Leeds Univ.: XRD, D. I. Green, *pers. comm.*).

Mexico mine As small pseudo-hexagonal crystals (*det.* UMIST: IR, R. S. W. Braithwaite, *pers. comm.*).

Red Gill mine Deep prussian blue crystals with caledonite etc. (*det.* Leeds Univ.: XRD, D. I. Green, *pers. comm.*).

Silver Gill Locally common as pseudo-hexagonal crystals to 0.25 mm on altered sulphides from an old ore pile at [NY 2995 2415]. Probably dump-formed (*det.* Leeds Univ.: XRD, D. I. Green, *pers. comm.*).

LEADHILLITE   Pb$_4$(SO$_4$)(CO$_3$)$_2$(OH)$_2$

Brae Fell mine Found here sparingly but in good specimens: as small, sharp, equant, colourless to greenish crystals (< 2 mm or so) with lanarkite, mattheddleite, cerussite and pyromorphite (King Collection, NMW; Kingsbury Collection, BM(NH)). Listed by Hartley (1984).

Brandy Gill Lead mine Minute, poorly crystalline brownish aggregates on quartz have been identified (BM(NH): XRD) as leadhillite–susannite (B. Yates Collection).

Driggith mine From the 30 fm level dumps (Hartley, 1984).

Red Gill mine Long famous for producing the finest leadhillite in England. Greg & Lettsom (1858: 399) recorded it as 'found recently' and a comment in the catalogue of the Allan–Greg Collection (BM(NH)) suggests that the species was first found here by Bryce Wright.

Fig. 70 LEADHILLITE: Red Gill mine. Tabular crystal 3 mm across with caledonite and minute fibres of mattheddleite. Found on the ore-dressing dump at the foot of Red Gill in 1986. D. I. Green Collection.

Crystals occur up to 35 mm across, but are generally much smaller; anything in excess of 15 mm being very rare. The habit is usually tabular, sometimes equant; associated minerals include caledonite, susannite, mattheddleite, and anglesite. Rarely found scattered on linarite crystals.

Roughton Gill As small tabular crystals, with linarite, caledonite, cerussite and anglesite (Goodchild, 1885). Fine, lustrous, pale yellow crystals to c.10 mm occur in the outcrop workings on the South vein in higher Roughton Gill (Kingsbury Collection, BM(NH), collected 1950). Recently found here *in situ* with lanarkite, caledonite, scotlandite etc. as tabular transparent crystals to 0.25 mm (D. I. Green *in prep.*).

Sandbeds mine From the 'top level dumps' (Hartley, 1984). Specimens in the Kingsbury Collection, BM(NH), show microcrystalline leadhillite with linarite, caledonite, and cerussite.

LIBETHENITE $Cu_2(PO_4)(OH)$

Old Potts Gill mine Very rare, known only from the dumps of the 'old No. 1 cross-cut' on specimens collected about 1949–1950 by Kingsbury and Hartley. Specimens in the Kingsbury Collection, BM(NH), show pseudo-octahedral to short prismatic, sparkling, dark olive-green crystals encrusting pseudomalachite. Listed by Hartley (1984).

LINARITE $PbCu(SO_4)(OH)_2$

The species is widespread in the Caldbeck Fells, but no specimens compare with those from the world-famous Red Gill locality.

Balliway Rigg As small, poor crystals in altered sulphides from an old working on the Silver Gill lode [NY 301 342].

Brae Fell mine As minute crystals and crusts on quartz-sulphide matrix. Listed by Hartley (1984).

Brandy Gill Lead mine In small amounts with duftite, mimetite, pyromorphite, stolzite etc. (Davidson & Thomson, 1951; Claringbull, 1951).

Carrock End mine (Hartley, 1984).

Carrock mine From an 'old cross-cut at, or near, the junction of the east–west lead veins with the Emerson vein' (Hartley, 1984: 36).

Driggith mine As bladed crystals (< 10 mm) with brochantite, malachite and aurichalcite (Kingsbury Collection, BM(NH); Hartley, 1984).

Dry Smale Gill In small amounts (Shaw, 1970).

Ingray Gill (Hartley, 1984).

Mexico mine Mentioned by Greg & Lettsom (1858). In traces from the Low level dumps in Todd Gill.

Old Potts Gill mine As sprays of incomplete, bladed, crystals (< 10 mm) in joints in a gossany matrix (Kingsbury Collection, BM(NH)); listed by Hartley (1984).

Poddy Gill (Hartley, 1984).

Red Gill mine The enduring fame of this locality rests with the fine linarite specimens found here in the nineteenth century, reputedly from the No. 2 or 'Old Dutch' level. These crystals, the world's best at the time (Greg & Lettsom, 1858; Hessenberg, 1864; Koksharov, 1869a,b), reached 25 mm in length by 10 mm and occurred in cavities in the quartz-sulphide veinstone. Unfortunately, the crystals are notoriously brittle and thus difficult to find undamaged, and commonly span the small cavities in the matrix. Nonetheless many fine specimens are known and are enhanced by the contrasting colours of such associated minerals as caledonite, anglesite, brochantite, malachite, pyromorphite etc. Malachite pseudomorphs after linarite were noted by Miers (1897) and, in the present study, brochantite, with or without admixed anglesite, pseudomorphs linarite. (J. Hartley Collection, Leeds Univ. (cf. Fig. 55, p. 85); M. P. Cooper Collection). Traces of linarite are still to be found on the dumps, but well crystallized specimens are very rare. Thin blue crusts on weathered sulphides are probably dump-formed.

Roughton Gill The earliest Caldbeck record for linarite (Dana, 1850) mentions only this locality and there are fine nineteenth century specimens in the BM(NH) showing good crystals (< 20 mm) but some authors (e.g. Davidson & Thomson, 1951) have doubted their provenance as few specimens have been found here since that time. Small crystals may be found in higher Roughton Gill, in the outcrop workings.

Sandbeds mine In small crystals, (rarely > 5 mm) with

Fig. 71 LINARITE: Caldbeck Fells. A group of thick deep blue tabular crystals to nearly 25 mm in a cavity in a matrix of quartz and sulphides. Acquired by R. P. Greg in 1852, these crystals were the model for the drawing in Fig. 72j from Greg and Lettsom's classic work on British mineralogy (1858). It was undoubtedly this specimen that was referred to by Bryce Wright (in Jenkinson, 1875: lxxxv) as 'truly one of the gems of the great national collection'. Although not specifically localised in the original Allan–Greg catalogue entry reproduced here (Fig. 72), it is generally assumed to have come from the Red Gill mine. Allan–Greg Collection, BM(NH) (BM 95313).

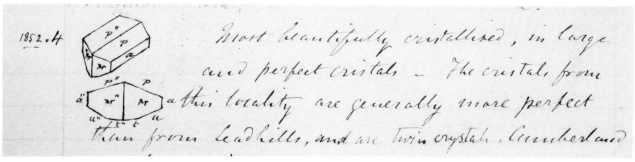

Fig. 72 LINARITE: the entry from the Allan–Greg catalogue (Vol. 1: 327) for the specimen shown in Fig. 71, with, below, published crystal drawings from: a–d Hessenberg (1864); e–i Koksharov (1869a, b); j Greg & Lettsom (1858); k Cesàro (1905).

leadhillite, brochantite, and cerussite (Kingsbury Collection, BM(NH)). Recorded by Davidson & Thomson, 1951; Hartley, 1984.

Silver Gill In small amounts from the 'lowest level at 1500 ft [450 m]' (Hartley, 1984); also as crusts of minute crystals on altered sulphides from the 'Golden Hugh' where it appears to still be forming on the mine walls.

Swinburn Gill A unique specimen showing excellent crystals (< 12 mm) was found by Kingsbury in 1950 in dumps from an 'old bell-pit' at the foot of Wet Smale Gill [NY 297 351] (Kingsbury Collection, BM(NH), Hartley, 1984).

LINDGRENITE $Cu_3(MoO_4)_2(OH)_2$

Brandy Gill Lead mine The first (and only) British occurrence (Kingsbury & Hartley, 1955). The mineral was found in specimens from the dumps of the eastern level as small (< 1.5 mm), dark olive-green bladed crystals on a yellowish-green crystalline mineral (which 'gives [an X-ray powder] pattern and spacings very close to those of the well-known pale blue Cumberland plumbogummite' *op. cit.*: 724). It was found in cavities in granophyre presumed to be from the vein-wall. Only a few specimens were obtained (Kingsbury and Russell Collections, BM(NH)) and, despite the exertions of a generation of collectors, none has been found since.

LIROCONITE $Cu_2Al(AsO_4)(OH)_4 . 4H_2O$

Old Potts Gill mine From the 'No. 1 cross-cut' and 'new to Cumb[erland]' (Kingsbury, MS 1). The occurrence is not mentioned in other Kingsbury MSS and is not known to his one-time colleague J. Hartley (*pers. comm.*). Requires confirmation.

LÖLLINGITE $FeAs_2$

Old Potts Gill mine 'in . . . small veins and strings carrying galena, pyrite and arsenopyrite' from the 'No. 1 cross-cut' dumps (Kingsbury & Hartley, 1960: 429).

MACPHERSONITE $Pb_4(SO_4)(CO_3)_2(OH)_2$

Red Gill mine Identified on a small specimen in the D. I. Green Collection (*det.* Leeds Univ.: XRD) as small prismatic crystals with triangular cross-section associated with caledonite, pyromorphite, leadhillite, and mattheddleite (Cooper, Green & Braithwaite, 1988).

MALACHITE $Cu_2(CO_3)(OH)_2$

Widespread in small amounts, the best specimens are from Roughton Gill and Potts Gill.

Brae Fell mine (Eastwood, 1921).

Brandy Gill Lead mine (Davidson & Thomson, 1951).

Carrock End mine (Greg & Lettsom, 1858). A Bryce Wright

specimen (BM(NH)) shows flat sprays to 10 mm across on quartz.

Carrock mine (Davidson & Thomson, 1951). With gold, from the Harding vein no. 1 level (Kingsbury, MS 2; BM(NH) Collection).

Driggith mine Eastwood (1921).

Dry Gill Hartley (1984).

Hay Gill Copper mine 'well crystallized, acicular and fibrous' (Greg & Lettsom, 1858: 311). No specimens have been seen to substantiate this claim.

Ingray Gill (Hartley, 1984).

Low Pike In small quantities as radiating fibrous masses with cornwallite, philipsburgite etc. from an old trial on the Low Pike vein at [NY 320 358] (*det.* Leeds Univ.: XRD).

Mexico mine (Greg & Lettsom, 1858).

Old Potts Gill mine (Hartley, 1984). Found as attractive masses of acicular crystals and as unique (for the district) thick botryoidal crusts (Kingsbury Collection, BM(NH)). Specimens collected recently show only traces.

Potts Gill Copper mine (Hartley, 1984).

Red Gill mine Sometimes occurs as attractive sprays, or spherical aggregates, of small emerald green crystals, with cerussite, baryte, chrysocolla etc. Commonly altered to chrysocolla. Malachite pseudomorphs after linarite were noted by Miers (1897).

Roughton Gill Long known for fine malachite (Greg & Lettsom, 1858; Goodchild, 1884). Once found here in specimens composed of masses of acicular emerald green crystals interspersed with needles of white cerussite. Also, although rarely, as well formed crystals and as botryoidal encrustations. Malachite was a valuable constituent of the large orebody in the South vein (Eastwood, 1921; Shaw, 1970).

Sandbeds mine (Eastwood, 1921). 'Good crystals' recorded by Davidson & Thomson (1951).

Silver Gill In 'traces' from an unspecified locality (Davidson & Thomson, 1951). As pretty acicular crystals with cerussite from the 'Golden Hugh' (D. R. Middleton, *pers. comm.*).

Fig. 73 MALACHITE: 'at Red Gill and Hay Gill' in this habit, after Greg & Lettsom (1858).

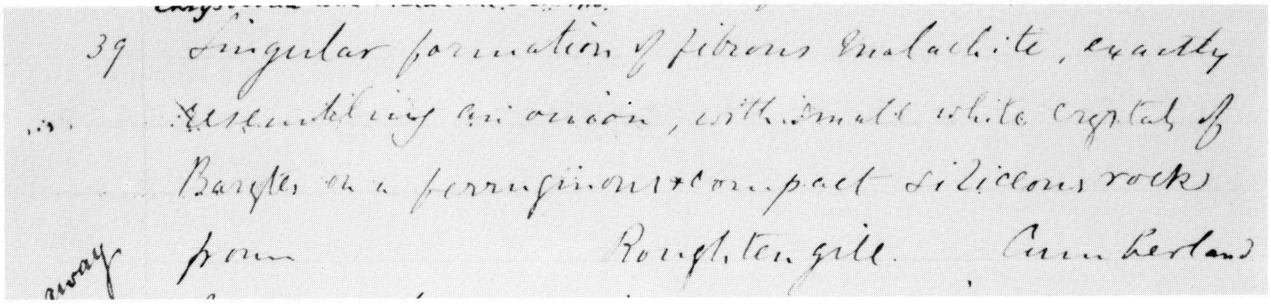
39 Singular formation of fibrous malachite, exactly resembling an onion, with small white crystals of Barytes on a ferruginous & compact siliceous rock from Roughtengill. Cumberland

MANGANITE $MnO(OH)$

Burdell Gill (Greg & Lettsom, 1858).

Thief Gills 'In one of the branches of the gill, a quartz vein, bearing either manganite or pyrolusite stands like a wall on the fellside ...' (Davidson & Thomson, 1951: 140).

MARCASITE FeS_2

Carrock mine 'common, both as a coating, and as crystals ... showed nice structures in the roof of one of the levels in 1946, being in the form of concentric circles about 6″ [15 cm] in diameter' (Davidson & Thomson, 1951: 143). R. J. King (*pers. comm.*) reports an 'asterate group of crystals 18 mm across' from the E–W lead vein in Carrock mine.

Old Potts Gill mine As 'fan-shaped aggregates of blade-like crystals' with chrysocolla, malachite, brochantite, and tenorite from 'a small copper vein above the present workings' (Davidson & Thomson, 1951: 140).

MATTHEDDLEITE $Pb_{20}(SiO_4)_7(SO_4)_4Cl_4$

A recently described member of the pyromorphite group (Livingstone *et al.*, 1987), mattheddleite has been found in several Caldbeck Fells localities during the present study (Cooper *et al.*, 1988). Specimens from the Red Gill mine are particularly fine.

Brae Fell mine Known from two specimens only: as minute colourless prismatic crystals and drusy pink encrustations on leadhillite and cerussite (King Collection, NMW, *det.* UMIST: IR); and as sharp, prismatic crystals on lanarkite with leadhillite (Kingsbury Collection, BM(NH), *det.*: XRD).

Red Gill mine Identified on a surprising number of specimens collected recently from the No. 2 or 'Old Dutch' level dumps (D. R. Middleton, D. I. Green Collections *det.* BM(NH), Leicester Univ., Leeds Univ.: XRD). Crystals are typically 0.25–0.50 mm long, colourless, steeply terminated prisms and may be found grown on caledonite, leadhillite, and susannite as sprays or crusts, or in cavities in altered galena with lanarkite. On some specimens the terminal faces have been etched away leaving what, at first sight, appear to be low pyramidal terminations.

Roughton Gill Cooper *et al.* (1988) knew of only one specimen of mattheddleite, associated with caledonite, cerussite, and a leadhillite group mineral, found on dump material from the old outcrop workings in higher Roughton Gill (D. I. Green Collection, *det.* Leeds Univ.: XRD). Since then a considerable number of specimens have been collected *in situ* in the same area where it is associated with lanarkite, caledonite, leadhillite, and scotlandite (D. I. Green *in prep.*).

Fig. 74 MALACHITE: Roughton Gill. A unique specimen from the Allan–Greg Collection, BM(NH). The original catalogue entry by Robert Greg, reproduced above, reads: 'Singular formation of fibrous malachite, exactly resembling an onion with small white crystals of Barytes on a ferruginous & compact siliceous rock from Roughtengill, Cumberland'. The malachite aggregate is 10 mm across (BM 91558).

Fig. 75 MATTHEDDLEITE: Brae Fell mine. Sprays of hexagonal prisms with characteristic pointed terminations, encrusting lanarkite. One of only two known specimens from this mine. SEM photograph, scale bar 20 µm. Kingsbury Collection, BM(NH).

Short Grain From the northern baryte trial, as extremely minute, sparkling colourless crystals lining small cavities in baryte with caledonite, susannite etc. (M. P. Cooper Collection, *det.* BM(NH): XRD).

METAVIVIANITE $Fe^{2+}_{3-x}Fe^{3+}_x(PO_4)_2(OH)_x \cdot 8-xH_2O$

For undifferentiated symplesite–metavivianite series, see symplesite.

MICROCLINE $KAISi_3O_8$

Carrock mine As drusy, white, crystalline aggregates to *c.*10 mm on octahedral fluorite from the recent workings on the adit level on the Smith vein (D. R. Hacker, *pers. comm.*, *det.* UMIST: IR).

Grainsgill As 'pale pink to cream-coloured ... crystals two or three inches [50–75 mm] in length ... often ... almost wholly converted into yellow mica in the vicinity of molybdenite-bearing fissures which traverse ... it' embedded in quartz in a vein a few metres east of the Emerson vein (Hitchen, 1934: 189). Microcline was also reported, from the Grainsgill granite, by Fortey (1978).

MIMETITE $Pb_5(AsO_4)_3Cl$

Widespread in the Caldbeck Fells and, as at Dry Gill, sometimes in considerable quantities. It is rarely of end-member composition and, with increasing phosphate content, grades insensibly into pyromorphite (q.v.). Specimens from old collections are sometimes labelled 'diarseniate of lead', probably after the description by Thomson (1839).

Arm o'Grain As small greyish prisms with well developed bipyramid faces, on quartz and feldspar (D. R. Middleton Collection, *det.* BM(NH): XRD). An undifferentiated pyromorphite–mimetite also occurs here in small greenish yellow prisms with mottramite.

Brandy Gill Lead mine Found in small crystals in a variety of habits often associated with bayldonite or a duftite-like mineral, both of which may replace mimetite. Also, rarely associated with vanadinite (from which it is, visually, indistinguishable), descloizite, mottramite etc. (Kingsbury & Hartley, 1956a). Small tapering colourless

Fig. 76 MATTHEDDLEITE: Red Gill mine. Radiating sprays of minute (< 0.25 mm) acicular crystals on caledonite in a cavity in a galena-quartz matrix. D. R. Middleton Collection.

Fig. 77 MATTHEDDLEITE: Short Grain. Sparkling colourless microscopic prisms line small cavities in baryte from an old trial on the north bank [NY 3130 3385]. The terminations of the crystals have been deeply etched, a common occurrence with mattheddleite from Caldbeck. Specimens showing only a partial resorption of the terminal faces may appear to terminate in a low bipyramid and might be mistaken for colourless pyromorphite-mimetite or even anglesite. SEM photograph, scale bar is 50 μm. M. P. Cooper Collection (off 8762).

Fig. 78 MIMETITE: Caldbeck Fells. Bright yellow crystals to 3 mm showing an interesting variation of habit from tablets, through crystals with increasingly concave pinacoids, to complete 'campylite' aggregates. This specimen has an attached printed label stating 'Diarseniate of lead, Caldbeck Fells, Cumberland' which is typical of several specimens seen showing the same type of mimetite. Unfortunately it is not possible to provenance this material any more accurately. This specimen formed part of the Herbert Willoughby-Ellis Collection sold by Watkins and Doncaster of the Strand, London, in 1945. It was bought by Leicester Museum (1945.7.212).

Fig. 79 MIMETITE: Dry Gill mine. Growth and colour zoning are common in Caldbeck pyromorphite and mimetite. The orange rounded prism and protruding terminations on this crystal are overgrowths on a yellow core. R. S. W. Braithwaite Collection (84-296).

crystals with beudantite and carminite from a vein exposure in the dry gully to the east [NY 3240 3385] have been shown by IR (UMIST) to be almost phosphate-free.

Burdell Gill From the old workings at the head of the gill, as an almost phosphate-free variety in small crystals with pharmacosiderite etc. (R. S. W. Braithwaite *pers. comm.*, *det.* UMIST: IR).

Driggith mine As small rounded milky green to khaki crystals on sugary quartz. Many specimens are highly phosphatian and approach the pyromorphite side of the binary solid solution series (see pyromorphite).

Dry Gill mine The deposit exploited here was one of the most remarkable occurrences of mimetite in the world. It is the main locality for the variety of phosphatian mimetite known as 'campylite' after the curved, barrel-shaped crystals so common here. Mimetite was the dominant lead mineral at Dry Gill, associated with pyromorphite and, rarely, plumbogummite in quartz, baryte, and manganese oxide gangue. The manganese oxides are characteristic of the deposit but are uncommon in association with mimetite from the Roughton Gill mines.

Although he did not specify a locality, the 'arseniate of lead' described by Allan (*in* Phillips, 1837) as '. . . aggregated in opake, orange-yellow coloured individuals, which consist each of three hexagonal prisms curved

Fig. 80 MIMETITE: Dry Gill mine. Seed-like rounded crystals to 10 mm encrusting a cavity in quartz. Although not as common as the globular 'campylite' habit, mimetite of this form is characteristic of the Dry Gill deposit. J. G. Wilson Collection.

Fig. 82 MIMETITE: Dry Gill mine. Highly lustrous 'campylite' crystals to 8 mm with unusual drusy faces caused by a subsequent sub-parallel overgrowth of mimetite. The larger crystals have yellow cores that are poorer in arsenate than the brown outer layer (ca. 43:57 and 40:60 PO_4:AsO_4 respectively). Dept. of Geology, Leeds University (41722/2).

Fig. 83 MIMETITE: Dry Gill mine. Rounded, lime green crystals with unusual spiky outgrowths. In some specimens of this sort the outgrowths are more symmetrically disposed and such crystals were described in the Allan–Greg catalogue (BM(NH)) as '. . . terminated with spicula, like bundles of fine needles . . .'. The figured specimen is from the D. R. Hacker Collection (84-12).

towards their terminations in a manner often beautifully symmetrical' (cf. Fig. 42, p. 68) may well be one of the first published descriptions of Dry Gill 'campylite'. The occurrence was first figured by Kurr (1858) but his illustration hardly does justice to the mineral.

The 'campylite' form of mimetite is the most common habit, but tabular, short to long prismatic, and acicular crystals are also found and may occur on, or with, 'campylite'. The colour is usually a shade of pale to dark orange brown, but yellow, greenish yellow and lime to olive greens are also found. The colour variation is not a reliable indicator of the phosphate:arsenate ratio. It is sometimes assumed that green and yellow varieties are pyromorphite, but this is not always the case. Crystal growth zones are illustrated by compositional and also colour variation; where such overgrowths are incomplete, or crystals broken, splendidly variegated specimens result (Fig. 85).

Crystals < 5–10 mm are typical, but may reach more than 30 mm in diameter. Matrix specimens to more than 20 cm and stalactites up to 50 mm in length (Fig. 81) were recovered when the mine was working.

The mine was accessible until recent times, and some

Fig. 81 *(opposite)* **MIMETITE:** Dry Gill mine, 90 × 70 mm. Stalactitic mimetite and pyromorphite specimens are relatively uncommon but some fine specimens are known from the Caldbeck Fells. One of the best is this group of olive green crystalline stalactites (to 50 mm long) spanning a cavity in solid mimetite. The stalactites are hollow and have orange cores. BM(NH) (BM 60767).

Fig. 84 MIMETITE: Dry Gill mine. Tabular crystals to 3 mm showing concave pinacoid faces, encrusting quartz. P. Briscoe Collection.

Fig. 86 MIMETITE: Dry Gill mine. Typical 'campylite' crystals to 7 mm on 'psilomelane' and quartz. R. J. King Collection, NMW (NMW 83.41G.M8374; K5756-51).

fine specimens recovered, some rivalling the best of the nineteenth century specimens.

Low Pike From an old trial on the Low Pike vein [NY 320 358] as a yellow crystalline crust with a duftite-like mineral (*det.* BGS: XRD, B. Young, *pers. comm.*). An intermediate mimetite–pyromorphite phase, occurring as small greenish crystals on baryte, has been identified by IR (M. P. Cooper Collection, *det.* UMIST).

Mexico mine Mentioned by Greg & Lettsom (1858). Brown crystalline specimens of similar habit to Dry Gill 'campylite' occur here on the dumps of the High Level.

Nether Row Brow From the Nether Row Farm level (Hartley, 1984).

Red Gill mine Listed by Kendall (1884) but not by subsequent authors. Lately identified as globular sprays on an unidentified clay mineral (D. I. Green *pers. comm.*, 1988, *det.* Leeds Univ.: XRD).

Roughton Gill mine Not as common as pyromorphite but occurs as fine specimens (Fig. 87). Bryce Wright collected 'arseniate of lead' underground in Roughton Gill mine in 1847 (*in* Sowerby, 1850); Greg & Lettsom (1858: 407) described mimetite in 'wax-yellow crystals, well defined' from here.

MOLYBDENITE MoS_2

Brandy Gill Lead mine Recorded by Davidson & Thomson (1951).

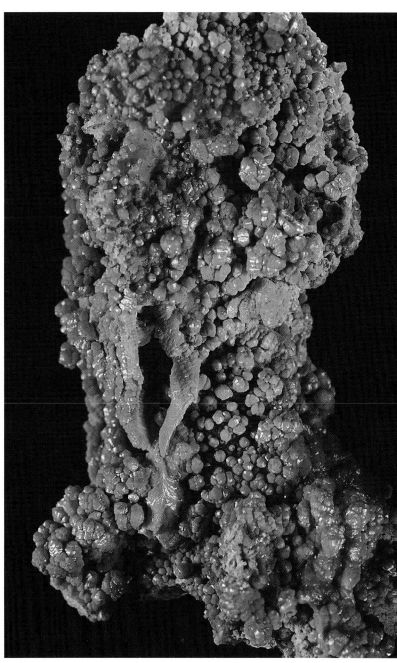

Fig. 85 MIMETITE: Dry Gill mine, 95 mm across. A rare, lime green 'campylite' specimen of 'old-time' quality, collected underground by the late Richard Barstow in 1979. Note the rich orange-brown cores to the broken crystals. R. Sutcliffe Collection.

Fig. 87 MIMETITE: Roughton Gill mine, 100 × 60 mm. A superb specimen of phosphatian mimetite showing globular aggregates and twisted stalactitic growths on a quartz matrix. BM(NH) (BM 25553).

Carrock mine A specimen of molybdenite from 'Caldbeck' was illustrated by Sowerby (1809); the first reproduction of a Caldbeck Fells' specimen. The occurrence in the Carrock tungsten veins was noted by many early writers (e.g. Lysons & Lysons, 1816; Borie, 1817; Phillips, 1819; Jameson, 1820) with varying degrees of accuracy. These variants were regarded as discrete occurrences by Greg & Lettsom (1858) who unwittingly cited no less than five versions of the one locality.

The mineral occurs as small flakes and veinlets disseminated in quartz and muscovite or concentrated along vein–greisen boundaries. It is common in microscopic amounts in most of the sulphide, sulpharsenide and telluride mineral assemblages from this locality. Fortey (1978) describes an unusual occurrence of molybdenite from the Harding vein as 'thin-walled spheres of the order of 1 mm in diameter, embedded in the margins of arsenopyrite patches and filled with Bi-sulphides. May involve development of droplets of a Bi-rich liquid'.

Quite rich specimens were once recovered from the 'molybdenite vein' to the east of the Emerson vein, now buried under waste. This may be the occurrence, described by Hitchen (1934), where molybdenite forms veinlets in altered microcline.

MOTTRAMITE $PbCu(VO_4)(OH)$

Arm o'Grain As minute, brownish black, rice-grain crystals with greenish yellow pyromorphite–mimetite on quartz (*det.* BM(NH): XRD, D. R. Middleton, *pers. comm.*).

Fig. 88 MOTTRAMITE: Iron Crag. An unusually transparent, dark green crystal (0.3 mm) of mottramite on 'limonite' and quartz, found in scree below the outcrop of the Roughton Gill (South) vein. Mottramite has also been found in the screes nearby as rounded brown masses of more typical appearance. D. R. Middleton Collection.

Brandy Gill Lead mine From the upper western level dump, but uncommon. It occurs as yellowish green to dark olive green crystalline aggregates in cavities in massive greyish brown mimetite with bayldonite, malachite, and yellow mimetite; as minute olive green crystals in cavities in quartz with bayldonite, beaverite, and beudantite; and as dark brown drusy botryoidal aggregates (< 15 mm across—Kingsbury & Hartley 1956*a*; Kingsbury Collection BM(NH)). Recently, in the form of minute sharp bipyramidal crystals of an unusually pale green colour on ?bayldonite (P. Braithwaite Collection, *det.* BM(NH): XRD).

Also, from the eastern dump, as very rare minute brownish crystals with descloizite and vanadinite in spongy quartz (Kingsbury & Hartley, 1956*a*).

Low Pike Very rare; as thin greenish brown encrustations with bayldonite from an old trial on the Low Pike vein [NY 320 358]. (N. Thomson Collection, *det.* BM(NH): XRD).

Nether Row Brow (Farm level) In small amounts as drusy botryoidal crusts on compact earthy beudantite with beaverite and cerussite (Kingsbury & Hartley, 1956*a*).

Roughton Gill mine In debris below Iron Crag, probably originating from the outcrop of the Roughton Gill (South) vein: as minute translucent pistachio green rounded crystals on goethite and quartz (D. Middleton Collection); and as greasy lustred brown rounded crystals encrusting quartz with pyromorphite (N. Thomson Collection). Both occurrences *det.* BM(NH): XRD.

MUSCOVITE $KAl_2(Si_3Al)O_{10}(OH,F)_2$

Carrock mine Common, as the variety 'gilbertite' in the tungsten veins and greisen with quartz, orthoclase, apatite, scheelite and wolframite. Spencer (1958) equated this with the 'nacrite' of Greg & Lettsom (1858).

OLIVENITE $Cu_2(AsO_4)(OH)$

The only known specimens are those collected by Kingsbury and Hartley, now in the Kingsbury Collection BM(NH).

Carrock mine Small tufts of minute, very pale green needles in cavities in quartz from dumps below the Harding vein (Kingsbury & Hartley, MS).

Dry Gill mine From the 'middle cross-cut dumps halfway up the gill': as small dark green crystals on manganese oxides (Kingsbury & Hartley, MS) and with beudantite (Kingsbury & Hartley, 1960).

Ingray Gill From the northern level as acicular olive green crystals in cavernous quartz (Kingsbury Collection and MS 1).

Old Potts Gill mine In good specimens showing crusts to 4 cm across of dark green crystals with cornwallite and conichalcite (Kingsbury & Hartley, MS).

Roughton Gill Kendall (1884) listed 'olivienite' among the 'metallic minerals' from Roughton Gill on the authority of Postlethwaite or Bryce Wright. However, neither of these authors cite any locality in the Caldbeck Fells for this species in their contemporary publications (Postlethwaite, 1877; 1899: Wright *in* Jenkinson, 1875 and subsequent editions).

ORTHOCLASE $KAlSi_3O_8$

Carrock mine 'present in vein margins where they cut altered gabbro of the Carrock Fell Complex' (Fortey, 1980).

PALYGORSKITE $(Mg, Al)_2Si_4O_{10}(OH).4H_2O$

East Potts Gill mine Specimens of 'mineral leather' were found in the New North Lode (Shaw, 1970).

PARAHOPEITE $Zn_3(PO_4)_2.4H_2O$

Roughton Gill mine Listed from the 60 fm level dumps by Hartley (1984).

PHARMACOSIDERITE $KFe_4^{3+}(AsO_4)_3(OH)_4.6-7H_2O$

Brandy Gill As minute pale green cubes on spongy quartz 'float' in the dry tributary gill to the east of Brandy Gill Lead mine [NY 324 338] (M. P. Cooper Collection).

Burdell Gill As sparkling crusts of small crystals on a characteristic matrix of spongy quartz, impregnated with iron and manganese oxides, from a vein in the head of the gill. Greg & Lettsom (1858) recorded it as a recent find. Some specimens seem to be susceptible to alteration, the green crystals discolouring to brown. Associated minerals include jarosite, scorodite etc.

Carrock mine Rare, as small crystals from the Emerson vein dumps (R. S. W. Braithwaite; T. F. Bridges, *pers. comm.*). Specimens in the BM(NH) labelled 'Grange Gill' [= Grainsgill?] have a matrix similar to Burdell Gill material and hence probably did not originate here.

Deer Hills Relatively common as pale green masses and small transparent cubes in altered veinstone from an old working on the Deer Hills Quartz vein [NY 3145 3626] (*det.* BM(NH): XRD on N. Thomson specimen). Associated with drusy crusts of brown scorodite (M. P. Cooper Collection).

Dry Gill 'An interesting find . . . made by a friend who unearthed a small group of pharmacosiderite crystals' (Davidson & Thomson, 1951: 141).

Ingray Gill From the north level as dark green lustrous cubes with beudantite, carminite, scorodite, arseniosiderite, and erythrite (Kingsbury & Hartley, 1957; 1960; Kingsbury Collection, BM(NH)).

Nether Row Brow From the Nether Row Farm level with beudantite, mimetite, mottramite, scorodite, plumbojaro-

site, and beaverite (Kingsbury & Hartley, 1960). As tiny pale green crystals on massive scorodite (M. P. Cooper Collection). Also reported from the 'Dumpy Stone' level (R. S. W. Braithwaite, *pers. comm.*).

Old Potts Gill mine With beudantite, carminite, and scorodite (Kingsbury & Hartley, 1960).

PHILIPSBURGITE $(Cu, Zn)_6(AsO_4, PO_4)_2(OH)_6.H_2O$

Low Pike Recently, in small amounts, from the dump of a small trial on the Low Pike vein [NY 320 358] where it occurs in three distinct forms: minute tabular apple green crystals; pale turquoise fibrous aggregates; and pale green to white minutely botryoidal crusts with a radiating foliated structure. It is associated with phosphatian cornwallite, bayldonite and mimetite (M. P. Cooper Collection and others, *det.* BM(NH): XRD, UMIST: IR; also on specimens collected by B. Young (*pers. comm.*) and *det.* BGS: XRD).

Although the high phosphate content of one specimen analysed by IR led Braithwaite & Ryback (1988) to suggest that it may in fact be a highly arsenatian kipushite this species has not so far been identified by XRD from Low Pike. Moreover a semi-quantitative analysis of a well crystallized sample shows an As/As + P ratio slightly higher than type philipsburgite (*det.* J. Faithfull, Leicester Univ.: EPMA).

Potts Gill Baryte mine As minutely crystalline encrustations on, or with, malachite in vuggy quartz on specimens collected in 1965; the first British occurrence (Braithwaite & Ryback, 1988).

PHOSGENITE $Pb_2(CO_3)Cl_2$

Driggith mine With anglesite in somewhat decomposed granular galena from a surface working on the Driggith – Sandbeds vein (Kingsbury, 1957).

PITTICITE   AMORPHOUS HYDROUS FERRIC ARSENATE-SULPHATE

Brandy Gill Lead mine As a dark reddish brown resinous mineral with carminite, beudantite, mimetite, and scorodite (Kingsbury & Hartley, 1951; Hartley, 1984).

PLANCHÉITE $Cu_8Si_8O_{22}(OH)_4.H_2O$

Driggith mine Known only from two small specimens from the 30 fm level dump (Kingsbury Collection, BM(NH); as a radiating fibrous mineral with chrysocolla. The first British occurrence. Listed by Kingsbury (MS 1) but otherwise unpublished.

PLUMBOGUMMITE $PbAl_3(PO_4)_2(OH)_5.H_2O$

Found in several Caldbeck Fells localities, but some of the Roughton Gill specimens are exceptional and probably the most beautiful in the world.

Brae Fell mine A single specimen from the upper level

Fig. 89 PLUMBOGUMMITE: Dry Gill mine. Epimorphs after pyromorphite prisms to 3 mm on quartz. Found in dump material in the upper part of Dry Gill. Pale blue encrustations of plumbogummite on pyromorphite, similar to those from Roughton Gill, have been found in the mine. Figured specimen from the P. Braithwaite Collection (D1/11).

dump (Kingsbury Collection, BM(NH)) has a blue-grey encrustation of plumbogummite partly epimorphous after pyromorphite. No other specimens have been located.

Brandy Gill Lead mine A pale yellowish green crystalline mineral associated with lindgrenite from the east level gave an X-ray powder photograph close to that of the 'well-known pale blue Cumberland plumbogummite' (Kingsbury & Hartley, 1955: 724). Also recorded from the upper west level (Hartley, 1984).

Dry Gill mine A great deal of plumbogummite was collected here in the 1970s much of which was of a dark turquoise blue colour, quite distinct from Roughton Gill specimens. It occurs in association with manganese oxides and acicular canary yellow pyromorphite crystals on quartz on specimens to 15 cm or so. It has also been identified on a few specimens as a very pale blue to colourless drusy encrustation on prismatic pyromorphite–mimetite (D. R. Hacker, *pers. comm.*, 1987) and as brown epimorphs after tapering pyromorphite–mimetite (P. Braithwaite Collection, *det.* UMIST: IR).

Mexico mine As brown to smoky grey minutely botryoidal crusts on quartz, with later yellow-green rounded pyromorphite crystals, from the Low level dumps in Todd Gill (Kingsbury Collection, BM(NH); Kingsbury & Hartley, MS).

Nether Row Brow From the Nether Row Farm Level (Hartley, 1984).

Old Potts Gill mine Listed by Hartley (1984); 'from the old No. 1 cross-cut dumps' (Kingsbury, MS 1).

Red Gill mine Reported by Berg (1985) on the basis of a visual identification of one small specimen in his collection (W. van den Berg, *pers. comm.*). An examination of this specimen by MPC suggests that the thin blue skin on pyromorphite is merely chrysocolla but the small amount of material precludes definite characterization.

Roughton Gill mine Initially, plumbogummite from this locality was confused with hemimorphite or smithsonite (q.v.), but the descriptions of the early authors are often unmistakably of plumbogummite specimens. The earliest record open to such reinterpretation is that of Blum (1843) who gives an elaborate description of a supposed hemimorphite ('kiesel-zinc') pseudomorph after pyromorphite that is a perfect account of the well known plumbogummite epimorphs. Subsequent authors, e.g. Greg & Lettsom, 1858; Goodchild, 1884, make much of the beautiful shades of lavender to cobalt blue exhibited by their 'calamine' or 'smithsonite' specimens and of their common association with pyromorphite; unequivocal descriptions of plumbogummite. Little attention was paid to Dana's (1850) reference to 'plumboresinite' [= plumbogummite] from Roughton Gill; Miers (1900) suggested the reference was to a brown, botryoidal aluminous pyromorphite since Dana did not allude to the characteristic blue colour of the plumbogummite. However, brown plumbogummite does occur at Mexico mine and at Dry Gill (both working prior to 1850), and may have been reported to Dana.

In 1897 Miers established that the mineral in question was a lead phosphate and identified it with 'plumboresinite'. Later, a series of related papers (Hartley, 1900; Miers, 1900; Prior, 1900) redefined the mineral as 'hitchcockite'. Since that time these names have been relegated to synonymy with plumbogummite. In 1967, Förtsch proposed that the Cumbrian mineral was a 'carbonate-bearing mix-crystal of hinsdalite, plumbogummite, and hidalgoite' but this is not supported by the analysis of Hartley (1900) which showed no sulphate and little arsenate. Moreover, although the infra-red absorption spectra of Roughton Gill plumbogummites always show carbonate peaks, there is none of the variation one might expect in a non-uniform mixture (R. S. W. Braithwaite, *pers. comm.*, 1987).

Typical Roughton Gill plumbogummite forms thin crusts on matrix (usually quartz) and often coats pyro-

Fig. 90 PLUMBOGUMMITE: Roughton Gill mine, 70 mm across. Several generations of plumbogummite coat and replace pyromorphite crystals to 5 mm. King Collection, NMW (NMW 83.41G.M7823; K1263).

Fig. 91 *(left and right)* **PYROMORPHITE on PLUMBOGUMMITE:** Roughton Gill mine. Two specimens collected in 1947 from the main (90 fm level) dumps chosen to show the variation in appearance of this association. *Left* shows yellowish globular pyromorphite (to 1.5 mm) of mid-series composition on minutely botryoidal plumbogummite; *right* has prismatic pyromorphite (to 2 mm) scattered on drusy plumbogummite. King Collection, NMW (NMW 83.41G.M7824 and M5918 (K4324 and K256); K4324 was once in the H. F. Harwood Collection no. 2599).

morphite crystals. It is also found as solid masses surrounding quartz crystals. The crusts may comprise several generations of varying colour and thickness interspersed with pyromorphite. The colour varies from almost colourless, through shades of blue-grey and lavender, to a deep cobalt blue (smalt-blue); the latter, particularly when sprinkled with greenish yellow pyromorphite, constitute the most prized specimens. The surface of the plumbogummite may be smooth to drusy and is often minutely botryoidal. Occasionally, underlying pyromorphite is partially or wholly altered and, in extreme cases, may be leached out to leave a sugary white to pale blue epimorph (see Blum, 1843; Miers, 1897). Such alteration may be selective and it is not unusual to observe epitaxial overgrowths of pyromorphite altered in this way while the original crystal remains untouched. The epimorphs are usually less than 3 mm.

Miers (1900: 240) states 'the specimens which now adorn most collections seem to have been obtained

Fig. 92 PLUMBOGUMMITE: Roughton Gill mine. Sugary pseudomorphs after pyromorphite (to 1.5 mm) on blue plumbogummite. Most of these are hollow epimorphs, but a green tinge due to residual pyromorphite can be seen in one 'crystal'. Found on the 90 fm level dump in 1947. King Collection NMW (NMW 83.41G.M7821; K5753).

shortly before ... 1834'. But a great deal of material was still present on the dumps over a hundred years later (Davidson & Thomson, 1951; Kingsbury & Hartley, MS; Kingsbury Collection, BM(NH); King Collection, NMW). There is no record of precisely where in the deposit the plumbogummite was found. Very little material has been collected in recent years from the dumps, and the few old specimens which come up for sale fetch high prices.

Sandbeds mine As small, sugary, pale apple green masses with lustrous green pyromorphite crystals on quartz (Kingsbury Collection, BM(NH)).

PLUMBOJAROSITE $PbFe_6^{3+}(SO_4)_4(OH)_{12}$

First British occurrence at Driggith and Nether Row Brow. In small amounts as a yellowish or yellowish brown powder from several localities.

Brandy Gill Lead mine With carminite and beaverite (Young, 1987).

Driggith mine From the outcrop of the Driggith–Sandbeds vein with beudantite and beaverite; partly derived by alteration of the former (Kingsbury & Hartley, 1957e; Hartley, 1984).

Nether Row Brow From the Nether Row Farm level with beudantite, mimetite, mottramite, scorodite, pharmacosiderite and beaverite (Kingsbury & Hartley, 1957e; 1960).

Roughton Gill From the workings on the South vein outcrop in higher Roughton Gill with galena, cerussite, chrysocolla, carminite, beudantite, jarosite, and beaverite (Kingsbury & Hartley, 1960)

POSNJAKITE $Cu_4(SO_4)(OH)_6 \cdot H_2O$

Silver Gill Rarely, as blocky turquoise blue crystals (< 0.2 mm) on altered sulphides in an old ore pile on the west bank of the gill [NY 2995 3415] *(det.* BM(NH): XRD on a specimen submitted by B. Young). Linarite, langite, and wroewolfeite also occur in this assemblage and all are probably the result of dump oxidation.

POWELLITE $CaMoO_4$

Carrock mine The first British occurrence (Hartley, 1984).

PREHNITE $Ca_2Al_2Si_3O_{10}(OH)_2$

Potts Gill Baryte mine A specimen of white, botryoidal prehnite labelled Potts Gill is in the Kingsbury Collection (BM(NH)) (Young, 1987). The label is not in Kingsbury's hand and there is no record of the occurrence in any of his unpublished MSS in the BM(NH), nor is this occurrence known to Kingsbury's one-time colleague J. Hartley (*pers. comm.*).

PSEUDOMALACHITE $Cu_5(PO_4)_2(OH)_4 \cdot H_2O$

Driggith mine From the 30 fm level dumps (Hartley, 1984).

Low Pike From an old trial on the Low Pike vein [NY 320 358] as thin porcellanous pale turquoise-blue crusts on quartz with bayldonite; significant arsenic substitutes for phosphorus in these specimens (M. P. Cooper Collection, *det.* UMIST: IR). Several specimens have also been identified by XRD at the BGS (B. Young, *pers. comm.*).

Old Potts Gill mine On the dumps from the No. 1 cross-cut as dark emerald green crusts and masses up to 100 mm across with malachite, bayldonite, baryte, brochantite, and libethenite. Although described by Kingsbury & Hartley (MS) as 'by no means rare here' specimens are seldom represented in collections.

'PSILOMELANE'   UNSPECIFIED HARD MANGANESE OXIDES

Dry Gill mine 'Psilomelane' here is probably either coronadite or romanèchite and, together with other manganese minerals, is a characteristic associate of 'campylite', quartz and baryte from this locality. It is occasionally botryoidal and sometimes forms as a smooth overgrowth on 'campylite' crystals. It also occurs as epimorphs after an unknown mineral, strongly resembling sheafy hemimorphite crystals (M. Leppington Collection).

Other localities are: *Arm o'Grain, Brae Fell mine, Brandy Gill Lead mine, Burdell Gill, Carrock End mine, Driggith mine, Hay Gill Copper mine, Ingray Gill, Mexico mine, Potts Gill Baryte mine, Red Gill mine, Roughton Gill mine, Sandbeds mine* and *Silver Gill.* See Appendix 1 for references.

PYRITE   FeS$_2$

Widespread, but nowhere in large amounts. It is mostly massive, although small crystals have been found on specimens from *Carrock mine.* Otherwise the occurrences are unremarkable. Published localities are *Brandy Gill Lead mine, Carrock mine, Driggith mine, Hay Gill Copper mine, Nether Row Brow, Potts Gill Copper mine, Sandbeds mine* and *Silver Gill.* See Appendix 1 for references.

PYROLUSITE   MnO$_2$

Powdery and earthy coatings are common, especially at *Dry Gill.* Other localities are *Arm o'Grain, Brandy Gill* (Day, 1928; Dunham & Hollingworth, 1947), *Burdell Gill, Driggith mine, Ingray Gill, Potts Gill Baryte mine* and 'Thief Gills' (Davidson & Thomson, 1951).

PYROMORPHITE   Pb$_5$(PO$_4$)$_3$Cl

The quality, variety and quantity of specimens from Caldbeck Fells localities makes the district unique. Almost all the lead veins contained pyromorphite or its arsenic-bearing equivalent, mimetite and in several mines these minerals formed in sufficient quantities to be mined as

Fig. 93 PYROMORPHITE: Brae Fell mine. Almost arsenate-free pyromorphite crystals to about 0.2 mm on cerussite. The substantial carbonate absorption shown in the infra-red spectrum of this material suggests substitution analogous to carbonate-apatite. Similar material occurs in higher Roughton Gill where it forms pseudomorphs after cerussite. Collected from a small dump near the lower level in 1979. King Collection, NMW (NMW 83.41G.M5919; K6141).

ore, notably at Roughton Gill, Driggith and Dry Gill.

Although many specimens are of undoubted secondary origin, Strens (1963) suggested that some may be primary, especially where associated with large amounts of manganese oxides.

The earliest specimen known is a small, unremarkable microcrystalline mass in the Woodward Collection (Sedgwick Museum, Cambridge Univ.): 'Lead ore . . . of a yellow colour, with a mixture of green. There's a little white spar amongst it. It yields 1/4 lead. From Caldbeck, Cumberland' (Woodward, 1729: specimen n. 52). The majority of specimens in the major collections, however, were obtained during the nineteenth century; many of these are labelled 'Caldbeck Fells' and lack a specific locality. The dealer Bryce Wright came by many fine specimens but as the mines declined the supply of specimens rapidly tailed off; in 1875 Wright (jnr.) (*in* Jenkinson)

Fig. 94 PYROMORPHITE-MIMETITE: Driggith mine. Rounded crystals of mid-series composition to 2 mm encrusting quartz breccia. Despite the variation in colour, the two generations of larger crystals (pale khaki and emerald green respectively) have essentially the same composition; the epitaxially overgrown paler crystals are slightly more phosphatian. Collected from the Driggith-Sandbeds vein outcrop workings in 1949. J. Hartley Collection, Leeds University.

lamented that pyromorphite, once the 'most common of Cumberland minerals, [was] now very scarce'. Since then fine specimens have been retrieved from the dumps, even as recently as the 1950s, but in general neither quality nor quantity compare with that of the nineteenth century. Good specimens are now scarce from the dumps but, occasionally, may be found *in situ* at the outcrop of the veins.

Brae Fell mine Common on the dumps as small, opaque, olive to emerald green crystals on quartz or, in an almost arsenate-free variety, as bright canary yellow microcrystalline crusts with cerussite. Most specimens are very weathered. The finest specimens appear to be those in the Kingsbury Collection (BM(NH)) which have small, olive green crystals of pyromorphite associated with silky, white, acicular cerussite on matrix (about 80 mm across). Plumbogummite encrusts and partially replaces pyromorphite on a separate specimen.

An off-white calcian pyromorphite occurs as matted fibrous masses with leadhillite, yellow pyromorphite and mattheddleite in the King Collection (NMW) (*det.* UMIST: IR; G. Ryback, *pers. comm.*).

Brandy Gill Lead mine (Davidson & Thomson, 1951); also reported by Kingsbury (MS) 'not very good, very pale and small'. The precise source of the pyromorphite recorded by Greg & Lettsom (1858) from 'Brandy Gill' is unknown.

Carrock mine (Dewey & Dines, 1923). From a 'cross-cut at, or near, the junction of the east–west lead veins with the Emerson vein at the foot of Brandy Gill' (Hartley, 1984: 36).

Carrock End mine (Hartley, 1984).

Driggith mine Pyromorphite was abundant here and still occurs in fair quantity in exposures of the Driggith–Sandbeds vein. The characteristic forms are rounded, prismatic, or seed-like, crystals of a milky green or khaki colour overgrowing quartz; or, less commonly, solid masses of radiating fibrous crystals. The latter are indistinctly colour-zoned from greenish yellow to green and have pitted sub-reniform surfaces (to over 100 mm across). Most specimens of the latter seen in collections seem to have been collected from the outcrop workings in the late 1940s. The arsenic content is often high and grades into mimetite.

Dry Gill mine Whereas 'campylite' may contain sufficient phosphorus to grade into an arsenatian pyromorphite, bright canary yellow tapering prisms on quartz as subparallel overgrowths on 'campylite', or associated with plumbogummite, are almost arsenic-free (P. Williams, *pers. comm.*). Davidson & Thomson (1951: 141) found pyromorphite 'in similar colours to the mimetite'.

Ingray Gill 'pyromorphite–mimetite' recorded by Hartley (1984).

Low Pike An intermediate pyromorphite–mimetite (*c.* 1:1 phosphate:arsenate) occurs as small olive green crystals on baryte from an old trial on the Low Pike vein [NY 320 358] (M. P. Cooper Collection, *det.* UMIST: IR).

Mexico mine 'phosphate ground' is mentioned in old mining reports of this mine almost from its opening in the 1850s. The upper levels appear to have been particularly rich in pyromorphite; the mineral is still the dominant lead ore on the dumps. Specimens were noted by Greg &

Fig. 95 PYROMORPHITE: Mexico mine, Low level dumps. Caldbeck pyromorphite is often colour-zoned but rarely so vividly as in these small (1 mm) crystals. R. S. W. Braithwaite Collection (74-27).

W. Braithwaite; G. Ryback, *pers. comm.*). Pyromorphite–mimetite was recorded by Hartley (1984).

Poddy Gill As green, minutely crystalline crusts with wulfenite and stolzite from an old trial at the foot of the Gill, first recorded by Davidson & Thomson (1951).

Red Gill mine Relatively uncommon here, but occurs as small yellow-green crystals and masses sometimes associ-

Fig. 96 PYROMORPHITE: Mexico mine, 80 mm high. An emerald green arsenatian variety encrusting quartz, collected from an exposure of the Roughton Gill (South) lode near the High level of the Mexico mine. The large vugh containing this and many similar specimens also yielded oil-green prismatic pyromorphite of near end-member composition (see Fig. 46). J. G. Wilson Collection.

Lettsom (1858: 405) 'of a rich golden-yellow colour, with the arseniate', but it has also been found in a honey brown, oil yellow or emerald green colour. Rounded aggregates of the 'campylite' habit are more common here than in specimens known to be from the main Roughton Gill mine, but they do not mimic Dry Gill 'campylite' in form or association sufficiently to be confused with it.

In 1978, a considerable quantity of fine pyromorphite was obtained by the late R. W. Barstow (the mineral dealer from Cornwall) from an exposure of the Roughton Gill South vein a little to the west of the Mexico mine High Level (although also known as the 'Mexico Mine open-cut' the exposure may be a collapsed stope). Further finds have been made from this same locality ('Barstow's Trench') by later collectors. The specimens show a wide range of colour and form from emerald green botryoidal aggregates (Fig. 96) to oil green prismatic crystals (cf. Fig. 46, p. 72). The former have a high arsenic content but most other specimens examined are near end-member pyromorphite (R. S. W. Braithwaite, *pers. comm.*). Crystals commonly occur to 10 mm in length; an exceptional crystal recently acquired by the BM(NH) is over 25 mm long.

Old Potts Gill mine An indistinctly crystallized mineral found by Kingsbury is a calcian pyromorphite (R. S.

Fig. 97 PYROMORPHITE: Roughton Gill mine. A group of prisms to 2 mm on dark blue drusy plumbogummite on quartz. Collected in 1947 from the main dump at the 90 fm level. King Collection, NMW (NMW 83.41G.7818; K256).

it is almost impossible to describe a typical specimen. Specimens in association with smalt blue plumbogummite are, however, unique. Perhaps the most well known are yellow-green to oil green tapering prismatic crystals (resembling spindles when doubly terminated) either in reasonably solid masses (cf. Fig. 47, p. 74) or on cavernous vein quartz. These crystals commonly exhibit rounded surface features giving ribbed or rippled faces, or may be overgrown by small sub-parallel prisms. Partial overgrowths on pinacoid faces give club or dumb-bell shaped crystals. Prismatic forms reach 20 mm in length but are generally less than 10–15 mm; these may form

Fig. 98 PYROMORPHITE: Roughton Gill mine. Delicately colour-zoned crystals (to 6 mm) of a magnificent oil green, lining a cavity in a gossany matrix. Collected from the main dump about 1950. King Collection, NMW (NMW 83.41G.M8303; K4292).

ated with linarite and brochantite. An unusual specimen recently examined at the BM(NH) gave an X-ray diffraction pattern close to that of pyromorphite, but has a blue-green colour and forms fibrous crystals on quartz with later more typical yellow pyromorphite (N. Carruth specimen).

Roughton Gill mine The Roughton Gill South vein contained one of the most remarkable deposits of pyromorphite on record. Many hundreds of tons of the mineral were raised and, in the early days, thrown away as useless. Later, more knowledgeable miners reworked the old waste heaps for 'coloured lead ore' and processed it. However, not all the pyromorphite met this fate: collectors and dealers also sought it, part of the 60 fm level workings yielding so many fine specimens that it became known as 'the specimen stope'.

Although the skilful mineralogist or collector can claim to readily recognize Roughton Gill pyromorphite, such is the variation of form and colour seen in collections that

Fig. 99 PYROMORPHITE: Roughton Gill mine. Green-tipped honey-coloured crystals to 10 mm on iron-stained quartz. Crystals showing this peculiar habit are well known from Roughton Gill and have also been found at the Mexico and Dry Gill mines. This specimen was bought by the BM from Bryce Wright in 1858 (BM 27548).

pure pyromorphite specimens 15–20 cm across. Pyromorphite also forms small tabular crystals; these are mostly indistinct but may form attractive rosettes or elongated stacks. The 'campylite' habit is common and grades into globular or botryoidal aggregates. Stalactites are rare but may be several centimetres long and covered in sparkling crystal faces. Acicular crystals, usually of a grey to pale green colour, may form fibrous vein fillings.

An attractive feature of many specimens is the variety of habits seen in the one piece, possibly enhanced by subtle changes in colour from form to form: honey brown rounded crystals overgrown by pale green prisms in singles or clusters, for instance (cf. Fig. 99), or oil green prisms scattered with milky green globular masses.

The full range of colours encompasses shades from white and grey through yellow, oil green to emerald green, brown and orange, Bicoloured crystals (green and

orange, yellow and green etc.) are not uncommon on smaller specimens. Colour is not a reliable guide to composition although an orange microcrystalline type is reputedly chromian (Bryce Wright, Unpubl. note, BM(NH); Goodchild, 1885). Chemical zoning is common and may coincide with colour changes but, although work has been done on phosphate:arsenate ratios (e.g. Jannettaz & Michel, 1881; Cockbain, 1968; Newby, 1981) a consistent relationship with colour has not been demonstrated.

The most common association is simply pyromorphite with quartz, but specimens associated with blue plumbo-gummite occur either as prisms or in the 'campylite' habit or both. Rarely, small pyromorphite crystals are seen embedded in hemimorphite crusts and fine-grained granular to sub-botryoidal pale yellow-green pyromorphite also forms epimorphs after cerussite crystals up to 20–30 mm. These last specimens are believed to have originated from the workings in higher Roughton Gill.

Sandbeds mine Small crystals (Davidson & Thomson, 1951).

Silver Gill From the 'lowest level at 1500 ft [450 m]' (Hartley, 1984) and the 'Golden Hugh' (D. R. Hacker Collection).

PYRRHOTINE $Fe_{1-x}S$

Carrock mine Massive pyrrhotine is common in the Harding and Smith veins, associated with quartz and carbonates. Fortey (1978) noted it as especially abundant where the country rock was gabbro. Sharp, tabular crystals to about 10 mm have been found in vughs or etched out of enclosing calcite from the recent workings on the Smith vein (J. G. Wilson, *pers. comm.*).

QUARTZ SiO_2

Quartz is the commonest gangue mineral in the metalliferous veins of the Caldbeck Fells. It is rarely found in good crystals but is mostly as massive or granular vein quartz or in chalcedonic varieties of little appeal to collectors. 'Hacked quartz' — a pseudomorphic variety of massive or granular quartz with hollow moulds after thin tabular baryte crystals — is common in the Roughton Gill veins and elsewhere. Only the notable occurrences are described below.

Brandy Gill Lead mine Drusy quartz epimorphs after ?galena (q.v.) have been found in a vein outcrop above the east level.

Carrock mine Large quartz crystals are to be found in vughs in the massive quartz veins. Dewey & Dines (1923) record crystals up to 2 feet [60 cm] long and 8 inches [20 cm] wide from the Harding vein. The larger crystals are mostly opaque and etched or stained, but smaller ones may be transparent and lustrous. Shaw (1970: 51)

Fig. 100 QUARTZ: epimorphs after ?GALENA, Brandy Gill. Hollow drusy quartz 'boxes' to 15 mm on edge from an outcrop on the flank of Brandy Gill just above the eastern level of Brandy Gill Lead mine. The boxes are coated with small mimetite crystals and the whole encrusted with fine brown clay. D. I. Green Collection (89/1).

Fig. 101 ROSASITE on HEMIMORPHITE: Roughton Gill mine. Pale turquoise blue globular aggregates of rosasite on radiating sprays of hemimorphite to 3 mm across. This is a very typical assemblage, and also occurs in dump material from workings on the Silver Gill vein on Balliway Rigg and in Silver Gill. David Hacker Collection (82-14).

reports 'very fine quartz crystals' from the trial on the Emerson vein in Coomb Height.

Iron Crag 'a pocket lined with well-grown pyramids upwards of three inches [7.5 cm] wide' in a vein outcrop 'high up in Iron Crags' (Day, 1928: 77).

QUEITITE $Pb_4Zn_2(SiO_4)(Si_2O_7)(SO_4)$

Red Gill mine This exceedingly rare mineral, previously reported only from Tsumeb, Namibia, was found on one small specimen collected from the No. 2 (Old Dutch) level dumps in 1987 by M. Rothwell. It forms thin, white, radiating-fibrous crusts with a minutely botryoidal surface on small susannite crystals in massive cerussite, associated with a scattering of later caledonite. Queitite was identified by XRD (BM(NH)) and IR (UMIST). The habit is completely different from type material (Braithwaite *et al.*, 1989).

RHODOCHROSITE $MnCO_3$

Carrock mine Listed by Fortey (1978) but Fortey & Bland (1979) state 'rhodochrosite may be present but has not

yet been located by the present writer'. The occurrence is doubtful.

RHODONITE $(Mn, Fe, Mg, Ca)SiO_3$

Caldbeck Young (1987) quoted the label of a specimen in the Geological Museum.

ROCKBRIDGEITE $(Fe^{2+}, Mn)Fe^{3+}(PO_4)_3(OH)_5$

Burdell Gill As drusy crusts of small, dark brown, crystals on gossany matrix (Kingsbury Collection, BM(NH); Kingsbury, MS 1).

ROMANÈCHITE $BaMn^{2+}Mn_8^{4+}O_{16}(OH)_4$

The majority of records for 'psilomelane' from Caldbeck would probably now be referred to romanèchite. A check of X-ray records in the BM(NH) shows that romanèchite has been confirmed from Dry Gill.

ROSASITE $(Cu, Zn)_2CO_3(OH)_2$

The first British occurrences were those noted by Kingsbury & Hartley (1957*b*) from various localities in the Caldbeck Fells. All the localities below with the exception of Balliway Rigg, were mentioned in their paper. They described rosasite as 'small bluish-green wart-like aggregates, though the colour may vary from malachite-green to pale blue, [with] . . . smithsonite, hemimorphite, malachite, aurichalcite and . . . ill-defined zinc-bearing varieties of malachite' (*op. cit.*: 501–502).

Balliway Rigg As small spherical aggregates on colourless hemimorphite from a small dump on the line of the Silver Gill vein [NY 301 342] (M. P. Cooper Collection).

Driggith mine 12 fm and 30 fm levels.

Old Potts Gill mine Although Kingsbury & Hartley (1957b: 501) give the locality as 'a copper vein near Potts Gill', unpublished MS notes by Kingsbury make it clear that the locality was the old No. 1 level dump of Old Potts Gill mine (see also Hartley, 1984).

Roughton Gill mine Specimens from the outcrop workings in higher Roughton Gill and from the 60 fm level dumps were noted by Kingsbury & Hartley (1957b). It also occurs on the 90 fm dumps as pale blue spherical aggregates and masses with colourless hemimorphite (Fig. 101).

Sandbeds mine From the upper level.

Silver Gill From the 'Middle level on north [Silver Gill] vein' (Kingsbury & Hartley, 1957b: 501).

RUTILE   TiO$_2$

Carrock mine Hartley (1984).

SCHEELITE   CaWO$_4$

Brandy Gill 'massive fawn scheelite occurs in N–S quartz veins in Higher Brandy Gill' (Young, 1987: 91).

Burdell Gill In stream sediments (Appleton & Wadge, 1976).

Carrock mine Fine scheelite crystals were noted in the tungsten veins in Brandy Gill and Grainsgill in the early nineteenth century. In 1837, it was independently recorded by Tooke ('tungsten in beautiful crystals'), by Lévy, and by Phillips. Lévy figured specimens from 'Caldbeckfels' in a catalogue of a collection bought by C. H. Turner from Henry Heuland in 1820, which suggests that its occurrence here had been known for some time.

The crystals are mostly less than 30 mm across; smaller crystals may be perfectly formed and transparent. Large crystals (< 20 cm) are uncommon and poorly formed and heavily fractured. The colour varies from colourless through wine yellow to clove brown. Scheelite is usually associated with quartz, 'gilbertite', wolframite and arsenopyrite. Partial replacement of wolframite by scheelite is common.

The formation of scheelite at Carrock mine is discussed in detail by Hitchen (1934), Fortey (1978) and Ball *et al.* (1985).

Although scheelite constituted a major ore mineral here, specimen grade material was always sporadic. Specimens found in the recent workings are as good as

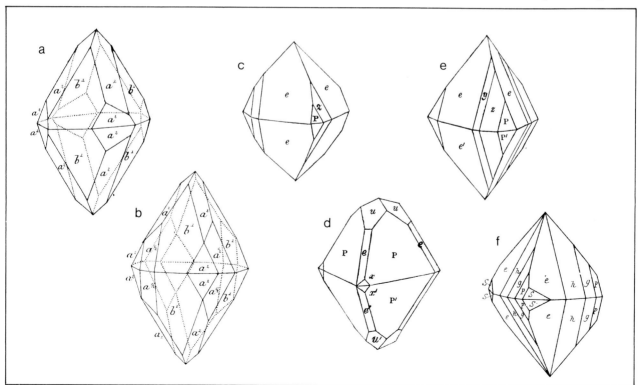

Fig. 102 SCHEELITE: from the Grainsgill tungsten veins. Drawings: a–b after Lévy (1837): c–e after Greg & Lettsom (1858); f after Bauer (1871).

Fig. 103 SCHEELITE: Carrock mine, 40 × 35 mm. A fine loose crystal collected from the 'New Tunnel level' [the Canadian level?] of the Harding vein about 1980 and bought by the BM(NH) from the late Richard Barstow in 1981 (BM 1981, 263).

any found in the past. A large 'walk-in' vugh lined with quartz crystals and containing large scheelite crystals was found in the Smith vein in the 1970s, but unfortunately, although its remains can still be seen, no record was made of this rare occurrence at the time of its discovery.

Wet Swine Gill In stream sediments (Appleton & Wadge, 1976).

SCORODITE $FeAsO_4.2H_2O$

Brandy Gill From a quartz vein just downstream of the waterfall at the foot of Brandy Gill as an alteration product of arsenopyrite (Day, 1928; Davidson & Thomson, 1951).

Burdell Gill As small, pale blue and colourless crystals from the vein in the north-east branch of the gill (Hartley, 1984).

Carrock mine As an alteration of massive arsenopyrite, first recorded by Hitchen (1934).

Deer Hills As yellow-brown glistening encrustations on quartz with pharmacosiderite from an old working on the

Deer Hills Quartz lode [NY 3145 3626] (M. P. Cooper Collection, *det.* UMIST: IR).

Ingray Gill From the northern level with arseniosiderite, pharmacosiderite, erythrite, carminite and beudantite (Kingsbury & Hartley, 1957a; 1960).

Nether Row Brow As green and brown crusts from the Nether Row Farm level with mimetite, mottramite, plumbojarosite, beaverite, beudantite, carminite and pharmacosiderite; and from the 'Dumpy Stone' level as reddish brown crusts with beaverite, carminite and beudantite (Kingsbury & Hartley, 1960).

Old Potts Gill mine From the old No. 1 cross-cut dumps with pharmacosiderite, beudantite and carminite (Kingsbury & Hartley, 1960).

SCOTLANDITE $PbSO_3$

Roughton Gill Recently found on a few small specimens collected from an outcrop of the Roughton Gill South vein in higher Roughton Gill. It occurs as a sparkling pale brown encrustation on altered galena with mattheddleite, lanarkite, leadhillite and caledonite (*det.* Leeds Univ.: XRD, D. I. Green *in prep.*).

SEMSEYITE $Pb_9Sb_8S_{21}$

Wet Swine Gill In the 'antimony vein' as tenuous coatings with fülöppite, and as rare, minute (< 20 μm), grains in zinckenite (Fortey *et al.*, 1984).

SENARMONTITE Sb_2O_3

Wet Swine Gill In the 'antimony vein' as grey masses and minute colourless octahedra derived from the alteration of stibnite (Fortey *et al.*, 1984).

Fig. 104 SENARMONTITE: Wet Swine Gill. Minute octahedra on altered stibnite from the 'antimony vein'. SEM photograph; scale bar is 200 μm. M. P. Cooper Collection.

SERPIERITE $Ca(Cu,Zn)_4(SO_4)_2(OH)_6 \cdot 3H_2O$

Driggith mine As aggregates of tiny, pale blue crystals on an altered chalcopyrite–sphalerite matrix (Kingsbury & Hartley MS, 1957*d*). Specimens in the Kingsbury Collection (BM(NH)) are typical of dump-formed serpierite.

Old Potts Gill mine As tufts of minute, pale blue needles with smithsonite, malachite, aurichalcite etc. from 'a small copper vein near Potts Gill' (Kingsbury & Hartley, 1957*d*: 605). Kingsbury (MS 1) makes it clear that the locality was the old No. 1 level dumps (see also Hartley, 1984).

Red Gill mine As soft, pale blue, micaceous aggregates on cerussite on one specimen from the P. Braithwaite Collection (*det.* BM(NH): XRD).

SIDERITE $FeCO_3$

Brandy Gill From an unspecified site ('the only locality in the Lake district') with galena and cerussite (Wright, *in* Jenkinson, 1875: lxxxi).

SILVER Ag

Driggith mine As minute dendrites in cerussite (D. R. Middleton Collection).

Red Gill mine Recently confirmed by a combination of XRD (BM(NH)) and EPMA (M. Rothwell) on one small specimen from the No. 2 level dumps. Silver forms minute arborescent growths with hydrocerussite, caledonite, susannite, leadhillite and mattheddleite (Wirth, 1989).

SMITHSONITE $ZnCO_3$

Smithsonite is uncommon in the Caldbeck Fells. Many early records of the mineral, especially those from Roughton Gill, being mis-identifications of hemimorphite (which may contain some included carbonate) or plumbogummite (which was mistaken for the hemimorphite).

Driggith mine As a pale blue coating (Day, 1928); confirmed by Hartley (1984) from the 12 fm and 30 fm dumps.

Old Potts Gill mine (Hartley, 1984).

Roughton Gill mine Greg & Lettsom's (1858: 424) description of smithsonite ('calamine') — 'botryoidal of a lavender colour, with barytes and arsenio-phosphate of lead' — is almost certainly a mistake for plumbogummite. The Allan–Greg Collection (BM(NH)) contains such a specimen catalogued as 'calamine'; other 'calamines' in the same collection are hemimorphite. Goodchild (1884: 197) also seems to have confused the minerals; his 'calamine, zinc carbonate' formed 'dull chalky-looking encrustations on the materials composing the fault-breccia. In tint these vary from smoke grey, or dull lead-colour, through sapphire-blue, or lavender, to nearly

a cobalt-blue', a good description of plumbogummite.

The only definite reports of smithsonite at Roughton Gill are those of Davidson & Thomson (1951: 138): 'a pale blue chalky substance, filling small cavities, and rarely, mammillated on old specimens in collections'; and R. J. King (*pers. comm.*) who found a specimen here in 1948 (*det.* BM(NH)).

Sandbeds mine Recorded as a 'pale blue coating' (Davidson & Thomson, 1951); also listed by Hartley (1984) from the 'top level'.

Silver Gill From 'the level at 1500 ft' [450 m] (Hartley, 1984). Young (1987) lists smithsonite with rosasite on a BM(NH) specimen from the same site.

SPHALERITE ZnS

Occurs in many of the metalliferous veins of the Caldbeck Fells, mostly as fine-grained aggregates or massive. Euhedral crystals are small and uncommon. Sphalerite was raised as ore from Driggith, Roughton Gill, and Dry Gill in the 1870s but proved difficult to separate from the associated sulphides and baryte. The recorded localities are:

Brae Fell mine; *Brandy Gill Lead mine*; *Carrock mine* (both in the tungsten veins and in the E–W lead veins); *Driggith mine*; *Dry Gill mine*; *Nether Row Brow* (the Nether Row Farm and 'Dumpy Stone' levels); *Potts Gill Baryte mine*; *Red Gill mine*; *Roughton Gill mine*; *Sandbeds mine*; *Silver Gill* (the 'level at 1500 m [450 m]' (Hartley, 1984)); *Wet Swine Gill* (in the 'antimony vein' in minute grains). For further references see Appendix 1.

STIBICONITE $Sb^{3+}Sb_2^{5+}O_6(OH)$

Caldew Valley Stibiconite was tentatively identified as light grey patches in a jamesonite-bearing vein at the foot of Coomb Height to the NE of Wet Swine Gill (Fortey *et al.*, 1984).

Wet Swine Gill A common alteration product of antimony sulphides and sulphosalts in the 'antimony vein' (Fortey *et al.*, 1984).

STIBNITE Sb_2S_3

Stibnite was recorded from 'Caldbeck' or 'Carrock Fells' by several authors (e.g. Greg & Lettsom, 1858; Hall, 1868) but no precise locality was given until Kingsbury & Hartley (1956*b*) identified stibnite from Carrock mine. In view of the predominance of other antimony-bearing minerals at the locality they considered the early records probably to have been misidentifications.

Carrock mine Found on one specimen by Kingsbury & Hartley (1956*b*). There have been no further finds.

Wet Swine Gill A common sulphide in the 'antimony vein' associated, predominantly, with zinckenite and berthierite. Small acicular crystals are sometimes found projecting into cavities; stibnite is commonly coated with, or pseudomorphed by, senarmonite or stibiconite, or both (Fortey *et al.*, 1984).

STOLZITE   PbWO$_4$

Stolzite is relatively common from localities in Brandy Gill where the N–S tungsten-bearing veins are cut by later E–W lead veins.

Brandy Gill Lead mine This occurrence is regarded by many as the first authenticated British locality for the species, an earlier record from Force Crag mine, Braithwaite, Cumbria (Greg & Lettsom, 1858) remains unsubstantiated by specimen or catalogue entry (Russell, 1944; Kingsbury & Hartley, MS) and unlikely from a study of the geochemistry of the Force Crag deposit (Freeman, 1982).

Kingsbury and Hartley first collected stolzite here in 1949; their find was first published by Claringbull (1951). An independent discovery was noted by Davidson &

Fig. 105 STOLZITE: Brandy Gill Lead mine. Sharp tabular crystal (0.5 mm) with malachite on cerussite. Crystals over 10 mm have been found at this locality, but are poorly formed. This specimen came from the upper west level. D. R. Middleton Collection (7-23).

Thomson (1951) but the most complete description is given in Kingsbury & Hartley (MS).

Kingsbury's original find was on dumps from the upper western level where stolzite occurred as poorly defined platy aggregates in quartz associated with a duftite-like mineral ('calcio-duftite') and, less commonly, malachite, mimetite, cerussite and bayldonite. The occurrence has been confirmed by many subsequent collectors, both on the dump and *in situ* in the old level. Crystals may reach over 10 mm across in small clusters often coated with duftite on matrix. Well formed tabular crystals, or less commonly, simple prisms, are rare and small. Although the visually similar wulfenite has been found on the eastern level dumps, none was found on the western level dumps by Kingsbury and Hartley. This distribution has been confirmed by recent work (T. F. Bridges, *pers. comm.*). However, stolzite is also recorded from the eastern level dumps where it is associated with 'a little galena and limonitic matter [and] a trace of mimetite' (Kingsbury & Hartley, MS).

Carrock mine Several habits of stolzite have been found in the dumps on the north side of Grainsgill. In 1950, Kingsbury & Hartley (MS) found stolzite as minute, slightly rounded, bi-pyramidal crystals of a pale olive brown colour on iron-stained quartz 'outside the old main adit-level on the Harding vein' and as a brownish, drusy, parallel growth on scheelite from the Harding vein dumps. Stolzite has recently been found as very thin, incomplete, creamy plates in a gossany quartz matrix from the main dump; it is not distinctive in appearance and may easily be overlooked (J. G. Wilson, *pers. comm.*, 1987, *det.* BM(NH): XRD).

In addition, Kingsbury & Hartley (MS) found a single specimen of stolzite in a dump from 'a level at, or near, the junction of the east–west lead veins and the Emerson vein at the foot of Brandy Gill' (Hartley, 1984: 36). It consists of pale brownish crystals of a 'truncated pyramidal habit showing a conspicuous basal plane' associated with pale green pyromorphite in spongy quartz.

Poddy Gill EPM analysis of several different habits of the 'wulfenite' well known from the E–W lead vein at the foot of Poddy Gill, showed considerable amounts of tungsten in all samples tested. The technique used did not, however, allow the detection of molybdenum and some specimens may be merely tungstatian wulfenite (M. Rothwell, *pers. comm.*). Follow-up EPM and XRD analysis at the BM(NH) on a specimen provided by N. Hubbard, bearing small orange-yellow pseudo-cubic crystals on pyromorphite–mimetite (Fig. 106, p. 129), showed the mineral in question to be almost pure stolzite. It is too early to say the proportion of stolzite to wulfenite that occurs here but a re-examination of the XRD film taken at the BM(NH) for Braithwaite *et al.* (1963) confirms that their specimen was wulfenite.

Fig. 106 STOLZITE: Poddy Gill. Pseudocubic crystals to 0.4 mm with pyromorphite from the outcrop of an east-west lead vein at the foot of Poddy Gill. Wulfenite also occurs in this assemblage and cannot readily be distinguished. N. Hubbard Collection.

STRENGITE $FePO_4.2H_2O$

Burdell Gill As small colourless to bluish crystals (Hartley, 1984). Young (1987: 98) describes a specimen in the BM(NH) as 'pale purple globules with goethite and cacoxenite'.

Carrock mine As minute, glassy, brown spherules on wolframite from an exposure of the Harding vein (*det.* BM(NH): XRD, D. McCallum, *pers. comm.*).

STRONTIANITE $SrCO_3$

Potts Gill Baryte mine Young (1987) cites a manuscript note of A. W. G. Kingsbury in the BM(NH).

SULPHUR S

Probably more common than the one record cited.

Wet Swine Gill Small quantities as an alteration product in the 'antimony vein' (Fortey *et al.*, 1984).

SUSANNITE $Pb_4(SO_4)(CO_3)_2(OH)_2$

Brae Fell mine A heavy mass of secondary lead minerals with baryte and quartz collected by Kingsbury in 1951 has crude, sheafy, yellowish tabular crystals to more than 10 mm which were originally identified as leadhillite. A recent examination of this specimen (BM(NH)) showed that these crystals, and a later generation in thin, brown, crystal aggregates, all gave an X-ray powder pattern identical to that of susannite.

Red Gill mine It occurs here as small, acute rhombohedral crystals of a distinctive aquamarine blue colour with cerussite, leadhillite, caledonite and mattheddleite (M. Wirth, R. E. Starkey Collections; *det.* BM(NH): XRD); also with queitite (q.v.).

Roughton Gill A specimen from the Ludlam Collection (BM(NH)) labelled 'leadhillite and aurichalcite' examined by the authors has been shown (BM(NH): XRD) to consist

Fig. 107 SUSANNITE on CALEDONITE: Roughton Gill mine. A nineteenth century specimen from the Ludlam Collection shows susannite (the crystal is 4 mm across) embedded in a velvety mass of caledonite. Although known in small amounts, this habit of caledonite is most unusual in the Caldbeck Fells; this rich piece seems to be unique. BM(NH) (BM 1985, Lud 7465).

of very pale blue equant to tabular susannite crystals to 10 mm embedded in acicular caledonite (Fig. 107, p. 129).

Short Grain From the northern trial as minute, pale aquamarine crystals in cavities in massive baryte with leadhillite, caledonite, cerussite, and mattheddleite (M. P. Cooper Collection, *det*. BM(NH): XRD).

SYLVANITE $AgAuTe_4$

Carrock mine The presence of sylvanite in 'grünlingite' is mentioned in a letter of 1943 from W. Hemingway to Anthony Wilson (leaseholder of the mine) preserved in the Cumbria Record Office, Carlisle (DX/955/3v). No other reference can be found.

SYMPLESITE $Fe_3(AsO_4)_2 \cdot 8H_2O$

Nether Row Brow An undifferentiated member of the symplesite–metavivianite series (*det*. BM(NH): XRD) occurs very rarely as small pale greenish grey flat radiating aggregates in quartz collected from the Nether Row Farm level dump in 1986 by B. Young (*pers. comm.*). The predominance of arsenic minerals at this locality suggests that the mineral is probably symplesite.

TENNANTITE $Cu_{10}Fe_2As_4S_{13}$

Driggith mine Tetrahedrite–tennantite was recorded from the 30 fm dumps and vein outcrop workings by Hartley (1984). Kingsbury (MS 1) described both tennantite from the 12 fm dumps and tetrahedrite–tennantite from the 30 fm dumps, as: 'intergrown with galena'.

Old Potts Gill mine (Hartley, 1984).

TENORITE CuO

Hay Gill Copper mine Listed as 'melaconite' by Greg & Lettsom (1858); also identified by Davidson & Thomson (1951).

Mexico mine The 'grey oxide' of copper recorded by Shaw (1970) may have been tenorite.

Old Potts Gill mine (Davidson & Thomson, 1951). Also, as an associate of chalcopyrite, malachite, and cornwallite, from a small copper vein intersected by the South lode (Shaw, 1970).

Roughton Gill mine (Greg & Lettsom, 1858). 'In small amounts' (Day, 1928). Davidson & Thomson (1951) found no trace on the dumps.

TETRADYMITE Bi_2Te_2S

Carrock mine Recorded by many authors (e.g. Greg & Lettsom, 1858). Many, if not most, records are errors for joseite or ingodite (q.v.); however, Clarke (1974) records an analysis (EPMA) of a Carrock mine sample that corresponds to tetradymite. Requires confirmation.

TETRAHEDRITE $Cu_{10}Fe_2Sb_4S_{13}$

Carrock mine As inclusions in iron-rich sphalerite (Thimmaiah, 1956).

Driggith mine Argentian tetrahedrite (10–12 wt% Ag) occurs as minute grains ($< 200 \mu m$) on quartz or included in galena (Stanley & Vaughan, 1981). Hartley (1984) records tetrahedrite–tennantite from the 30 fm dumps and from the Driggith–Sandbeds outcrop workings; Kingsbury (MS 1) described tetrahedrite–tennantite as 'intergrown with galena' from the former.

Nether Row Brow From the dumps of the Nether Row Farm level as small masses, (< 3 mm) in granular quartz (M. P. Cooper Collection, *det*. BM(NH): XRD).

Roughton Gill mine Tetrahedrite–tennantite was recorded from the old workings in higher Roughton Gill by Hartley (1984).

TOURMALINE GROUP
Mostly schorl $NaFe_3^{2+}Al_6(BO_3)_3Si_6O_{18}(OH)_4$

Burdell Gill Schorl as 'brush-like clusters in quartz' (Hitchen, 1934: 186); in a vein at the foot of the gill (R. S. W. Braithwaite, *pers. comm.*).

Caldew Valley From the flank of Coomb Height (Davidson & Thomson, 1951: 144) schorl 'about $\frac{1}{4}$ mile [0.4 km] east of Burdle Gill'. In a quartz vein with jamesonite north-east of Wet Swine Gill (Fortey *et al.*, 1984).

Carrock mine Occasionally, as bundles of fibrous crystals 'mainly on the dumps from the Emmerson [*sic*] Vein' (Davidson & Thomson, 1951: 143). Common as a wall-rock alteration product where the tungsten veins pass through hornfels; Thimmaiah (1956) described the mineral as a ferroan indicolite. Fortey (1978) also records euhedral needle-like crystals of tourmaline in dolomite at the margin of a quartz vein running through hornfels.

Poddy Gill As bundles of black crystals in a N–S quartz vein about half-way up the gill (Hitchen, 1934; Davidson & Thomson, 1951).

TREMOLITE $Ca_2(Mg, Fe)_5Si_8O_{22}(OH)_2$

Carrock mine 'sparingly in a fibrous form, as an alteration product, on metamorphosed diabase from the Harding vein' (Davidson & Thomson, 1951: 143).

TSUMEBITE $Pb_2Cu(PO_4)(SO_4)(OH)$

Carrock Fell An arsenatian tsumebite was recorded by Embrey (1977*b*) from 'Carrock Fell', but the collector of the material subsequently reported the locality more precisely as Roughton Gill at [NY 302 343]; i.e. between the 60 and 90 fm levels (Moffit, 1979).

Roughton Gill mine The authors have found tsumebite to be an occasional associate of brochantite in specimens collected from the mains dumps of Roughton Gill. It

Fig. 108 TSUMEBITE: Roughton Gill mine. Light green drusy globular aggregates to 0.1 mm with emerald green brochantite on quartz pseudomorphous after baryte. Collected from the main dump in 1985. D. R. Middleton specimen, M. P. Cooper Collection (86103).

forms tiny (*c*.0.25 mm) pale apple green drusy aggregates and rare scaly crystals on compact quartz. Associated brochantite crystals reach 2–3 mm and cerussite is occasionally present. First identified on a specimen collected by D. R. Middleton (*det.* BM(NH): XRD; UMIST: IR).

TUNGSTITE WO₃ . H₂O

$WO_3 . H_2O$

Carrock mine As a yellow powdery alteration product of wolframite (Greg & Lettsom, 1858, 'wolframine'; Hitchen, 1934; Davidson & Thomson, 1951).

TURQUOISE $CuAl_6(PO_4)_4(OH)_8 . 5H_2O$

Driggith mine From the 30 fm dumps (Hartley, 1984).

TYROLITE $CaCu_5(AsO_4)_2(CO_3)(OH)_4 . 6H_2O$

Potts Gill Baryte mine Known only on specimens from the 'old No. 1 cross-cut' in the Kingsbury Collection (BM(NH)) which have blue-green small platy crystals of tyrolite encrusting matrix. Kingsbury (MS 1) noted this occurrence as new to Britain but it was not published until 1984 (Hartley).

URANINITE UO_2

Carrock mine Found as minute grains (0.01–0.20 mm) in the greisen wall-rock of a vein 'immediately west of the former smithy serving Carrock Mine'. Since radioactivity was restricted to the vicinity of the vein, the authors (Dawson & Harrison, 1966) suggested that the uraninite was associated with the vein mineralization.

VANADINITE $Pb_5(VO_4)_3Cl$

Brandy Gill Lead mine Very rare, it occurs as small (1–2 mm) cream to reddish brown short prismatic or barrel-shaped crystals or globular aggregates sometimes associated with mottramite or descloizite (Kingsbury & Hartley, 1956a). Specimens in the Kingsbury Collection (BM(NH)) match this description and are labelled as from the eastern level. It also occurs as small aggregates of creamy radiating fibrous crystals on quartz from the upper western level found by T. Wolloxall (*pers. comm.*) and identified at the BM(NH) (XRD).

Carrock mine It forms short prismatic buff to almost colourless crystals in specimens from 'an old cross-cut driven close to the point where an east–west copper–lead vein meets an ankerite vein and the Emerson vein' (Kingsbury & Hartley, 1956a: 291). Specimens in the Kingsbury Collection (BM(NH)) show small lustrous crystals on a fine-grained reddish rock.

Ingray Gill Listed from the dumps of the northern trial by Kingsbury (MS 1) but specimens could not be traced in the Kingsbury Collection, BM(NH). The occurrence was not known to J. Hartley (*pers. comm.*).

Old Potts Gill mine As small brown prismatic crystals in cellular quartz with baryte and calcite from the 'old No. 1 cross-cut' (Kingsbury & Hartley, 1956a: 292).

VIVIANITE $Fe_3(PO_4)_2 . 8H_2O$

Burdell Gill Crusts of minute black crystals on goethite (Kingsbury Collection, BM(NH)). Listed by Hartley (1984).

WITHERITE $BaCO_3$

Potts Gill Baryte mine Shaw (1970: 65) noted the presence of up to 0.5 wt% BaCO₃ in assays of baryte from Potts Gill, but although fluorescent spots assumed to be witherite could be seen *in situ* by UV light the mineral 'could not be discerned with the naked eye in ordinary light'. Listed by Hartley (1984). Young (1987: 102) quoted the label of a specimen in the BM(NH): 'Cream-coloured massive. From the old No. 2 cross-cut'.

WOLFRAMITE $(Mn,Fe)WO_4$

Burdell Gill In stream sediments (Appleton & Wadge, 1976).

Carrock mine Wolframite was the earliest ore mineral to form in the Carrock tungsten veins (Fig. 12, p. 20); the euhedral habit suggests that it grew unimpeded in open fractures. Individual blades to more than 20 cm occur but almost all are completely embedded in quartz. Crystals remaining in open voids after the quartz deposition are usually altered to scheelite by subsequent mineralization. It varies in composition from 35 to 55 mole % hübnerite (Beddoe-Stephens & Fortey, 1981; Ball *et al.*, 1985).

Dry Swine Gill Shaw (1970: 52) records 'float quartz

containing wolfram' from 'near Dry Swine Gill' [between Wet Swine Gill and Grainsgill].

Wet Swine Gill In stream sediments (Appleton & Wadge, 1976).

WROEWOLFEITE $Cu_4(SO_4)(OH)_6 \cdot 2H_2O$

The two records are of specimens in the D. I. Green Collection, identified by the collector at Leeds University (XRD). At both sites the mineral is almost certainly dump-formed.

Red Gill mine Occurs on one specimen as minute (0.2 mm) bladed crystals and crusts on altered chalcopyrite and galena.

Silver Gill Relatively common in small amounts as deep blue blades to 0.5 mm with langite on oxidized sulphides from an old ore pile in the west bank of the gill [NY 2995 3415].

WULFENITE $PbMoO_4$

Arm o' Grain Very rarely; as minute tabular yellow crystals on quartz with pyromorphite–mimetite (C. M. Leppington Collection, *det.* BM(NH): XRD).

Brandy Gill Lead mine J. G. Goodchild (1875, 1885) first recorded wulfenite from the Caldbeck Fells, associated with pyromorphite, anglesite, cerussite and 'various other species of more or less interest', but gave no more precise locality than 'one of the gills running up from the Cawda [Caldew] to the west side ... of Carrick' (Goodchild, 1885: 188). One of his specimens, labelled 'Brandy Gill', was seen in Carlisle Museum by Arthur Russell (1936) who discovered, or rediscovered, wulfenite of similar appearance on the dumps of Brandy Gill Lead mine. Here, wulfenite forms aggregates of crude, micaceous crystals to 1–2 mm on iron-stained quartz. It seems to be confined to specimens from the dump of the east level. Specimens of a similar mineral from the west level have all proved to be stolzite (q.v.).

Carrock mine Reported from the dump of an old level 'at, or near, the junction of the east–west lead veins with the Emerson vein at the foot of Brandy Gill' (Hartley, 1984: 36). Surprisingly rich specimens of wulfenite (for Britain) are labelled as having been found at this locality in the Kingsbury Collection with further specimens in the Russell Collection (donated by Kingsbury), BM(NH). Crystals reach 5–6 mm square and form aggregates to 25 mm across; they vary in colour from yellow to grey and in habit from square tablets to thin plates modified by a low pyramid.

Driggith mine From an outcrop working on the Driggith–Sandbeds vein as 'minute yellow plates (0.5–2 mm) ... showing the forms c(001), n(011) and e(112) ... implanted on yellowish-green pyromorphite and mimetite' (Kingsbury & Hartley, MS). Listed by Hartley (1984).

Ingray Gill As the variety 'eosite' from the northern level (Hartley, 1984). Specimens in the BM(NH) donated by Kingsbury show small (*c.* 1 mm) blood red rounded bipyramidal crystals with bright green acicular pyromorphite on quartz.

Mexico mine Found recently as tiny, rounded, orange, steeply bipyramidal crystals with cerussite and other, unidentified, lead minerals, from a vein exposure above the Mexico mine High Level (D. R. Middleton, *pers. comm.*, 1986). Also, as small (< 2 mm) tabular translucent to transparent yellow plates and bipyramids of variable thickness with pyromorphite–mimetite on quartz from the dumps of the Low Level in Todd Gill (M. P. Cooper Collection). Both occurrences *det.* BM(NH): XRD.

Poddy Gill Davidson & Thomson (1951) first recorded wulfenite from a small dump at the foot of Poddy Gill, on the authority of Dr W. Goodchild (son of J. G. Goodchild of the Geological Survey). More information was given on its occurrence by Braithwaite *et al.* (1963). Small (< 2 mm) tabular, pseudo-cubic, or bipyramidal orange-yellow crystals are relatively common on green pyromorphite from the outcrop of the vein or from the dump from an old trial on it and all have, until recently, been assumed to be wulfenite. However, qualitative analysis of samples representing the three common habits mentioned, have shown significant tungsten in all the tested specimens (M. Rothwell, *pers. comm.*) and analyses at the BM(NH) show that some, at least, are stolzite (q.v.). A re-examination of the X-ray film taken by the BM(NH) for Braithwaite *et al.* (*ibid.*) shows their material to have been wulfenite.

Silver Gill Recently identified on a few small specimens as thin, yellow to orange square plates to 1 mm on cerussite or iron-stained quartz from an old ore pile found on the west bank of the gill [NY 2995 3415] in 1988 (P. Braithwaite, N. Hubbard Collections, *det.* BM(NH): XRD).

ZINCKENITE $Pb_9Sb_{22}S_{42}$

Carrock mine The first British occurrence: in small amounts as dark grey fibrous crystals or aggregates in quartz with small amounts of carbonates and other sulphides. Virtually impossible to distinguish in the hand specimen from boulangerite and jamesonite that occur here in a similar habit (Kingsbury & Hartley, 1956b).

Wet Swine Gill In the 'antimony vein' as fibrous patches to 15 mm across in quartz with stibnite, berthierite etc. (Fortey *et al.*, 1984).

UNKNOWN MINERALS

UNKNOWN COPPER CALCIUM SODIUM PHOSPHATE HYDRATE

Roughton Gill mine Sprays of tapering bladed aquamarine

lections; it generally forms sprays of extremely small pale green acicular crystals with ?langite on altered sulphides and is assumed to be dump-formed.

Silver Gill Very rarely as minutely crystalline crusts with ?langite and cerussite on oxidized sulphides from the 'Golden Hugh' (D. R. Middleton Collection, *det.* BM(NH): XRD). Specimens very similar to those from Esgair-Hir have recently been found in an old ore pile on the west bank of the gill [NY 2995 3415] (D. I. Green, *pers. comm.*).

Work is continuing on both of these minerals.

Fig. 109 UNKNOWN COPPER CALCIUM SODIUM PHOSPHATE HYDRATE: Roughton Gill mine. To date, only four specimens are known from Caldbeck of this attractive species. It forms small (here to 1 mm) glassy, turquoise blue blades on chrysocolla in a gossany quartz. J. Dickinson Collection.

Fig. 110 UNKNOWN COPPER SULPHATE HYDRATE: Red Gill mine. Prismatic crystals to 0.1 mm on altered galena. Several specimens of this mineral have been collected in Caldbeck, typically associated with a langite group mineral and probably of post-mining formation. Specimens from localities in Silver Gill have much smaller crystals, and thus lack the depth of colour of the illustrated specimen. P. Braithwaite Collection.

blue transparent crystals to 1.5 mm on chrysocolla in quartz have been shown by XRD (BM(NH) & Leeds Univ.) and semi-quantitative EPMA (M. Rothwell, *pers. comm.*) to be a probable new species. Only two very small specimens have been found (J. Dickinson & P. Braithwaite Collections). The XRD pattern is closely related to that of the magnesium phosphate bobierrite (D. I. Green, *pers. comm.*).

UNKNOWN COPPER SULPHATE HYDRATE

Red Gill mine A bright grass green mineral forming transparent square section rods to 0.15 mm on altered sulphides was found on the No. 2 level dumps by P. Braithwaite. XRD analysis (BM(NH)) showed it to be identical with a mineral previously found at Esgair-Hir in Wales by S. Rust; the X-ray pattern could not otherwise be matched to any known mineral. Small amounts of the mineral have subsequently been identified (BM(NH) & Leeds Univ.: XRD) in various private col-

APPENDIX 1

The following lists contain all the species reported for each of the important collecting localities in the Caldbeck Fells. The species are given in alphabetical order: valid names begin with a capital letter; discredited, vague, or unknown names are given in quotation marks. An asterisk by a name indicates that the locality was the site of the first British record for that species. Exclamation marks after names indicate species for which that locality is notable; the more marks (to a maximum of three) the better. Loosely, the importance of the occurrence varies as: local!, national!!, international!!!.

The mineral names are followed by a list of citations of all the important publications that mention the given species. Some lesser papers have been omitted but, in most cases, the earliest known reference is included. Passing references to species in recent papers, unless constituting a rare or first reference, are omitted. No attempt has been made to provide full citations for the common species quartz, baryte, galena, chalcopyrite and 'psilomelane'. In general, citations are limited to the earth sciences' press, although several early references are to county histories and the like that contained sections on geology, mineralogy, mining etc. Square brackets around a reference indicate that its relevance was inferred by later authors, the original paper not being specific about locality.

Previously unpublished reports are cited according to the source of the identification. Those by or for the present authors are cited as a collection name (. . . Coll.); those by other independent researchers or collectors are cited as personal communications (*pers. comm.*). Where known, such entries are followed by the establishment carrying out the determination (*det.*), the method used and the date. Abbreviations used here are those used elsewhere in the text: BGS—British Geological Survey; BM(NH)—British Museum (Natural History); UMIST—University of Manchester Institute of Science and Technology. Methods are: IR—Infra Red spectrophotometry; EPMA—Electron Probe Micro Analysis; XRD—X-Ray Diffraction.

Fig. 111 PLUMBOGUMMITE with PYROMORPHITE: Roughton Gill mine, 100 × 60 mm. A. W. G. Kingsbury inherited this fine specimen from the collection of his grandfather Thomas Kingsbury (1777–1854). It was collected about 1834 and thus probably originated in the higher reaches of the mine above the 30 fm level. Kingsbury Collection, BM(NH).

ARM O'GRAIN [NY 316 333]

Beudantite	D. R. Middleton Coll. (*det.* BM(NH): XRD, 1987)
Mimetite	D. R. Middleton Coll. (*det.* BM(NH): XRD, 1989)
Mottramite!	Young 1987
'psilomelane'	Day 1928
Pyrolusite	Day 1928
Pyromorphite-mimetite	R. E. Starkey Coll.
Quartz	
Wulfenite	C. M. Leppington Coll. (*det.* BM(NH): XRD, 1989)

BRAE FELL MINE [NY 2985 3565]

Anglesite!	Greg & Lettsom 1858; Hartley 1984
Baryte	Hartley 1984
Caledonite	Hartley 1984
Cerussite	Greg & Lettsom 1858; Hartley 1984
Chalcopyrite	Hartley 1984
Chrysocolla	Hartley 1984
Cuprite	C. M. Leppington Coll. (*det.* M. Rothwell: EPMA, 1988)
Galena	Eastwood 1921; Hartley 1984
Goethite	Kingsbury MS1
Hemimorphite	M. P. Cooper Coll. (*det.* UMIST: IR, 1987)
Hydrocerussite	Kingsbury & Hartley MS; Hartley 1984
Lanarkite!	Kingsbury & Hartley MS; Hartley 1984
Langite	C. M. Leppington Coll. (*det.* Leeds Univ.: XRD, 1988)
Leadhillite!	Hartley 1984
Linarite	Hartley 1984
Malachite	Eastwood 1921; Shaw 1970; Hartley 1984
Mattheddleite!	Cooper *et al.* 1988
Mimetite	Kingsbury MS1
Plumbogummite!	Kingsbury Coll. BM(NH) (Young 1987)
'psilomelane'	Hartley 1984
Pyromorphite! (pyromorphite-mimetite)	Eastwood 1921; Shaw 1970; Hartley 1984
Quartz	
Sphalerite	Hartley 1984

Susannite!	Kingsbury specimen BM(NH) (*det*. BM(NH): XRD, 1987)

BRANDY GILL LEAD MINE [NY 3225 3385]

Agardite	W. van den Berg specimen (*det*. BM(NH): XRD and EPMA, 1988)
Anglesite	[Goodchild 1875]; Hartley 1984
Ankerite	Claringbull 1951; Davidson & Thomson 1951
*Arseniosiderite	Kingsbury & Hartley 1957a; Hartley 1984
Arsenopyrite	Davidson & Thomson 1951; Hartley 1984
Baryte	Hartley 1984
Bayldonite!	Kingsbury & Hartley MS, 1956a; Hartley 1984
*Beaverite	Kingsbury & Hartley 1956a, 1957e; Hartley 1984
Beudantite	Kingsbury & Hartley MS, 1956a, 1957e, 1960; Hartley 1984
Brochantite	Hartley 1984
'calcio-duftite'	Kingsbury & Hartley MS [= calcian duftite?]
Caledonite	Hartley 1984
Carminite	Kingsbury & Hartley MS, 1957e, 1960; Hartley 1984
Cerussite	[Goodchild 1884]; Davidson & Thomson 1951; Hartley 1984
Chalcopyrite	Davidson & Thomson 1951; Hartley 1984
Chalcosine	Hartley 1984
Chenevixite	Hartley 1984
Chrysocolla	Hartley 1984
Conichalcite	Young 1987; (cf Kingsbury & Hartley MS)
Covelline	Hartley 1984
Cuprite	Hartley 1984
Descloizite	Kingsbury & Hartley 1956a; Hartley 1984
Devilline	Berg 1985 [perhaps an error, requires confirmation]
*Duftite	Claringbull 1951; Davidson & Thomson 1951; Kingsbury & Hartley MS; Guillemin 1956; Hartley 1984
Galena	Davidson & Thomson 1951; Hartley 1984
Goethite	Hartley 1984
*Hedyphane!	R. E. Starkey *pers. comm.* (*det*. BM(NH): XRD, 1985)
Hematite	Hartley 1984
Hisingerite	Hartley 1984
Jarosite	Kingsbury & Hartley 1958; Hartley 1984
Leadhillite-susannite	B. Yates Coll. (*det*. BM(NH): XRD, 1987)
Linarite	Davidson & Thomson 1951; Claringbull 1951; Hartley 1984
*Lindgrenite!!	Kingsbury & Hartley 1955; Hartley 1984
Malachite	Davidson & Thomson 1951; Hartley 1984
Mimetite!	[Greg & Lettsom 1858]; Davidson & Thomson 1951; Hartley 1984
Molybdenite	Davidson & Thomson 1951
Mottramite	Kingsbury & Hartley 1956a; Hartley 1984
Muscovite	Kingsbury MS1
Pitticite	Kingsbury & Hartley MS; Hartley 1984

Plumbogummite	Kingsbury & Hartley 1955; Hartley 1984
Plumbojarosite	Young 1987
'psilomelane'	Hartley 1984
Pyrite	Davidson & Thomson 1951; Hartley 1984
Pyromorphite	[Greg & Lettsom 1858]; Claringbull 1951; Davidson & Thomson 1951
Quartz	
Sphalerite	Hartley 1984
*Stolzite!!	Davidson & Thomson 1951; Claringbull 1951; Kingsbury & Hartley 1951, MS; Hartley 1984
Vanadinite	Kingsbury & Hartley 1956a; Hartley 1984
Wulfenite!	[Goodchild 1875]; Russell 1936; Kingsbury & Hartley MS, 1955; Hartley 1984

BURDELL GILL [NY 3075 3245]

Baryte	Young 1987
Beraunite	Hartley 1984 (Braunite, Young 1987: a misinterpretation of beraunite)
Beudantite	D. R. Middleton Coll. (*det*. BM(NH): XRD, 1987)
Cacoxenite	Hartley 1984
Dufrenite	Hartley 1984
Goethite	Hartley 1984
Jarosite	Kingsbury & Hartley 1958; Hartley 1984
Manganite	Greg & Lettsom 1858; Davidson & Thomson 1951
Mimetite	R. S. W. Braithwaite *pers. comm.* 1985 (*det*. UMIST: IR)
Pharmacosiderite!	Greg & Lettsom 1858; Goodchild 1885; Davidson & Thomson 1951; Kingsbury & Hartley 1958; Hartley 1984
'psilomelane'	Hartley 1984
Pyrolusite	Davidson & Thomson 1951
*Rockbridgeite	Kingsbury Coll. BM(NH) (Young 1987)
Scorodite	Hartley 1984
*Strengite	Hartley 1984
Tourmaline	Hartley 1984
Vivianite	Hartley 1984

CARROCK MINE [NY 323 330]

Including references to minerals characteristic of the deposit (e.g. bismuth, scheelite, molybdenite) but recorded as 'Brandy Gill', 'Carrock Fell' etc. before the mine was opened.

*Aikinite	Kingsbury & Hartley 1956b; Hartley 1984
Alunite	Kingsbury & Hartley 1958
Ankerite	Smythe & Dunham 1947; Davidson & Thomson 1951; Eastwood 1959; Eastwood *et al.* 1968; Beddoe-Stephens & Fortey 1981; Brown 1983; Hartley 1984
Apatite!!	Borie 1817; Phillips 1823; Lévy 1837; Greg & Lettsom 1858; Wright *in* Jenkinson 1875; Rudler 1905; Finlayson 1910; Day 1928; Davidson & Thomson 1951; Fortey 1978; etc.
Aragonite	Goodchild 1884; Davidson & Thomson 1951; Hartley 1984
Arseniosiderite	Kingsbury & Hartley 1957a; Hartley 1984

Arsenopyrite!	Greg & Lettsom 1858; Finlayson 1910; Dewey & Dines 1923; Davidson & Thomson 1951; Patrick 1980; etc.
Azurite	Kingsbury MS2; Young 1987
Baryte	Dewey & Dines 1923
Beryl	Kingsbury MS1; Hartley 1984
Bismite	Goodchild 1882 ('bismuth ochre'); Davidson & Thomson 1951
Bismuth	Tooke 1837; Greg & Lettsom 1858; Goodchild 1882; Hitchen 1934; Davidson & Thomson 1951; Hartley 1984
Bismuthinite!	Phillips 1823; Greg & Lettsom 1858; Goodchild 1882; Davidson & Thomson 1951; Hartley 1984
Bismutite	Goodchild 1882 ('bismuth ochre'); Hitchen 1934; Hartley 1984
Bornite	Davidson & Thomson 1951
*Boulangerite	Kingsbury & Hartley 1956b; Hartley 1984
Calcite	Davidson & Thomson 1951; Fortey 1978; Brown 1983; Hartley 1984
*Carpholite	Kingsbury & Hartley 1957c; Hartley 1984
Cassiterite	Kingsbury MS1; Hartley 1984; Young 1987
Chalcopyrite	Dewey & Dines 1923; Davidson & Thomson 1951; Kingsbury & Hartley 1956b; Fortey 1978; Brown 1983; Hartley 1984
Chalcosine	Davidson & Thomson 1951; Thimmaiah 1956; Hartley 1984
Chrysocolla	Davidson & Thomson 1951; Hartley 1984
Columbite	Beddoe-Stephens & Fortey 1981
Corundum	Greg & Lettsom 1858; Davidson & Thomson 1951
*Cosalite!	Thimmaiah 1956; Kingsbury & Hartley 1956b; Hartley 1984
Covelline	Thimmaiah 1956
Cubanite	Ewart 1957; Hartley 1984
Dolomite	[Smythe & Dunham 1947]; Davidson & Thomson 1951; Fortey 1978; Brown 1983
Epidote	Young 1987
feldspar	Greg & Lettsom 1858
Ferrimolybdite	Lévy 1837 ('acide molybdique jaune'); Greg & Lettsom 1858 ('molybdine'); Wright in Jenkinson 1875 ('molybdic ochre'); Hartley 1984
Fluorite	Rastall & Wilcockson 1915; Rastall 1942; Davidson & Thomson 1951; Fortey 1978; Stanley 1979; Hartley 1984
Galena	Finlayson 1910; Davidson & Thomson 1951; Kingsbury & Hartley 1956b; Hartley 1984
'gilbertite'	see muscovite
Gold	Dewey & Dines 1923; Kingsbury MS2; Shaw 1970; Hartley 1984
'grünlingite'	Muthmann & Schröder 1897; Garrido & Feo 1938; Peacock 1941; (= mixtures of josëite-A, bismuthinite, and ingodite: Zav'yalov & Begizov 1981a, b)
Gypsum	BM(NH) Coll. (Young 1987)
Hedleyite	BM(NH) Coll. (det. BM(NH): EPMA)
Hematite	Hartley 1984
*Hübnerite	Kingsbury 1958 (in Spencer 1958); (see also wolframite)
*Ingodite	Zav'yalov & Begizov 1981a
Jamesonite	Kingsbury & Hartley 1956b; Hartley 1984
Jarosite	Kingsbury & Hartley 1958; Hartley 1984
*Josëite-A!!	Peacock 1941; Davidson & Thomson 1951; Zav'yalov & Begizov 1981a, b; see also refs to tetradymite
Josëite-B	BM(NH) Coll. (det. BM(NH): EPMA)
Krupkaite	BM(NH) Coll. (det. BM(NH): EPMA)
Malachite	Davidson & Thomson 1951; Kingsbury MS2; Hartley 1984
Marcasite	Davidson & Thomson 1951; Brown 1983; Young 1987
Microcline	Hitchen 1934
Molybdenite!	Sowerby 1809; Lysons & Lysons 1816; Phillips 1819, 1823; Lévy 1837; Greg & Lettsom 1858; Finlayson 1910; Hitchen 1934; Fortey 1978 etc.
Muscovite	Greg & Lettsom 1858 (also as 'margarodite' and 'nacrite'); Finlayson 1910; Fortey 1978; etc.
Olivenite	Kingsbury & Hartley MS; Hartley 1984
Orthoclase	Fortey 1980; (see also feldspar)
Pharmacosiderite	T. F. Bridges (pers. comm. 1984)
*Powellite	Hartley 1984
Pyrite	Dewey & Dines 1923; Davidson & Thomson 1951; Kingsbury & Hartley 1956b; Patrick 1980; etc.
Pyromorphite	Dewey & Dines 1923
Pyrrhotine	Davidson & Thomson 1951; Fortey 1978; Patrick 1980; Hartley 1984
Quartz	Dewey & Dines 1923; Day 1928; Fortey 1978; etc.
Rutile	Fortey 1978; Hartley 1984
Scheelite!!	Phillips 1823; Lévy 1837; Tooke 1837; Greg & Lettsom 1858; Bauer 1871; Goodchild 1885; Hitchen 1934; Fortey 1978; Ball et al. 1985; etc.
Scorodite	Hitchen 1934; Davidson & Thomson 1951; Hartley 1984; Young 1987
Sphalerite	Dewey & Dines 1923; Hitchen 1934; Davidson & Thomson 1951; El Shazly et al. 1957; etc.
(Stilbite	Hartley 1984 = stibnite, Hartley pers. comm. 1988)
Stibnite	Greg & Lettsom 1858; Kingsbury & Hartley 1956b; Ewart 1957
Stolzite	Kingsbury & Hartley MS; Hartley 1984; Young 1987
Strengite	D. McCallum pers. comm. (det. BM(NH): XRD, 1985)
Sylvanite	W. Hemingway (letter in Cumbria Record Office DX/955/3v)
Tetradymite	Greg & Lettsom 1858; Goodchild 1882; Day 1928; etc. (the occurrence was suggested by Clarke 1974 but remains

unconfirmed; see josëite, 'grünlingite', ingodite etc.)

Tetrahedrite	Thimmaiah 1956; Ewart 1957
Tourmaline group	Dewey & Dines 1923; Davidson & Thomson 1951; Thimmaiah 1956; Fortey 1978; Hartley 1984
Tremolite	Davidson & Thomson 1951
Tungstite	Greg & Lettsom 1858 ('wolframine'); Goodchild 1884 (ditto); Rudler 1905; Finlayson 1910; Davidson & Thomson 1951; Hartley 1984; etc.
Uraninite	Dawson & Harrison 1966
Wolframite	Borie 1817; Phillips 1823; Greg & Lettsom 1858; Finlayson 1910; Fortey 1978; Beddoe-Stephens & Fortey 1981; Brown 1983; etc. (see also hübnerite)
*Zinckenite	Kingsbury & Hartley 1956b; Hartley 1984

'Material collected around an old cross-cut at, or near, the junction of the east–west lead veins with the Emerson vein at the foot of Brandy Gill' (Hartley 1984). The same species are also listed by Kingsbury (MS1).

Bayldonite	Kingsbury & Hartley MS; Hartley 1984
Beaverite	Hartley 1984
Beudantite	Kingsbury & Hartley 1960; Hartley 1984
Bismite	Hartley 1984
Cerussite	Hartley 1984
Galena	Hartley 1984
Hematite	Hartley 1984
Hydrocerussite	Kingsbury & Hartley MS; Hartley 1984
Linarite	Hartley 1984
Pyromorphite-Mimetite	Hartley 1984
Stolzite	Kingsbury & Hartley MS; Hartley 1984
Vanadinite	Kingsbury & Hartley 1956a; Hartley 1984
Wulfenite	Kingsbury & Hartley MS; Hartley 1984

CARROCK END MINE (QUEEN MINE) [NY 352 342]

Cerussite	Hartley 1984
Chalcopyrite	Dewey & Eastwood 1925; Davidson & Thomson 1951; Shaw 1970; etc.
Chrysocolla	Greg & Lettsom 1858; Davidson & Thomson 1951; Hartley 1984
Cuprite	Hartley 1984
Galena	Hartley 1984
Linarite	Hartley 1984
Malachite	Greg & Lettsom 1858; Goodchild 1884; Dewey & Eastwood 1925; Davidson & Thomson 1951; Shaw 1970; Hartley 1984
'psilomelane'	Hartley 1984
Pyromorphite	Hartley 1984

DEER HILLS [NY 3145 3626]

An old working on the Deer Hills Quartz vein outcrop.

Arsenopyrite	M. P. Cooper Coll.
Beudantite	N. Thomson pers. comm. (det. BM(NH): XRD, 1988)
Carminite	N. Thomson pers. comm. (det. BM(NH): XRD, 1988)
Pharmacosiderite	N. Thomson pers. comm. (det. BM(NH): XRD, 1988)
Scorodite	M. P. Cooper Coll. (det. UMIST: IR, 1987)

DEER HILLS BARYTE MINE

Adamite	M. P. Cooper Coll. (det. BM(NH): XRD, 1989)
Agardite	B. Young specimen (and others) (det. BM(NH): XRD, 1988, 1989)
Aurichalcite	M. P. Cooper Coll. (det. BM(NH): XRD, 1989)
Baryte	Shaw, 1970
Cuprite	Shaw, 1970
Quartz	

DRIGGITH MINE [NY 328 353]

Including outcrop workings on the Driggith–Sandbeds vein. (Old) Sandbeds mine is listed separately.

Adamite	D. R. Middleton Coll. (det. BM(NH): XRD, 1987)
Allophane	Hartley 1984
Anglesite	Davidson & Thomson 1951; Kingsbury 1957; Hartley 1984
Antimony	Stanley & Vaughan 1981
Arsenopyrite	Stanley & Vaughan 1981
Aurichalcite	Kingsbury & Hartley MS; Hartley 1984
Azurite	Thimmaiah 1956; Stanley & Vaughan 1981
Baryte	Eastwood 1921; Dunham & Dines 1945; Shaw 1970; Hartley 1984
Bayldonite	Kingsbury & Hartley MS; Hartley 1984
Beaverite	Kingsbury & Hartley MS, 1957e; Hartley 1984
Beudantite	Kingsbury & Hartley 1957e, 1960; Hartley 1984
Bindheimite	Young 1987
Bornite	Thimmaiah 1956
Bournonite	Stanley & Vaughan 1981
Brochantite	Davidson & Thomson 1951; Hartley 1984
Calcite	Thimmaiah 1956; Stanley 1979
Caledonite	Kingsbury Coll. BM(NH); Kingsbury MS4
Carminite	Kingsbury & Hartley MS, 1960; Hartley 1984
Cerussite	Greg & Lettsom 1858; Hall 1868; Davidson & Thomson 1951; Shaw 1970; Hartley 1984
Chalcopyrite	Eastwood 1921; Dewey & Eastwood 1925; Dunham & Hollingworth 1947; Shaw 1970; Hartley 1984; etc.
Chalcosine	Shaw 1970; Hartley 1984
Chlorargyrite	Hartley 1984
Chrysocolla	Davidson & Thomson 1951; Hartley 1984
Conichalcite	Kingsbury & Hartley MS; Hartley 1984
Copper	Stanley & Vaughan 1981
Covelline	Thimmaiah 1956; Stanley & Vaughan 1981; Hartley 1984
Cuprite	Kingsbury MS1
Devilline	Hartley 1984

Djurleite	Stanley & Vaughan 1981
Duftite	Kingsbury & Hartley MS; Hartley 1984
Galena	Dunham & Hollingworth 1947; Davidson & Thomson 1951; Kingsbury 1957; Stanley & Vaughan 1981; etc.
Goethite	Stanley & Vaughan 1981; Hartley 1984
Hemimorphite	Hartley 1984
Hydrocerussite	Kingsbury & Hartley MS; Hartley 1984
Jarosite	Hartley 1984
Leadhillite	Hartley 1984
Linarite!	Hartley 1984
Malachite	Eastwood 1921; Day 1928; Davidson & Thomson 1951; Stanley & Vaughan 1981; Hartley 1984
Mimetite!!	Young 1987
Phosgenite	Kingsbury 1957
Plumbojarosite	Kingsbury & Hartley 1957e; Hartley 1984
*Planchéite	Kingsbury specimens BM(NH) (Young 1987)
Pseudomalachite	Hartley 1984
'psilomelane'	Davidson & Thomson 1951; Stanley & Vaughan 1981; Hartley 1984
Pyrite	Stanley & Vaughan 1981
Pyrolusite	Davidson & Thomson 1951; Stanley 1979
Pyromorphite!!	Greg & Lettsom 1858; Dunham & Hollingworth 1947; Davidson & Thomson 1951; Shaw 1970; Hartley 1984
Quartz	
Rosasite	Kingsbury & Hartley 1957b
*Serpierite	Kingsbury & Hartley MS, 1957d; Hartley 1984
Silver	D. R. Middleton pers. comm. 1986
Smithsonite	Hartley 1984
Sphalerite	Eastwood 1921; Dunham & Hollingworth 1947; Shaw 1970; Stanley & Vaughan 1981; etc.
Tennantite	Kingsbury MS1; Hartley 1984 (tetrahedrite-tennantite)
Tetrahedrite	Stanley & Vaughan 1981; Hartley 1984 (tetrahedrite-tennantite)
Turquoise	Hartley 1984
Wulfenite	Kingsbury & Hartley MS; Hartley 1984

DRY GILL MINE [NY 324 345]

Anglesite	Young 1987
Azurite	Kingsbury & Hartley 1960; Hartley 1984
Baryte	Greg & Lettsom 1858; Eastwood 1921; Davidson & Thomson 1951
Beudantite	Kingsbury & Hartley 1960; Hartley 1984
Calcite	Hall 1868; Hartley 1984
'campylite'!!!	Breithaupt 1841 (var. of mimetite q.v.)
Cerussite	Hartley 1984
*Coronadite	Hartley 1959; Hartley 1984
Galena	Eastwood 1921; Shaw 1970
Malachite	Hartley 1984
Mimetite!!!	[Allan in Phillips 1837]; Breithaupt 1841; Wright in Sowerby 1850; Dana 1850; Greg & Lettsom 1858; Goodchild 1885;

	Rudler 1905; Davidson & Thomson 1951; Newby 1981; Hochleitner 1984; etc.
Olivenite	Kingsbury & Hartley MS, 1960; Hartley 1984
Pharmacosiderite	Davidson & Thomson 1951
Plumbogummite!!	Palache et al. 1951; Berg 1985; Young 1987
'psilomelane'	Greg & Lettsom 1858; Goodchild 1882; Eastwood 1921; etc.
Pyrolusite	Goodchild 1885
Pyromorphite!!	Eastwood 1921; Davidson & Thomson 1951; El Shazly et al. 1957
Quartz	
Romanèchite	see 'psilomelane'
Sphalerite	Eastwood 1921; Wilson et al. 1922

HAY GILL COPPER MINE [NY 308 360]

Atacamite!	Kingsbury & Hartley 1956c; Hartley 1984
Brochantite	Hartley 1984
Calcite	Hartley 1984
Chalcopyrite	Greg & Lettsom 1858; Dewey & Eastwood 1925; Hartley 1984
Chrysocolla	Hartley 1984
Cuprite	Hartley 1984
Malachite	Greg & Lettsom 1858; Goodchild 1884; Davidson & Thomson 1951; Hartley 1984
'psilomelane'	Day 1928; Hartley 1984
Pyrite	Hartley 1984
Tenorite	Greg & Lettsom 1858 ('melaconite'); Goodchild 1882

INGRAY GILL North level [NY 307 367]

Arseniosiderite	Kingsbury & Hartley 1957a; Hartley 1984
Arsenopyrite	Hartley 1984
Baryte	Hartley 1984
Bayldonite	Kingsbury MS1
Beaverite	Kingsbury & Hartley 1957e; Hartley 1984
Beudantite	Kingsbury & Hartley 1960; Hartley 1984
Carminite	Kingsbury & Hartley 1960; Hartley 1984
Cerussite	Hartley 1984
Chalcopyrite	Hartley 1984
Chrysocolla	Hartley 1984
Erythrite	Kingsbury & Hartley 1957a; Hartley 1984
Galena	Dunham & Dines 1945; Kingsbury & Hartley 1957e, 1960; Hartley 1984
Gold	Kingsbury MS2; Young 1987
Hemimorphite	Hartley 1984
Jarosite	Kingsbury & Hartley 1958; Hartley 1984
Linarite	Hartley 1984
Malachite	Hartley 1984
Olivenite	Kingsbury MS1, MS2
Pharmacosiderite	Kingsbury & Hartley 1957a, 1960; Hartley 1984
'psilomelane'	Hartley 1984
Pyrolusite	Kingsbury MS1

Pyromorphite-mimetite	Hartley 1984
Quartz	Dunham & Dines 1945
Scorodite	Kingsbury & Hartley 1957a, 1960; Hartley 1984
Vanadinite	Kingsbury MS1
Wulfenite	Hartley 1984

LOW PIKE [NY 320 358]

Trial on the Low Pike vein

Baryte	Dunham & Dines 1945
Bayldonite	M. P. Cooper Coll. (det. UMIST: IR, 1987)
Beudantite	M. P. Cooper Coll. (det. BM(NH): XRD, 1987)
Brochantite	D. I. Green pers. comm. (det. Leeds Univ.: XRD, 1987)
Chalcopyrite	M. P. Cooper Coll.
Cornwallite!	D. R. Middleton Coll. (det. BM(NH): XRD, 1986); M. P. Cooper Coll. (det. UMIST: IR, 1987)
Duftite	B. Young pers. comm. (det. BGS: XRD)
Kipushite?	Braithwaite & Ryback 1988 [doubtful]
Malachite	D. I. Green pers comm. (det. Leeds Univ.: XRD)
Mimetite	M. P. Cooper Coll. (det. UMIST: IR, 1987); B. Young pers. comm. (det. BGS: XRD)
Mottramite	N. Thomson pers. comm. (det. BM(NH): XRD)
Philipsburgite!	M. P. Cooper Coll. (det. UMIST: IR, Braithwaite & Ryback 1988); (also det. BM(NH): XRD, 1987)
Pseudomalachite	M. P. Cooper Coll. (det. UMIST: IR, 1987)
Pyromorphite-mimetite	M. P. Cooper Coll. (det. UMIST: IR, 1987)
Quartz	Dunham & Dines 1945

MEXICO MINE [NY 305 345]

Anglesite	Greg & Lettsom 1858; Bristow 1861
Bindheimite	M. P. Cooper Coll. (det. Leicester Univ.: XRD, 1988)
Brochantite	Kingsbury MS2; Hartley 1984
Chalcopyrite	Kingsbury MS2
Chalcosine	Berg 1985
Cerussite	Greg & Lettsom 1858; Kingsbury MS2
*Corkite!!	D. Middleton, M. Wirth pers. comms. (det. BM(NH) and RSM: XRD, 1978)
Cuprite	Shaw 1970
Galena	Shaw 1970
Goethite	D. R. Middleton pers. comm.
Gold	Kingsbury MS2; Young 1987
Langite	R. S. W. Braithwaite pers. comm. (det. UMIST: IR)
Linarite	Greg & Lettsom 1858; Bristow 1861; Hall 1868
Malachite	Greg & Lettsom 1858; Hartley 1984
Mimetite!!	Greg & Lettsom 1858; Wright in Jenkinson 1875; Berg 1985

Plumbogummite!	Kingsbury & Hartley MS; Hartley 1984; Young 1987
'psilomelane'	Hartley 1984
Pyromorphite!!!	Greg & Lettsom 1858; Wright 1875; Shaw 1970; Hartley 1984; Berg 1985
Tenorite?	Shaw 1970 ('grey oxide of copper')
Wulfenite	D. R. Middleton Coll., M. P. Cooper Coll. (det. BM(NH): XRD, 1989)

NETHER ROW BROW

NETHER ROW FARM LEVEL [NY 3230 3705]

Arseniosiderite	Kingsbury & Hartley 1960
Arsenopyrite	Kingsbury & Hartley 1956a, 1960; Hartley 1984
Beaverite	Kingsbury & Hartley 1956a, 1957e, 1960; Hartley 1984
Beudantite	Kingsbury & Hartley 1956a, 1957e, 1960; Hartley 1984
Boulangerite	B. Young pers. comm. (det. BGS and BM(NH): XRD, 1988)
Bournonite	B. Young pers. comm. (det. BGS and BM(NH): XRD, 1988)
Carminite	Kingsbury & Hartley 1960; Hartley 1984
Cerussite	Kingsbury & Hartley 1956a; Hartley 1984
Chalcopyrite	Kingsbury & Hartley 1956a, 1960
Galena	Kingsbury & Hartley 1956a, 1960; Hartley 1984
Jamesonite	B. Young pers. comm. (det. BGS: XRD)
Jarosite	Kingsbury & Hartley 1958; Hartley 1984
Mimetite	Kingsbury & Hartley 1960; Hartley 1984
Mottramite	Kingsbury & Hartley 1956a, 1960; Hartley 1984
Pharmacosiderite	Kingsbury & Hartley 1960; Hartley 1984
Plumbogummite	Hartley 1984
Plumbojarosite	Kingsbury & Hartley 1957e, 1960; Hartley 1984
Pyrite	Kingsbury & Hartley 1956a, 1960; Hartley 1984
Quartz	
Scorodite	Kingsbury & Hartley 1960; Hartley 1984
Sphalerite	Kingsbury & Hartley 1956a, 1960; Hartley 1984
Symplesite-metavivianite	B. Young pers. comm. (det. BM(NH): XRD)
Tetrahedrite	M. P. Cooper Coll. (det. BM(NH): XRD, 1987; also det. BGS: XRD, B. Young pers. comm.)

NETHER ROW BROW

'DUMPY STONE' LEVEL [NY 327 364]

Adamite	Hartley 1984
Arseniosiderite	Kingsbury & Hartley 1957a; Hartley 1984
Arsenopyrite	Hartley 1984
Baryte	Hartley 1984
Beaverite	Kingsbury & Hartley 1957e, 1960; Hartley 1984
Beudantite	Kingsbury & Hartley 1957e, 1960; Hartley 1984

Carminite	Kingsbury & Hartley 1960
Galena	Hartley 1984
Jarosite	Kingsbury & Hartley 1958
Quartz	
Pharmacosiderite	R. S. W. Braithwaite *pers. comm.* (*det.* UMIST: IR)
Scorodite	Kingsbury & Hartley 1960; Hartley 1984
Sphalerite	Hartley 1984

PODDY GILL [NY 328 328]
Trial on E–W lead vein

Bayldonite	Kingsbury & Hartley MS; Hartley 1984
Cerussite	Davidson & Thomson 1951; Hartley 1984
Crocoite	Kingsbury Coll., BM(NH) (*det.* BM(NH): XRD, 1987) [requires confirmation]
Galena	Davidson & Thomson 1951; Hartley 1984
Hydrocerussite	Hartley 1984
Linarite	Hartley 1984
Pyromorphite	Davidson & Thomson 1951; Hartley 1984
Quartz	
Stolzite	M. Rothwell Coll. (*det.* EPMA, 1988, M. Rothwell *pers. comm.*); also N. Hubbard Coll. (*det.* BM(NH): EPMA and XRD, 1988)
Wulfenite	Davidson & Thomson 1951; Braithwaite *et al.* 1963

OLD POTTS GILL MINE [NY 320 366]

Adamite	Hartley 1984
Allophane	Kingsbury MS1
Anglesite	Hartley 1984
Ankerite	Shaw 1970; Hartley 1984
Antlerite	Kingsbury & Hartley MS; Hartley 1984
Arsenopyrite	Kingsbury & Hartley 1960; Shaw 1970; Hartley 1984
Atacamite	Kingsbury & Hartley MS, 1956c; Hartley 1984
Aurichalcite	Kingsbury & Hartley MS, 1957d; Hartley 1984
Azurite	Shaw 1970; Hartley 1984; Young 1987
Baryte	Greg & Lettsom 1858; Wilson *et al.* 1922; Dunham & Dines 1945; Davidson & Thomson 1951; Shaw 1970; etc.
Bayldonite	Kingsbury & Hartley MS; Hartley 1984; Young 1987
Beaverite	Kingsbury & Hartley 1957e; Hartley 1984
Beudantite	Kingsbury & Hartley 1960; Hartley 1984
Bornite	Hartley 1984
Breithauptite	Kingsbury Coll., BM(NH); Kingsbury MS1
Brochantite	Davidson & Thomson 1951; Kingsbury & Hartley MS, 1957e; Hartley 1984
Calcite	Kingsbury & Hartley 1956a; Hartley 1984
Carminite	Kingsbury & Hartley 1960; Hartley 1984
Chalcophyllite	Hartley 1984
Chalcopyrite	Kingsbury & Hartley 1960; Shaw 1970; Hartley 1984

Chalcosine	Kingsbury & Hartley MS; Hartley 1984
Chrysocolla	Davidson & Thomson 1951; Shaw 1970; Hartley 1984
*Conichalcite	Kingsbury & Hartley MS; Hartley 1984
Connellite	Kingsbury MS1 [requires confirmation]
Cornubite	Claringbull *et al.* 1959
Cornwallite	Kingsbury & Hartley MS; Claringbull *et al.* 1959; Shaw 1970; Hartley 1984
Covelline	Kingsbury MS1
Cuprite	Hartley 1984
Cyanotrichite	Hartley 1984
Descloizite	N. Thomson *pers. comm.* (*det.* BM(NH): XRD, 1989)
*Dioptase	Hartley 1984
Dolomite	Hartley 1984
Duftite	N. Thomson *pers. comm.* (*det.* BM(NH): XRD, 1989)
Galena	Kingsbury & Hartley 1960; Shaw 1970; Hartley 1984
Goethite	Kingsbury & Hartley 1960; Hartley 1984
Hematite	Hartley 1984
*Hinsdalite	Hartley 1984
Hydrozincite	Kingsbury MS1
Jarosite	Kingsbury & Hartley 1958
Libethenite	Kingsbury & Hartley MS; Hartley 1984; Young 1987
Linarite	BM(NH) (Young 1987)
Liroconite	Kingsbury MS1
Löllingite	Kingsbury & Hartley 1960; Hartley 1984
Malachite	Davidson & Thomson 1951; Kingsbury & Hartley 1957d; Shaw 1970; Hartley 1984
Marcasite	Davidson & Thomson 1951
Olivenite	Kingsbury & Hartley MS; Hartley 1984
Palygorskite	Shaw 1970 ('mountain leather')
Pharmacosiderite	Kingsbury & Hartley 1960; Hartley 1984
*Philipsburgite	Braithwaite & Ryback 1988
Plumbogummite	Hartley 1984
Prehnite	Kingsbury Coll., BM(NH) [doubtful]
Pseudomalachite	Kingsbury & Hartley MS; Hartley 1984; Young 1987
'psilomelane'	Davidson & Thomson 1951; Shaw 1970; Hartley 1984
Pyrolusite	Shaw 1970
Pyromorphite-mimetite	Hartley 1984
Quartz	
Rosasite	Kingsbury & Hartley 1957b; Hartley 1984
Scorodite	Kingsbury & Hartley 1960
*Serpierite	Kingsbury & Hartley 1957d; Hartley 1984
Smithsonite	Kingsbury & Hartley 1957d; Hartley 1984; Young 1987
Sphalerite	Kingsbury & Hartley 1960; Shaw 1970; Hartley 1984
Strontianite	Kingsbury Coll., BM(NH) (Young 1987)
Tennantite	Hartley 1984
Tenorite	Davidson & Thomson 1951; Shaw 1970
Tyrolite	Hartley 1984; Young 1987

Vanadinite	Kingsbury & Hartley 1956a; Hartley 1984
Witherite	Shaw 1970; Hartley 1984

POTTS GILL COPPER MINE [NY 318 370]

Chalcopyrite	Shaw 1970; Hartley 1984
Hematite	Hartley 1984
Malachite	Hartley 1984
Pyrite	Hartley 1984

RED GILL MINE [NY 2950 3478]

Anglesite!	Greg & Lettsom 1858; Goodchild 1885; Rudler 1905; Davidson & Thomson 1951
Baryte	Eastwood 1921; Wilson et al. 1922
Brochantite	Davidson & Thomson 1951
Calcite	M. P. Cooper Coll.
Caledonite!!!	Greg & Lettsom 1858; Hessenberg 1870; Goodchild 1885; Davidson & Thomson 1951; etc.
Cerussite	Greg & Lettsom 1858; Davidson & Thomson 1951; etc.
Chalcopyrite	Davidson & Thomson 1951; Shaw 1970; etc.
Chalcosine	Kendall 1884
Chrysocolla	Greg & Lettsom 1858; Davidson & Thomson 1951; etc.
Cuprite	Berg 1985
Digenite	Davidson & Thomson 1951
Elyite	Briscoe 1986
Galena	Eastwood 1921; Davidson & Thomson 1951
Gold	Sweet 1960; Kingsbury MS2; Young 1987
Hemimorphite	Berg 1985
Hydrocerussite	Kingsbury & Hartley MS; Hartley 1984
Lanarkite	Cooper et al. 1988
Langite	D. I. Green pers. comm. (det. Leeds Univ.: XRD)
Leadhillite!!	Greg & Lettsom 1858; Goodchild 1885; Davidson & Thomson 1951; Harley 1984; etc.
Linarite!!!	Greg & Lettsom 1858; Hessenberg 1864; Koksharov 1869a, b; Cesàro 1905; Davidson & Thomson 1951; etc.
Macphersonite	Cooper et al. 1988
Malachite	Greg & Lettsom 1858; Miers 1897; Davidson & Thomson 1951; etc.
Mattheddleite!!	Cooper et al. 1988; Wirth 1989
Mimetite	Kendall 1884; D. I. Green pers. comm. (det. Leeds Univ.: XRD, 1988)
Plumbogummite	Berg 1985 [an error for ?chrysocolla]
'psilomelane'	Hartley 1984
Pyromorphite	Kendall 1884; Davidson & Thomson 1951; Hartley 1984
Quartz	
*Queitite!!	Braithwaite et al. 1989
Serpierite	P. Braithwaite Coll. (det. BM(NH): XRD, 1989)
Silver	M. Wirth pers. comm. (det. BM(NH): XRD; M. Rothwell: EPMA, 1988)
Sphalerite	Berg 1985

Susannite!	M. Wirth pers. comm. (det. BM(NH): XRD, 1987)
Wroewolfeite	D. I. Green pers. comm. (det. Leeds Univ.: XRD, 1987)
Unknown copper sulphate	P. Braithwaite Coll. (det. BM(NH): XRD, 1987)

ROUGHTON GILL MINE [NY 302 344]

combining records from all workings in Roughton Gill proper. Silver Gill and the Mexico Mine are listed separately.

Anglesite!	Greg & Lettsom 1858; Goodchild 1885; Day 1928; Davidson & Thomson 1951; Hartley 1984
Aragonite	Goodchild 1884; Davidson & Thomson 1951
*Atacamite	Bannister et al. 1950, [cf. Kingsbury & Hartley 1956c]
Aurichalcite	Greg & Lettsom 1858; Rudler 1905; Day 1928; Davidson & Thomson 1951; Hartley 1984
Azurite	Hartley 1984; Young 1987
Baryte	Greg & Lettsom 1858; Carruthers et al. 1915; Eastwood 1921; Wilson et al. 1922; Davidson & Thomson 1951; etc.
Beaverite	Kingsbury & Hartley MS, 1957e; Hartley 1984
Beudantite	Kingsbury & Hartley MS, 1958, 1960; Hartley 1984
Bindheimite	Hartley 1984
Bornite	Young 1987
Bournonite	Kingsbury MS1
'brewsterite'	Hall 1868; Branston 1910; Postlethwaite 1913; [= cuprite? Not the brewsterite of Brooke? cf. Young 1987]
Brochantite!	[Wright in Sowerby 1850]; Dana 1854; Greg & Lettsom 1858; Goodchild 1885; Rudler 1905; Davidson & Thomson 1951; Hartley 1984
Calcite	Melmore 1920; Eastwood 1921; Dewey & Eastwood 1925; Davidson & Thomson 1951
Caledonite!	[Wright in Sowerby 1850]; Bristow, 1861; Hall 1868; Goodchild 1885; Davidson & Thomson 1951; Hartley 1984
Carminite	Kingsbury & Hartley MS, 1960; Hartley 1984
Cerussite!	Greg & Lettsom 1858; Rudler 1905; Davidson & Thomson 1951; Hartley 1984
Chalcopyrite	Greg & Lettsom 1858; Dewey & Eastwood 1925; Davidson & Thomson 1951; etc.
Chalcosine	Kendall 1884
Chrysocolla	Greg & Lettsom 1858; Miers 1897; Rudler 1905; Davidson & Thomson 1951; Hartley 1984
Covelline	Hartley 1984
Cuprite	(see 'brewsterite')
Dolomite	Day 1928; Davidson & Thomson 1951
Erythrite	Young 1987
Galena	

Goethite | Davidson & Thomson 1951
Gold | Kingsbury MS2; Young 1987
Hematite | Davidson & Thomson 1951
Hemimorphite!!! | Greg & Lettsom 1858; Goodchild 1885; Davidson & Thomson 1951; Hartley 1984
Hidalgoite? | Förtsch 1967
Hinsdalite? | Förtsch 1967
Hydrocerussite | Kingsbury & Hartley MS; Hartley 1984
Jarosite | Kingsbury & Hartley 1958; Hartley 1984
Lanarkite! | Hartley 1984
Leadhillite! | Goodchild 1885; Hartley 1984
Linarite!! | Dana 1850; [Wright *in* Sowerby 1850]; Greg & Lettsom 1858; Goodchild 1885; Day 1928; Davidson & Thomson 1951; Hartley 1984
Malachite!! | Greg & Lettsom 1858; Goodchild 1884; Davidson & Thomson 1951; Shaw 1970; Hartley 1984
Mattheddleite! | Cooper *et al.* 1988
Mimetite!!! | Wright *in* Sowerby 1850; Greg & Lettsom 1858; Hall 1868
Mottramite | D. R. Middleton Coll. 1986, N. Thomson Coll. 1988 (*det.* BM(NH): XRD)
Olivenite | Kendall 1884 ('olivienite') [doubtful]
*Parahopeite | Hartley 1984
*Plumbogummite!!! | Blum 1843 ('kiesel zinc'); 'plumboresinite' or 'hitchcockite': Dana 1850; Miers 1897, 1900; Hartley 1900; Prior 1900; Rudler 1905; plumbogummite: Kingsbury & Hartley MS; Davidson & Thomson 1951; Förtsch 1967; Hartley 1984
Plumbojarosite | Kingsbury & Hartley 1960; Hartley 1984
'psilomelane' | Day 1928; Davidson & Thomson 1951; Hartley 1984
Pyromorphite!!! | Greg & Lettsom 1858; Goodchild 1885; Day 1928; Davidson & Thomson 1951; El Shazly *et al.* 1957; Cockbain 1968; Newby 1981; Hartley 1984; etc.
Quartz |
Rosasite! | Kingsbury & Hartley 1957*b*
Scotlandite! | D. I. Green *pers. comm.* (*det.* Leeds Univ.: XRD, 1988)
Smithsonite | Greg & Lettsom 1858 [= plumbogummite]; Goodchild 1884 [ditto]; Davidson and Thomson 1951
Sphalerite | Eastwood 1921; Davidson & Thomson 1951; Hartley 1984
Susannite | Ludlam Coll. BM(NH) (*det.* BM(NH): XRD, 1988)
Tenorite | Greg & Lettsom 1858 ('melaconite'); Goodchild 1882 (ditto); Day 1928
Tetrahedrite-Tennantite | Hartley 1984
*Tsumebite | [Embrey 1977*b*]; Moffitt 1979
*Unknown copper calcium phosphate | J. Dickinson Coll. (*det.* BM(NH): XRD; Leeds Univ.: XRD; M. Rothwell: EPMA)

(OLD) SANDBEDS MINE [NY 332 636]

i.e. the Sandbeds levels on the Driggith–Sandbeds vein

*Adamite | Kingsbury & Hartley MS; [Spencer 1958]; Hartley 1984; Young 1987
Anglesite | Hartley 1984
(Antlerite | R. J. King Coll. (NMW) (Young 1987) [misidentified, = malachite, *det.* NMW; XRD, 1989])
Aurichalcite | Kingsbury & Hartley 1951; Hartley 1984
Azurite | Hartley 1984
Baryte | Eastwood 1921; Wilson *et al.* 1922; Shaw 1970; Hartley 1984
Bayldonite | Davidson & Thomson 1951; Kingsbury & Hartley 1951; Claringbull 1951; Hartley 1984
Brochantite | Hartley 1984
Caledonite | Davidon & Thomson 1951; Hartley 1984
Carminite | J. G. Wilson *pers. comm.*
Cerussite | Hartley 1984
Chalcopyrite | Eastwood 1921; Hartley 1984
Chrysocolla | Hartley 1984
Cornwallite | R. J. King Coll. (NMW) (Young 1987)
Devilline | Hartley 1984
Galena | Wilson *et al.* 1922; Davidson & Thomson 1951; Hartley 1984
Goethite | Hartley 1984
Hematite | Hartley 1984
Hemimorphite | Davidson & Thomson 1951; Hartley 1984; Young 1987
Hydrocerussite | Kingsbury & Hartley MS; Hartley 1984
Hydrozincite | Young 1987
Leadhillite | Hartley 1984
Linarite | Davidson & Thomson 1951; Hartley 1984; Young 1987
Malachite | Eastwood 1921; Day 1928; Davidson & Thomson 1951; Hartley 1984
Plumbogummite | Kingsbury Coll., BM(NH)
Pseudomalachite | Kingsbury & Hartley MS; Hartley 1984
'psilomelane' | Eastwood 1921; Hartley 1984
Pyrite | Hartley 1984
Pyromorphite! | Eastwood 1921; Davidson & Thomson 1951; Hartley 1984
Quartz |
Rosasite | Kingsbury & Hartley 1957*b*; Hartley 1984
Smithsonite | Day 1928; Davidson & Thomson 1951; Hartley 1984
Sphalerite | Wright, *in* Sowerby 1850; Greg & Lettsom 1858; Eastwood 1921; Davidson & Thomson 1951; Hartley 1984

SHORT GRAIN [NY 3130 3585]

Baryte trial in north bank

Specimens in M. P. Cooper Coll.

Anglesite |
Baryte |
Caledonite | D. I. Green *pers. comm.* (*det.* Leeds Univ.: XRD, 1987)

Cerussite	det. Leeds Univ.: XRD (D. I. Green pers. comm.)
Chalcopyrite	
Galena	
Linarite	
Mattheddleite	(det. BM(NH): XRD, 1987)
Pyromorphite-mimetite	
Susannite	(det. BM(NH): XRD, 1987)

SILVER GILL

A collation of all reported species from the various workings in Silver Gill, including material recently identified from an old ore pile in the west bank of the gill at [NY 2995 3415]. For details see text.

Anglesite	M. P. Cooper Coll.
Brochantite	D. I. Green pers. comm. (det. Leeds Univ.: XRD, 1989)
Calcite	Shaw 1970
Caledonite	D. R. Middleton pers. comm.
Cerussite	Davidson & Thomson 1951
Chalcopyrite	Hartley 1984
Chrysocolla	Hartley 1984
Covelline	Hartley 1984; Young 1987
Cuprite	M. Rothwell pers. comm. (det. EPMA)
Galena	Shaw 1970; Hartley 1984
Hemimorphite	Hartley 1984
Langite	D. I. Green pers. comm. (det. Leeds Univ.: XRD, 1988)
Linarite	Davidson & Thomson 1951; Hartley 1984
Malachite	Davidson & Thomson 1951; Hartley 1984
Posnjakite	B. Young specimen (det. BM(NH): XRD, 1988)
'psilomelane'	Hartley 1984
Pyrite	Greg & Lettsom 1858
Pyromorphite	Hartley 1984
Quartz	
Rosasite	Kingsbury & Hartley 1957b; Hartley 1984
Smithsonite	Hartley 1984
Sphalerite	Hartley 1984
Wroewolfeite	D. I. Green pers. comm. (det. Leeds Univ.: XRD, 1988)
Wulfenite	P. Braithwaite Coll. (det. BM(NH): XRD, 1989)
unknown copper sulphate	D. R. Middleton Coll. (det. BM(NH): XRD, 1987)

WET SWINE GILL 'ANTIMONY VEIN' [NY 3144 3215] from Fortey et al. 1984

Antimony
Arsenopyrite
Berthierite
Bindheimite
*Fülöppite
Jamesonite
Kermesite?
Quartz
Semseyite
Senarmontite
Sphalerite
Stibiconite
Stibnite
Sulphur
Zinckenite

APPENDIX 2

To compensate for the bias in favour of the vein minerals in the text we give here a list of the minerals recorded from the country rocks together with the major references for each species. For more information the reader is referred to the glossary by Young (1987) which attempts to give equal status to all minerals reported from the Lake District, and which contains a fuller bibliography for the species below.

Actinolite	Carrock Fell gabbro	Harker 1894, 1895
	Carrock mine	Fortey 1978
Albite	Carrock Fell gabbro	Eastwood *et al.* 1968;
	Carrock Fell granophyre	Holmes 1917
	Skiddaw granite	Eastwood *et al.* 1968
Almandine	Carrock Fell hornfels	Eastwood *et al.* 1968
Amphibole group	[see individual minerals]	
Anatase	Skiddaw granite	Rastall & Wilcockson 1917
Andalusite	Skiddaw metasediments	Rastall 1910
	Skiddaw Granite	Rastall & Wilcockson 1917
Andesine	Roughton Gill area	Eastwood *et al.* 1968
Andradite	Carrock Fell	BM(NH) specimen (Young 1987)
Anorthoclase	Carrock Fell hornfels	Eastwood *et al.* 1968
	Harestones felsite	Eastwood *et al.* 1968
Apatite	Carrock Fell gabbro	Harker 1894
	Carrock Fell granophyre	Harker 1895
	Carrock Fell dolerites	Eastwood *et al.* 1968
	Grainsgill greisen	Eastwood *et al.* 1968
	Roughton Gill area	Eastwood *et al.* 1968
	Skiddaw granite	Rastall & Wilcockson 1915; Eastwood *et al.* 1968
Augite	Carrock Fell granophyre	Harker 1895
	Carrock Fell diabase	Eastwood *et al.* 1968
	Carrock Fell gabbro	Eastwood *et al.* 1968
	Carrock Fell dolerites	Eastwood *et al.* 1968
Biotite	Carrock Fell gabbro	Harker 1894; Eastwood *et al.* 1968
	Carrock Fell granophyre	Eastwood *et al.* 1968
	Carrock Fell hornfels	Eastwood *et al.* 1968
	Carrock mine	Fortey 1978
	Skiddaw granite	Rastall 1910
Brookite	Skiddaw granite	Rastall & Wilcockson 1915
Calcite	Carrock Fell	Melmore 1920
Chlorite	widespread	
Chloritoid	Carrock Fell hornfels	Eastwood *et al.* 1968
Chromite	Carrock Fell gabbro	Eastwood *et al.* 1968
Clinochlore	Grainsgill	Roberts 1983
Cordierite	Carrock mine	Stanley 1979; Roberts 1983
	Skiddaw hornfels	Eastwood *et al.* 1968
Corundum	Carrock Fell	Greg & Lettsom 1858; Davidson & Thomson, 1951

Enstatite	Carrock Fell gabbro	Harker 1895; Eastwood *et al.* 1968
Epidote	Carrock Fell	Eastwood *et al.* 1968
	Grainsgill greisen	Rastall & Wilcockson 1915; Firman 1978*a*
	Grainsgill	Rastall 1910
	Skiddaw granite	Rastall & Wilcockson 1915
Feldspar group	[see individual minerals]	
Garnet group	[see individual minerals]	
Grossular	Carrock Fell	BM(NH) specimen (Young 1987)
Hedenbergite	Carrock Fell gabbro	Eastwood *et al.* 1968
Hematite	Carrock Fell	Thimmaiah 1956
Hornblende	Carrock Fell diabase	Goodchild 1885; Eastwood *et al.* 1968
	Carrock Fell gabbro	Harker 1894, 1895; Eastwood *et al.* 1968
	Carrock Fell granophyre	Eastwood *et al.* 1968
Hypersthene	Carrock Fell gabbro	Goodchild 1885; Harker 1894; Eastwood *et al.* 1968
Illite	Carrock mine, Driggith mine, Potts Gill mine, Roughton Gill mine, Sandbeds mine	Ineson & Mitchell 1974
Ilmenite	Carrock Fell diabase	Eastwood *et al.* 1968
	Carrock Fell gabbro	Harker 1894; Eastwood *et al.* 1968
	Skiddaw granite	Rastall & Wilcockson 1915; Eastwood *et al.* 1968
Kaolinite	China Clay mine	Day 1928; Shaw 1970; Young 1987
	Skiddaw granite	Hitchen 1934
Labradorite	Carrock area gabbro	Fortey 1978
	Carrock Fell dolerite	Eastwood *et al.* 1968
Magnetite	Carrock Fell gabbro	Harker 1894; Melmore 1920; Eastwood *et al.* 1968
	Carrock Fell granophyre	Harker 1895
	Skiddaw granite	Eastwood *et al.* 1968
Microcline	Skiddaw granite	Fortey 1978
Muscovite	Skiddaw granite	Rastall 1910; Hitchen 1934
	Grainsgill greisen	Fortey 1978; Roberts 1983
Oligoclase	Carrock Fell hornfels	Eastwood *et al.* 1968
	Carrock Fell granophyre	Harker 1895
	Skiddaw granite	Rastall 1910; Eastwood *et al.* 1968
Orthoclase	Carrock Fell granophyre	Harker 1895
	Skiddaw granite	Fortey 1978
Ottrelite	Skiddaw area	Rastall 1910
Pectolite	Carrock Fell	Melmore 1920
Prehnite	Carrock Fell gabbro	Eastwood *et al.* 1968
Pyroxene group	[see individual minerals]	
Quartz	widespread	
Rutile	Grainsgill greisen	Eastwood *et al.* 1968
	Skiddaw granite	Rastall & Wilcockson 1915
Sericite	widespread	
Smectite	China Clay mine	Young 1987
Titanite	Carrock Fell gabbro	Eastwood *et al.* 1968
	Skiddaw granite	Rastall & Wilcockson 1915
Topaz	Carrock Fell gabbro	Thimmaiah 1956
Tourmaline	Skiddaw granite	Rastall & Wilcockson 1915
Tremolite	Carrock Fell gabbro	Harker 1894
	Carrock mine	Davidson & Thomson 1951
Xenotime-(Y)	Grainsgill greisen	Dawson & Harrison 1966
Zircon	Carrock Fell granophyre	Holmes 1917; Harker 1895
	Skiddaw granite	Rastall & Wilcockson 1915

REFERENCES &
BIBLIOGRAPHY

ABRAHAMS, I. (1899–1901) Joachim Gaunse: a mining incident in the reign of Queen Elizabeth. *Transactions of the Jewish Historical Society of Great Britain* **4**, 83–101.

ADAMS, J. (1988) *Mines of the Lake District Fells*. Dalesman Books, Clapham, Lancaster. 160 pp.

ADDISON, P. L. (1889–1890) Description of the Cleator Iron Ore Company's barytes and umber mines and refining mills in the Caldbeck Fells. *Minutes of Proceedings of the Institution of Civil Engineers*, **102**, 283–291.

AGRICOLA, G. (G. Bauer) (1556) *De Re Metallica*. Basel. [English translation by H. C. & L. H. Hoover published as *De Re Metallica*. 'Translated from the first latin edition of 1556, with biographical introduction, annotations and appendices upon the development of mining methods [etc.] from the earliest times to the 16th century.' *Mining Magazine*, London. 1912. 640 pp. subsequent reprints].

ALLEN, M. (1987) *Caldbeck*. Airey and Stephenson, Penrith. 32 pp [not numbered].

ANONYMOUS (1747) A journey to Caudebec Fells, with a map and description of the same. *The Gentleman's Magazine, and Historical Chronicle* **17**, 522–525.

ANONYMOUS (1842) Copper mine *in* 'Mining notices'. *Mining Journal* **12**, 171 (21 May 1842). [taken from the *Carlisle Journal*, 14 May, 1842]

ANONYMOUS (1875) Obituary notice. The late Mr Bryce M. Wright. *Canadian Naturalist* **7**, 431–432.

ANONYMOUS (1977) Carrock Fell. *Mining Magazine* **136**, 169–175.

APPLETON, J. D. & WADGE, A. J. (1976) Investigation of tungsten and other mineralisation associated with the Skiddaw granite near Carrock Mine, Cumbria. *Mineral Reconnaissance Programme. Report of the Institute of Geological Sciences* No. 7.

ARMSTRONG, A. M., MAWER, A., STENTON, F. M. & DICKINS, B. (1950–1952) *The Place-names of Cumberland*. English Place Name Society. 3 vols., Cambridge University Press. vi, 1xxx, 565 pp.

ARX, R. VON (1987) Caldbeck Fells stationery. *British Mining* **34**, 34.

ATKINSON, S. (1619) *The discoverie and historie of the gold mynes in Scotland*. Printed for the Bannatyne Club in 1825 by James Ballantyne and Co, Edinburgh. vii, 119 pp. [includes a contemporary description of the Mines Royal by Bevis Bulmer who leased mines in Cornwall from the Company].

BALL, T. K., FORTEY, N. J. & SHEPHERD, T. J. (1985) Mineralisation at the Carrock Fell Tungsten Mine, N. England: Paragenetic, fluid inclusion and geochemical study. *Mineralium Deposita* **20**, 57–65.

BAMFORD, D., FABER, S., JACOB, B., KAMINSKI, W., NUNN, K., PRODEHL, C., FUCHS, K., KING, R. & WILLMORE, P. (1976) A lithospheric seismic profile in Britain. 1: preliminary results *Geophysical Journal of the Royal Astronomical Society* **44**, 145–160.

BANNISTER, F. A., HEY, M. H. & CLARINGBULL, G. F. (1950) Connellite, buttgenbachite, and tallingite. *Mineralogical Magazine* **29**, 280–286.

BAUER, M. (1871) Krystallographische Untersuchung des Scheelits. *Wurttembergische Naturwissenschaftliche Jahreshefte* (for 1871), pp. 129–198 [describes scheelite from 'Carrockfells' on p. 192 with crystal drawing].

BEAN, J. M. (1958) *The Estates of the Percy family 1416–1537*. Oxford University Press, London. x, 176 pp.

BEDDOE-STEPHENS, B. & FORTEY, N. J. (1981) Columbite from the Carrock Fell tungsten deposit. *Mineralogical Magazine* **44**, 217–223.

BERG, W. VAN DEN (1985) Mineralien zoeken in de Caldbeck Fells (Lake District) *Gea (Driemaandelijks tijdschrift van de Stichting Geologische Aktiviteiten)* **18**, 39–48.

BERRY, L. G. (1951) The unit cell of linarite. *American Mineralogist* **51**, 511–512 [determined on Red Gill material].

BLUM, J. R. (1843) *Die Pseudomorphosen des Mineralreichs*. Vol. 1. E. Schweizerbart'sche, Stuttgart. x, 378 pp.

BLUNDELL, D. (1987) Carrock Mine, a short history. *The Mine Explorer: The Journal of the Cumbria Amenity Trust* **2**, 95–101.

BORIE, Mr (1817) Caldbeck Fells. *Annals of Philosophy* **9**, 161.

BOTT, M. H. P (1974) The geological interpretation of a gravity survey of the English Lake District and the Vale of Eden. *Journal of the Geological Society of London* **130**, 309–331.

BOUCH, C. M. L. & JONES, G. P. (1961) *A short economic and social history of the Lake Counties 1500–1830*. Manchester University Press. xi, 371 pp.

BRAITHWAITE, R. S. W., COOPER, M. P. & HART, A. D. (1989) Queitite, a mineral new to Britain, from the Caldbeck Fells. *Mineralogical Magazine* **53**, 508–509.

BRAITHWAITE, R. S. W., GREENLAND, T. B. & RYBACK, G. (1963) Wulfenite from Poddy Gill, Caldbeck Fells. *Mineralogical Magazine* **33**, 720.

BRAITHWAITE, R. S. W. & RYBACK, G. (1988) Philipsburgite from the Caldbeck Fells and kipushite from Montana, and their infrared spectra. *Mineralogical Magazine* **53**, 529–533.

BRANSTON, J. W. (1910) The minerals of Cumberland. *Transactions of the Carlisle Natural History Society* **2**, 14–29.

BREARLEY, D. (1974) *Lake District place names*. Frank Graham, Newcastle upon Tyne. 64 pp.

BREITHAUPT, J. F. A. (1841) *Vollständiges Handbuch der Mineralogie*, vol. 2. Arnoldische, Dresden and Leipzig. 406 pp.

BRISCOE, P. (1986) Red gill mine. *U.K. Journal of Mines and Minerals* no. 1, 2–4.

BRISTOW, H. W. (1861) *A glossary of mineralogy*. Longman, Green, Longman and Roberts, London. x1vii, 420 pp.

BRITTON, J. & BRAYLEY, E. W. (1802) *The beauties of England and Wales*, vol. 3. Vernor and Hood, London. pp. 22–33.

BROWN, G. C., IXER, R. A., PLANT, J. A. & WEBB, P. C. (1987) Geochemistry of granites beneath the north Pennines and their role in orefield mineralization. *Transactions of the Institution of Mining and Metallurgy* 96, B65–76.

BROWN, M. J. (1983) Mineral investigations at Carrock Fell, Cumbria. Part 2—Geochemical investigations. *Mineral Reconnaissance Programme, Report of the Institute of Geological Sciences* no. 60.

BROWN, W. (1921) Caldbeck in 1642 *in* Addenda antiquaria. *Transactions of the Cumberland and Westmorland Antiquarian and Archaeological Society* (new series) 21, 276–279.

BURCHARD, U. & BODE, R. (1986) *Mineral museums of Europe.* Walnut Hill Publishing, Carson City, Nevada. 269 pp.

BURT, R. (1982a) *A short history of British metal mining technology in the eighteenth and nineteenth centuries.* De Archaeologische Pers Nederland, Aalst-Waalre. 105 pp.

BURT, R. (1982b) *A short history of the British ore preparation techniques in the eighteenth and nineteenth centuries.* De Archaeologische Pers Nederland, Aalst-Waalre. 69 pp.

BURT, R. (1984) *The British lead mining industry.* Dyllansow Truran, Redruth. 344 pp.

BURT, R., WAITE, P. & BURNLEY, R. (1982) *The Cumberland mineral statistics: metalliferous and associated minerals 1845–1913.* Department of Economic History, University of Exeter with the Northern Mines Research Society and The Peak District Mines Historical Society. xxi, 156 pp.

CALVERT, J. (1853) *The gold rocks of Great Britain and Ireland . . .* Chapman and Hall, London. 324 pp. [Facsimile R. Bird, 1989].

CARRUTHERS, R. G., EASTWOOD, T., WILSON, G. V., POCOCK, R. W. & WRAY, D. A. (1915) Barytes and witherite. *Special Report of the Mineral Resources of Great Britain* vol. 2, *Memoirs of the Geological Survey of Great Britain.*

CESARO, G. (1905) Formes nouvelles dans la Linarite et dans la Mélinose. *Bulletin de l'Académie Royale des Sciences, des Lettres et des Beaux-Arts de Belgique* (for 1905), 328–333.

CLARINGBULL, G. F. (1951) New occurrences of duftite. *Mineralogical Magazine* 29, 609–614.

CLARINGBULL, G. F., HEY, M. H. & DAVIS, R. J. (1959) Cornubite, a new mineral dimorphous with cornwallite. *Mineralogical Magazine* 32, 1–5.

CLARK, J. W. & HUGHES, T. MCK. (1890) *The life and letters of the Reverend Adam Sedgwick.* 2 vols. Cambridge University Press.

CLARKE, G. M. (1974) *The mineralogy and geochemistry of tellurium with special reference to the bismuth sulphotellurides.* Unpublished MSc thesis, University College, Cardiff.

CLEEVELY, R. J. (1983) *World palaeontological collections.* British Museum (Natural History) and Mansell Publishing Ltd, London. 365 pp. [despite the title contains a great deal of information on mineral collectors and collections].

COCKBAIN, A. G. (1968) Lead apatite solid-solution series. *Mineralogical Magazine* 36, 1171–1173.

COLLINGWOOD, W. G. (1910) Germans at Coniston in the seventeenth century. *Transactions of the Cumberland and Westmorland Antiquarian and Archaeological Society (new series)* 10, 369–394

COLLINGWOOD, W. G. (1912) Elizabethan Keswick: extracts from the original accounts books 1564–1577, of the German miners, in the archives of Augsburg. *Transactions of the Cumberland and Westmorland Antiquarian and Archaeological Society.* Tract Series No. 8. vii, 219 pp. [also a facsimile reprint by Michael Moon, Whitehaven, 1986].

COLLINGWOOD, W. G. (1928) The Keswick and Coniston mines in 1600 and later. *Transactions of the Cumberland and Westmorland Antiquarian and Archaeological Society* 28, 1–32.

COOPER, M. P. (1988) An early account of mineral collecting in the Caldbeck Fells, Cumbria. *U.K. Journal of Mines and Minerals* no. 4, 5–7 [a reprint of 'Collecting minerals' by B. M. Wright from Sowerby, 1850].

COOPER, M. P., GREEN, D. I. & BRAITHWAITE, R. S. W. (1988) The occurrence of mattheddleite in the Caldbeck Fells, Cumbria: a preliminary note. *U.K. Journal of Mines and Minerals* no. 5, 21.

CROSTHWAITE, J. F. (1876) The Crosthwaite registers. *Transactions of the Cumberland and Westmorland Antiquarian and Archaeological Society* 2, 225–241.

CROSTHWAITE, J. F. (1883) The colony of German miners at Keswick. *Transactions of the Cumberland and Westmorland Antiquarian and Archaeological Society* 6, 344–354.

CUMBERLAND GEOLOGICAL SOCIETY (1982) *The Lake District.* Unwin, London. [field excursion guide to the 'Carrock Fell region' pp 50–57].

DANA, J. D. (1850) *System of mineralogy.* 3rd ed. Putnam, New York and London. 711 pp.

DANA, J. D. (1854) *System of mineralogy* 4th ed. Vol 1. (of 2). Putnam and Co., New York. 534 pp.

DAVIDSON, W. F. (1957) Mines and minerals. *In* The Changing scene. *Joint Transactions of the Eden Field Club, Penrith and District Natural History Society, and Kendal Natural History Society* 1, 61–63.

DAVIDSON, W. F. & THOMSON, N. (1951) Some notes on the minerals of Westmorland and Cumberland. *North West Naturalist* 23 (for 1948), 136–154.

DAVIES, D. (1693) Two letters concerning several copper mines, in answer to some queries proposed by Dr. Lister, F.R.S. who communicated them to the publisher. *Philosophical Transactions* 17, 737–745.

DAVIES, D. S. (1936–1937) The records of the Mines Royal and the Mineral and Battery Works. *Economic History Review* 7, 209–213.

DAVIES, T. (1881) Obituary, Henry Ludlam. *Mineralogical Magazine* 4, 132.

DAWSON, J. & HARRISON, R. K. (1966) Uraninite in the Grainsgill greisen, Cumberland. *Bulletin of the Geological Survey of Great Britain* 25, 91.

DAY, F. H. (1928) Some notes on the minerals of the Caldbeck Fells. *Transactions of the Carlisle Natural History Society* 4, 66–79.

DE LA BECHE, H. T. (1839) *Report on the geology of Cornwall, Devon and west Somerset.* Longman, Orme, Brown, Green and Longmans, London. 648 pp.

DEAN, A. (1852) *The Roughtengill silver lead mines, Caldbeck, Cumberland. Report.* [Printed in a prospectus of the Roughtengill Silver Lead and Copper Mining Co.]. Druid's Inn collection (package no. 57), National Library of Wales, Aberystwyth. 2 pp.

DEWEY, H. & DINES, H. G. (1923) Tungsten and manganese ores. *Special Report on the Mineral Resources of Great Britain, No. 1. Memoirs of the Geological Survey of Great Britain.*

DEWEY, H. & EASTWOOD, T. (1925) Copper ores of the Midlands, Wales, the Lake District and the Isle of Man. *Special Report on the Mineral Resources of Great Britain, No. 30. Memoirs of the Geological Survey of Great Britain.*

DICKENS, C. (1857) *Lazy tour of the two idle apprentices.* [Originally published in '*Household Words*' magazine, October 1857; cited pagination is from the 1890 reprint by Chapman and Hall, London].

DONALD, M. B. (1955) *Elizabethan copper: the history of the Company of Mines Royal, 1568–1605.* Pergamon Press, London. viii, 405 pp. [facsimile reproduction Michael Moon, Whitehaven, 1987].

DONALD, M. B. (1961) *Elizabethan monopolies: the history of the Company of Mineral and Battery Works from 1565 to 1604.* Oliver and Boyd, London. xx, 256 pp.

DOWNIE, C. & SOPER, N. J. (1972) Age of the Eycott Volcanic Group and its conformable relationship to the Skiddaw Slates in the English Lake District. *Geological Magazine* **109**, 259–268.

DUNHAM, K., BEER, K. E., ELLIS, R. A., GALLAGHER, J., NUTT, M. J. C., & WEBB, B. C. (1978) United Kingdom. pp. 263–317 in *Mineral deposits of Europe vol. 1: Northwest Europe*, Eds. BOWIE, S. H. U., KVALHEIM, A. & HASLAM, H. W. Institution of Mining and Metallurgy; Mineralogical Society of Great Britain.

DUNHAM, K. C. & DINES, H. G. (1945) Barium minerals of England and Wales. *Wartime Pamphlet no. 46, Geological Survey of Great Britain.*

DUNHAM, K. C. & HOLLINGWORTH, S. E. (1947) Excursion to Penrith and the north-west. *Mineralogical Magazine* **28**, 248–254.

DURRANCE, E. M., BROMLEY, A. V., BRISTOW, C. M., HEATH, M. J. & PENMAN, J. M. (1982) Hydrothermal circulation and post-magmatic changes in granites of SW England. *Proceedings of the Ussher Society* **5**, 304–319.

EASTWOOD, T. (1921) The lead and zinc ores of the Lake District. *Special Report on the Mineral Resources of Great Britain No. 22, Memoirs of the Geological Survey of Great Britain.*

EASTWOOD, T. (1959) The Lake District mining field. pp. 149–174 in TAYLOR (Ed.), 1959.

EASTWOOD, T., HOLLINGWORTH, S. E., ROSE, W. C. C. & TROTTER, F. M. (1968) Geology of the country around Cockermouth and Caldbeck. *Memoirs of the Geological Survey of Great Britain.*

ELLIS, R. (1851) *Official descriptive and illustrated catalogue of the Great Exhibition of the works of industry of all nations.* Spicer Bros, London. 3 vols.

EL SHAZLY, E. M., WEBB, J. S. & WILLIAMS, D. (1957) Trace elements in sphalerite, galena and associated minerals from the British isles. *Transactions of the Institution of Mining and Metallurgy* **66**, 241–271.

EMBREY, P. G. (1977a) Foreword. pp. vii–xvii in the 1977 reprint of Greg & Lettsom (1858); Lapidary Publications, Broadstairs.

EMBREY, P. G. (1977b) Fourth supplementary list of British minerals. pp. xlviii–lxcii in the 1977 reprint of Greg & Lettsom (1858). *Mineralogical Magazine* **42**, 169–177 (1978).

EMBREY, P. G. & SYMES, R. F. (1987) *Minerals of Cornwall and Devon.* British Museum (Natural History), London; Mineralogical Record Inc., Tucson. vi, 154 pp.

EWART, A. (1957) *The Carrock Fell wolfram deposit.* Unpublished MSc thesis, University of London. [unseen; quoted on the authority of Young, 1987].

EWART, A. (1962) Hydrothermal alteration in the Carrock Fell area, Cumberland, England. *Geological Magazine* **99**, 1–8.

EYLES, V. A. (1965) John Woodward, F.R.S. (1665–1728) Physician and geologist. *Nature* (London) **206**, 868–870.

FERGUSON, R. S. (Ed.) (1889) Description of the county of Cumberland by Sir Daniel Fleming of Rydal, A.D. 1671. *Cumberland and Westmorland Antiquarian and Archaeological Society*, Tract Series No. 3. iv, 36 pp.

FERGUSON, R. S. (1890) Sandford's history of Cumberland ['A Cursory relation of all the antiquities & familyes in Cumberland writt about the year 1675']. *Transactions of the Cumberland and Westmorland Antiquarian and Archaeological Society* Tract Series No. 4. 54 pp.

FINLAYSON, A. M. (1910) The ore-bearing pegmatites of Carrock Fell. *Geological Magazine* **7**, 19–28.

FIRMAN, R. J. (1978) Epigenetic mineralization in the Lake District. pp. 226–241 in Moseley (Ed.), 1978.

FIRMAN, R. J. & LEE, M. K. (1986) Age and structure in the concealed English Lake District batholith and its probable influence on subsequent sedimentation, tectonics, and mineralization. pp. 117–127 in R. W. NESBITT & I. NICHOLL (Eds) *Geology in the real world the Kingsley Dunham volume.* Institution of Mining and Metallurgy, London.

FITTON, J. G. & HUGHES, D. J. (1970) Volcanism and plate tectonics in the British Ordovician. *Earth and Planetary Science Letters* **8**, 223–238.

FLEISCHER, M. (1987) *Glossary of mineral species.* 5th ed. Mineralogical Record Inc., Tucson. 234 pp.

FORTEY, N. J. (1978) Mineral parageneses of the Harding vein tungsten deposit, Carrock Fell mine, Cumbria. *Mineralogy Unit Report No. 228, Institute of Geological Sciences.*

FORTEY, N. J. & BLAND, D. J. (1979) Heavy mineral dispersion profiles in altered granite at Carrock Fell mine, Cumbria. *Applied Mineralogy Unit Report No. 245, Institution of Geological Sciences.*

FORTEY, N. J. (1980) Hydrothermal mineralization associated with minor late Caledonian instrusions in northern Britain: preliminary comments. *Transactions of the Institution of Mining and Metallurgy* **89**, B173–176.

FORTEY, N. J., INGHAM, J. D., SKILTON, B. R. H., YOUNG, B. & SHEPHERD, T. J. (1984) Antimony mineralisation at Wet Swine Gill, Caldbeck Fells, Cumbria. *Proceedings of the Yorkshire Geological Society* **45**, 59–65.

FÖRTSCH, E. B. (1967) 'Plumbogummite' from Roughten Gill, Cumberland. *Mineralogical Magazine* **36**, 530–538.

FREEMAN, F. J. B. (1982) *The geology and geochemistry of Force Crag mine, Cumbria.* Unpublished MSc thesis, Camborne School of Mines.

GARRARD, G. F. G. (1974–1975) *The geology and mineralization of the Caldbeck Fells and upper Caldew valley.* Unpublished undergraduate dissertation, Leicester University. [contains, amongst other information, a comprehensive listing of workings, trials etc. in Caldbeck].

GARRIDO, J. & FEO, R. (1938) Sur les sulfotellurures de bismuth. *Bulletin de la Société Française de Minéralogie et Cristallographie* **61**, 196–204.

GEIKIE, A. (1882) *Text book of geology.* Macmillan, London. xi, 971 pp.

GENTLE, R. & FEILD, R. (1975) *English domestic brass 1680–1810 and the history of its origins.* Paul Elak, London. 232 pp.

GIACOVAZZO, C., MENCHETTI, S. & SCORDARI, F. (1973) The crystal structure of caledonite. *Acta Crystallographica* **B29**, 1986–1990 [determined on Red Gill material].

GOODCHILD, J. G. (1875) Wulfenite at Caldbeck Fell. *Geological Magazine* **2**, 565–566.

GOODCHILD, J. G. (1882) Contributions towards a list of minerals occurring in Cumberland and Westmorland [part 1]. *Transactions of the Cumberland Association for the Advancement of Literature and Science* **7**, (for 1881–1882) 101–126.

GOODCHILD, J. G. (1884) ditto (part 2). *Ibid.* **8**, (for 1882–1883) 189–204.

GOODCHILD, J. G. (1885) ditto (concluding part). *Transactions of the Cumberland and Westmorland Association for the Advancement of Literature and Science* **9**, (for 1883–1884) 175–199.

GRANT, D. (1985) The sixth duke of Somerset, Thomas Robinson and the Newlands mines. *Transactions of the Cumberland and Westmorland Antiquarian and Archaeological Society* **85**, 141–162.

GRANT-FRANCIS, G. (1881) *The smelting of copper in the Swansea district of South Wales from the time of Elizabeth to the present day.* 2nd ed., Henry Sotheran and Co., London. x, 193 pp. [transcripts of documents relating to the Mines Royal].

GRAVES, H. G (1928) Notes on copper smelting, 1567–1616. *Transactions of the Newcomen Society* 7, 121–125 (for 1926–1927). [transcription of smelting notes by Emanuel Höchstetter in the archive of Sir Daniel Fleming (1633–1701)].

GREEN, D. I. (in prep.) Scotlandite from higher Roughton Gill, Caldbeck Fells, Cumbria. *Mineralogical Magazine* 53, 653.

GREEN, J. F. N. (1918) The Skiddaw Granite—a structural study. *Proceedings of the Geologists' Association* 29, 126–136.

GREEN, J. F. N. (1921) The tungsten mine and the Skiddaw aureole. *Proceedings of the Geologists' Association* 32, (part 3) 130–131 [superficial account of a field trip].

GREENOP, J. (1905) 'The anatomy of the Earth' by Thomas Robinson, Rector of Ousby in Cumberland, 1694—with a note by the author. *Transactions of the Cumberland and Westmorland Antiquarian and Archaeological Society* (new series) 5, 243–265.

GREG, R. P. (1851) A description of matlockite, a new oxychloride of lead. *Philosophical Magazine* 2 (series 4), 120–121.

GREG, R. P. & LETTSOM, W. G. (1858) *Manual of the mineralogy of Great Britain and Ireland.* John van Voorst, London. ix, 483 pp. [facsimile reprint, with addenda, by Lapidary Publications, Broadstairs, 1977].

GUILLEMIN, C. (1956) Contribution a la minéralogie des arséniates, phosphates et vanadates de cuivre. *Bullétin de la Société Française de Minéralogie et Crystallographie* 79, 7–95.

HALL, T. M. (1868) *The Mineralogist's directory: or a guide to the principal mineral localities in the United Kingdom and Ireland.* Edward Stanford, London. 168 pp.

HAMILTON, H. (1926) *The English brass and copper industries to 1800.* Longmans, London. xxvii, 388 pp. [reissued in 1967 with a new introduction by J. R. Harris; Frank Cass, London. xxxvi, 388 pp].

HAMMERSLEY, G. (1973) Technique or economy? The rise and decline of the early English copper industry, c.1550–1660. *Economic History* 15, 1–31.

HARKER, A. (1894) Carrock Fell: a study in the variation of igneous rock masses—part I. The Gabbro. *Quarterly Journal of the Geological Society of London* 50, 311–337.

HARKER, A. (1895) Carrock Fell: a study in the variation of igneous rock masses—part II the Carrock Fell granophyre, part III the Grainsgill greisen. *Quarterly Journal of the Geological Society of London* 51, 125–148.

HARKNESS, R. (1858) On the geology of the Caldbeck Fells and the lower sedimentary rocks of Cumberland. *Report of the British Association for the Advancement of Science 1857, Transactions of the Sections* p. 67 [brief superficial commentary].

HARRIS, P. & DAGGER, G. W. (1987) The intrusion of the Carrock Fell Gabbro Series (Cumbria) as a sub-horizontal body. *Proceedings of the Yorkshire Geological Society* 46, 371–380.

HARTLEY, E. G. J. (1900) On the constitution of the natural arsenates and phosphates. Part III Plumbogummite and Hitchcockite. *Mineralogical Magazine* 12, 223–233.

HARTLEY, J. (1959) Coronadite from Cumberland. *Mineralogical Magazine* 32, 343–344.

HARTLEY, J. (1984) A list of minerals associated with the ore deposits of the Caldbeck Fells, Cumbria. *Transactions of the Leeds Geological Association* 10, 22–39.

HEDDLE, M. F. (1901) *The Mineralogy of Scotland.* David Douglas, Edinburgh. 2 vols.

HESSENBERG, F. (1864) Linarit (Bleilasur) aus Cumberland. *Abhandlungen der Senckenbergische Naturforschende Gesellschaft, Frankfurt am Main* 5, 263–273.

HESSENBERG, F. (1870) Caledonit von Red Gill, Cumberland. *Abhandlungen der Senckenbergische Naturforschende Gesellschaft, Frankfurt am Main* 7, 304–308.

HETON, T. (1707) *Some account of mines, and the advantage of them to the kingdom. With an appendix relating to the mine adventure in Wales.* J. Wyat, London. 171 pp.

HITCHEN, C. S. (1934) The Skiddaw granite and its residual products. *Quarterly Journal of the Geological Society of London* 90, 158–200.

HOCHLEITNER, R. (1984) Kampylite von Cumberland. *Lapis* 9, 27 [history and status of name; colour plate].

HOLLAND, P. (1610) *Britain, or, a Chorographicall description of . . . England, Scotland and Ireland . . . written first in Latine by W. Camden . . . with sundry additions.* Georgii Bishop and Ioannis Norton, London.

HOLLINGWORTH, S. E. (1938) Carrock Fell and adjoining areas. *Proceedings of the Yorkshire Geological Society* 23, 208–218 [a brief geological guide].

HOLMES, A. (1917) Albite granophyre and quartz-porphyry from Brandy Gill, Carrock Fell. *Geological Magazine*, decade 6, 4, 403–407.

HOUSMAN, J. (1800) *A topographical description of Cumberland, Westmorland, Lancashire and a part of the West Riding of Yorkshire.* Carlisle.

HUDSON, S. (1842) *A complete guide to the lakes, comprising minute directions to the tourist with Mr. Wordsworth's description of the country etc. and three letters on the geology of the Lake District by the Rev. Prof. Sedgwick.* J. Hudson, Kendal, 259 pp.

HUNT, R. (1884) *British Mining.* Crosby Lockwood and Co., London. xx, 944 pp. [a facsimile reprint of 'Book 1' and the appendix and index of the 2nd, revised, edition of 1887 (pp. 1–186, 885–925) was published as *A historical sketch of British Mining* by E. P. Publishing in 1978].

HUTCHINSON, W. (1794) *The history of the county of Cumberland.* F. Jollie, Carlisle. 2 vols; 600, 686 pp [facsimile reprint by E. P. Publishing Ltd/Cumbria County Library, 1974, with an introduction by C. R. Hudleston, 1, v–xxiii].

INESON, P. R. & MITCHELL, J. G. (1974) K-Ar isotopic age determinations from some Lake District mineral localities. *Geological Magazine* 111, 521–537.

INGHAM, J. K. & MCNAMARA, K. J. (1978) The Coniston Limestone Group. pp. 121–129 in MOSELEY (Ed.), 1978.

JACKSON, D. (1978) The Skiddaw Group. pp. 79–98 in MOSELEY (Ed.), 1978.

JAMESON, R. (1816) *A system of mineralogy.* Archibald Constable, Edinburgh. 3 vols. [second edition].

JAMESON, R. (1820) *A system of mineralogy in which minerals are arranged according to the natural history method.* Archibald Constable, Edinburgh. 3 vols. [third edition].

JANNETTAZ, E. & MICHEL, L. (1881) Note sur les relations de la composition chimique et les caractères optiques dans la groupe pyromorphites et mimétites. *Bulletin de la Société Française de Minéralogie et Cristallographie* 4, 196–225.

JENKINS, R. (1938) The society for the Mines Royal and the German colony in the Lake District. *Transactions of the Newcomen Society* 18, 225–234.

JENKINSON, H. I. (1875) *Practical guide to the English Lake District*, 4th ed. Carlisle. [a chapter on 'Mineralogy' (pp. lxxi–xciii) was contributed by Bryce M. Wright Jr and was reprinted in all subsequent editions].

KENDALL, J. D. (1884) The mineral veins of the Lake District. *Transactions of the Manchester Geological Society* 17, 292–341. [Early theory of vein formation. Mineral lists derived from previous authors].

KINGSBURY, A. W. G. (1957) New occurrences of phosgenite. *Mineralogical Magazine* 31, 500–501.

KINGSBURY, A. W. G. & HARTLEY, J. (1955) On the occurrence of the rare copper molybdate, lindgrenite, at Brandy Gill, Carrock Fell, Cumberland. *Mineralogical Magazine* 30, 723–726.

KINGSBURY, A. W. G. & HARTLEY, J. (1956a) New occurrences of vanadium minerals (mottramite, descloizite, and vanadinite) in the Caldbeck area of Cumberland. *Mineralogical Magazine* 31, 289–295.

KINGSBURY, A. W. G. & HARTLEY, J. (1956b) Cosalite and other lead sulpho-salts at Grainsgill, Carrock Fell, Caldbeck, Cumberland. *Mineralogical Magazine* 31, 296–300.

KINGSBURY, A. W. G. & HARTLEY, J. (1956c) Atacamite from Cumberland and Cornwall. *Mineralogical Magazine* 31, 349–350.

KINGSBURY, A. W. G. & HARTLEY, J. (1957a) New occurrences of arseniosiderite. *Mineralogical Magazine* 31, 499–500.

KINGSBURY, A. W. G. & HARTLEY, J. (1957b) New occurrences of rosasite in Britain. *Mineralogical Magazine* 31, 501–502.

KINGSBURY, A. W. G. & HARTLEY, J. (1957c) Carpholite from Cumberland and Cornwall. *Mineralogical Magazine* 31, 502.

KINGSBURY, A. W. G. & HARTLEY, J. (1957d) Serpierite from the Lake District. *Mineralogical Magazine* 31, 604–605.

KINGSBURY, A. W. G. & HARTLEY, J. (1957e) Beaverite from the Lake District. *Mineralogical Magazine* 31, 700–702.

KINGSBURY, A. W. G. & HARTLEY, J. (1958) Jarosite and natrojarosite from the Lake District. *Mineralogical Magazine* 31, 813–815.

KINGSBURY, A. W. G. & HARTLEY, J. (1960) Carminite and beudantite from the northern part of the Lake District and from Cornwall. *Mineralogical Magazine* 32, 423–432.

KOKSHAROV, N. I. (1869a) Ueber Linaritkrystalle. *Memoires de l'Académie Impériale des Sciences de Saint-Pétersbourg* 13, no. 3.

KOKSHAROV, N. I. (1869b) Notiz über Linaritkrystalle. *Bulletin de l'Académie Impériale des Sciences de Saint-Pétersbourg* 8, 472–476 [a short summary of work already published—see Koksharov 1869a].

KURR, J. G. VON (1858) *Das Mineralreich in Bildern.* Schreiber und Schill, Stuttgart. ['kampylite' figured in Table XX. An English translation published as *The Mineral Kingdom* by Edmonston and Douglas, Edinburgh, 1859].

LAMBOURNE, L. (1979) *Ernest Griset: Fantasies of a Victorian illustrator.* Thames and Hudson, London. 88 pp.

LAST, C. E. (1945) The old road at Caldbeck. *Transactions of the Cumberland and Westmorland Antiquarian and Archaeological Society* 44, 142–145.

LAWSON, J. (1972) Statistics of mineral production of the Pennines. Part 2 Westmorland & the Lake District. *Memoirs of the Northern Cavern and Mine Research Society* 2, 44–59. [despite the overall title gives statistics for the Caldbeck Fells].

LEE, M. K., BROWN, G. C., WEBB, P. C., WHEILDON, J. & ROLLIN, K. E. (1987) Heat flow, heat production and thermotectonic setting in mainland U.K. *Journal of the Geological Society of London* 144, 35–42.

LEWIS, W. J. (1967) *Lead mining in Wales.* University of Wales Press, Cardiff. 415 pp.

LÉVY, A. (1837) *Description d'une collection de minéraux formée par M. Henri Heuland et appartenant a M. Ch. Hampden Turner* . . . London, 3 vols and atlas.

LIVINGSTONE, A., RYBACK, G., FEJER, E. E. & STANLEY, C. J. (1987) Mattheddleite, a new mineral of the apatite group from Leadhills, Strathclyde Region. *Scottish Journal of Geology* 23, 1–8.

LYSONS, D. & LYSONS, S. (1816) *Magna Brittania; being a concise topographical account of the several counties of Great Britain,* vol. 4 *Cumberland.* Cadell and Davies, London. 200 pp.

MCDERMOTT, J. (1986) *The account books of Michael Lok relating to the northwest voyages of Martin Frobisher 1576–1578. Text and Analysis.* Unpublished M.Phil thesis, University of Hull.

MACKAY, C. (1846) *The scenery and poetry of the English Lakes. A summer ramble.* Longman, Brown, Green and Longman, London.

MANNIX, . . . & WHELLAN, W. (1847) *History, gazeteer and directory of Cumberland.* Printed for the authors by W. B. Johnson, Beverley. 647 pp. [facsimile reprint by Michael Moon, Beckermet, 1974].

MARSHALL, J. H. (1973) Mineral collecting in northern England and Scotland. *Rocks and Minerals* 48, 507–515.

MELMORE, S. (1920) The metamorphism of the Carrock Fell gabbro; with a note on the origin of the sulphide veins of the Caldbeck Fells. *Geological Magazine* 57, 266–268.

MIERS, H. A. (1897) On some British pseudomorphs. *Mineralogical Magazine* 11, 263–285.

MIERS, H. A. (1900) Note on the hitchcockite, plumbogummite and beudantite analysed by Mr. Hartley. *Mineralogical Magazine* 12, 239–243.

MILLWARD, D., MOSELEY, F. & SOPER, N. J. (1978) The Eycott and Borrowdale Volcanic rocks. pp. 99–120 in MOSELEY (Ed.), 1978.

MITCHELL, M., TAYLOR, B. J. & RAMSBOTTOM, W. H. C. (1978) Carboniferous. pp. 168–187 in MOSELEY (Ed.) 1978.

[MOFFIT, C.] (1979) New mineral discovered. *Northern Mines Research Society Newsletter* August 1979, p. 2.

MOLYNEUX, S. G. & RUSHTON, A. W. A (1985) Discovery of Tremadoc rocks in the Lake District. *Proceedings of the Yorkshire Geological Society* 45, 123–127.

MONKHOUSE, F. J. (1943) Some features of the historical geography of the German mining enterprise in Elizabethan Lakeland. *Geography* 28, 107–113.

MOORBATH, S. (1962) Lead isotope abundance studies on mineral occurrences in the British Isles. *Philosophical Transactions of the Royal Society of London* A254, 295–360.

MOORE, A. J. MCM. (1977) Carrock Fell tungsten mine, Cumbria. *Journal of the Royal School of Mines, London* 26, 7–14.

MOORE, A. J. MCM. (1982) Mineral zonation near the granitic batholiths of south-west and northern England and some geothermal analogues. pp. 229–242 in EVANS, A. M. (Ed.) *Metallization associated with acid magmatism.* John Wiley, New York.

MOSELEY, F. (Ed.) (1978) *The geology of the Lake District.* Yorkshire Geological Society. Occasional Publication No. 3. viv, 284 pp.

MOSELEY, F. (1978) The geology of the English Lake District— an introductory review. pp. 1–16 in MOSELEY (Ed.), 1978.

MOSELEY, F. (1984) Lower Palaeozoic lithostratigraphic classification in the English Lake District. *Geological Journal* 19, 237–247.

MUTHMANN, W. & SCHRÖDER, E. (1897) Ueber die Zussammensetzung einiger Tellurmineralien. *Zeitschrift für Krystallographie und Mineralogie* 29, 140–145.

NEVILL, W. (1872) *Descriptive catalogue of minerals, being the collection of William Nevill, F.G.S., Godalming, Surrey.* Taylor and Francis, London. 175 pp.

NEWBY, H. P. (1981) *Rare earth elements in pyromorphite group minerals.* Unpublished PhD thesis, University of London.

NICHOLSON, J. & BURN, R. (1777) *The history and antiquities of the counties of Westmorland and Cumberland.* 2 vols. [facsimile reprint by E. P. Publishing/Cumbria County Library 1976 including an index by Henry Hornyold-Strickland].

NICHOLSON, N. (1955) *The Lakers. The adventures of the first tourists.* Robert Hale, London. 235 pp.

O'BRIEN, C., PLANT, J. A., SIMPSON, P. R. & TARNEY, J. (1985) The geochemistry, metasomatism and petrogenesis of the granites of the English Lake District. *Journal of the Geological Society of London* 142, 1139–1158.

OTLEY, J. (1820) Remarks on the succession of rocks in the district of the Lakes. *Philosophical Magazine* 56, 257–261. (from the *Lonsdale Magazine* 1, 433.).

OTLEY, J. (1823) *A concise description of the English Lakes and adjacent mountains with general directions to tourists: and observations on the mineralogy and geology of the district.* L. Otley, Keswick.

PALACHE, C., BERMAN, H. & FRONDEL, C. (1951) *The system of mineralogy of James Dwight Dana ... vol. 2* John Wiley and Sons, New York. xi, 1124 pp.

PARKIN, J. S. (1921) Greenrigg, Caldbeck. *Transactions of the Cumberland and Westmorland Antiquarian and Archaeological Society (new series)* 21, 234–236.

PARSON, W. & WHITE, W. (1829) *History, directory, and gazeteer of the counties of Cumberland and Westmorland ...* xxxiv, 732 pp. [facsimile reprint by Michael Moon, Beckermet, Cumbria 1976].

PATRICK, D. J. (1980) Mineral investigations at Carrock Fell, Cumbria. Part 1—geophysical survey. *Mineral Reconnaissance Program, Report of the Institute of Geological Sciences* No. 33.

PEACOCK, M. A. (1941) On josëite, grünlingite, oruetite. *University of Toronto Studies, Geology Series* 46, 83–105.

PEARSALL, W. H. & PENNINGTON, W. (1973) *The Lake District, a landscape history.* Collins New Naturalist, London. 320 pp.

PETTUS, SIR J. (1670) *Fodinae Regales, or the history, laws and places of the chief mines and mineral works in England, Wales, and the English Pale in Ireland.* T. Basset, London. 108 pp. [also a facsimile reprint by the Institution of Mining and Metallurgy, 1981].

PHILLIPS, W. (1819) *An elementary introduction to the knowledge of mineralogy.* William Phillips, London. 325 pp. [1st edition].

PHILLIPS, W. (1823) *An elementary introduction to the knowledge of mineralogy ... with accounts of the places and circumstances in which they are found; and especially the localities of British minerals.* 3rd edition. Published by the author, London. 407 pp.

PHILLIPS, W. (1837) *An elementary introduction to mineralogy.* [4th edition, considerably augmented by Robert Allan]. Longman, Rees, Orme, Brown, Green and Longman, London. 425 pp.

POOL, R. (1862) *A few thoughts on the natural, social and religious aspect of the parish of Caldbeck.* H. Hoodless, Wigton, Cumbria.

PORTER, R. (1979) John Woodward: 'A droll sort of a philosopher' *Geological Magazine* 116, 335–343.

POSTLETHWAITE, J. (1891) The deposits of metallic and other minerals surrounding the Skiddaw Granite. *Transactions of the Cumberland and Westmorland Association for the Advancement of Literature and Science* 15 (for 1889–1890), 75–86.

POSTLETHWAITE, J. (1913) *Mines and mining in the (English) Lake District.* 3rd ed. Moss and Sons, Whithaven. 164 pp. 1st ed.: 1877; 2nd ed.: 1889. [facsimile reprints of 3rd ed. by Michael Moon, Beckermet 1976 and later].

PRIOR, G. T. (1900) Hamlinite, florencite, plumbogummite (hitchcockite), beudantite, and svanbergite, as members of a natural group of minerals. *Mineralogical Magazine* 12, 249–254.

RABONE, P. (1945) A short-wave ultra-violet prospecting set for fluorescent minerals. *Transactions of the Institution of Mining and Metallurgy* 54, 231–241, 256.

RASTALL, R. H. (1910) The Skiddaw granite and its metamorphism. *Quarterly Journal of the Geological Society of London* 66, 116–141.

RASTALL, R. H. (1942) The ore deposits of the Skiddaw district. *Proceedings of the Yorkshire Geological Society* 24, 328–343.

RASTALL, R. H. & WILCOCKSON, W. H. (1915) The accessory minerals of the granitic rocks of the English Lake District. *Quarterly Journal of the Geological Society of London* 71, 592–622.

ROBERTS, D. E. (1971) Structures of the Skiddaw Slates in the Caldew Valley, Cumberland. *Geological Journal* 7, 225–238.

ROBERTS, D. E. (1983) Metasomatism and the formation of greisen in Grainsgill, Cumbria, England. *Geological Journal* 18, 43–52.

ROBINSON, T. (1709) *An essay towards a natural history of Cumberland and Westmoreland, wherein is given an account of their several mineral and surface productions, &c.* W. Freeman, London. 227 pp.

RUDLER, F. W. (1905) *A handbook to a collection of the minerals of the British Islands ... in the Museum of Practical Geology ... London.* H.M.S.O., London. x, 241 pp.

RUNDLE, C. C. (1979) Ordovician intrusions in the English Lake District. *Journal of the Geological Society of London* 136, 29–38.

RUSSELL, A. (1936) Notes on the occurrence of wulfenite at Brandy Gill, Cumberland, and of leadhillite at Drumruck Mine, Kirkcudbrightshire. *Mineralogical Magazine* 24, 321–323.

RUSSELL, A. (1944) Notes on some minerals either new or rare to Britain. *Mineralogical Magazine* 27, 1–10.

SCHÖTTLER, G. (1979) Roughtongill Mine, Cumberland. Paradies für Kleinstufensammler. *Lapis* 4, 26. [brief note on selected 'micro-minerals'].

SCOTT, J. W. (1972) Technological and economic changes in the metalliferous mining and smelting industries of Tudor England. *Albion (Proceedings of the Conference on British Studies)* 4, 94–110.

SCOTT, J. W. (1973) Theory and practice in early metalliferous mining in the British Isles: some comments on the state of geological knowledge in Tudor and Stuart times. *Albion (Proceedings of the Conference on British Studies)* 5, 211–225.

SCOTT, W. R. (1907) The constitution and finance of an English copper mining company in the 16th and 17th centuries. [in English]. *Vierteljahrschrift für Social und Wirtschaftgeschichte* 5, 525–552. [incorporated in Scott, 1911, vol. 2, 383–405].

SCOTT, W. R. (1911) *The Constitution and Finance of English, Scottish and Irish joint stock companies to 1720.* 3 vols. University Press, Cambridge. [mining companies in vol. 2].

SCRIVENOR, J. B. (1916) The Grainsgill greisen of Carrock Fell. *Geological Magazine*, decade 6, 3, 239–240.

SEDGWICK, A. (1831) Introduction to the general structure of the Cumbrian mountains; with a description of the great dislocations by which they have been separated from the neighbouring Carboniferous chains. *Transactions of the Geological Society of London*, Series 2, 4, 47–68.

SEDGWICK, A. (1832) On the geological relations of the stratified and unstratified groups of rocks composing the Cumbrian mountains. *Proceedings of the Geological Society of London* 1, 399–401.

SHAW, W. T. (1959) Potts Ghyll and Sandbeds barytes mines. pp. 221–223 in TAYLOR (Ed.), 1959.

SHAW, W. T. (1970) *Mining in the Lake Counties*. Dalesman Books, Kendal. 128 pp. [2nd ed. 1975 incorporating minor changes].

SHEPHERD, T. J., BECKINSALE, R. D., RUNDLE, C. C. & DURHAM, J. (1976) Genesis of Carrock Fell tungsten deposits, Cumbria: fluid inclusion and isotopic study. *Transactions of the Institution of Mining and Metallurgy* **85**, B63–73.

SHEPHERD, T. J. & WATERS, P. (1984) Fluid inclusion gas studies, Carrock Fell tungsten deposit, England: implications for regional exploration. *Mineralium Deposita* **19**, 304–314.

SIMONS, W. V. (1866) *A catalogue of foreign minerals in the possession of the Mining Department, Melbourne, Victoria*. John Ferres, Melbourne. 74 pp.

SKILLEN, I. E. (1973) The igneous complex of Carrock Fell. *Proceedings of the Cumberland Geological Society* **3**, 71–85 [a good guide to exposures].

SMITH, F. W. (1973) Fluid inclusion studies on fluorite from the north Wales orefield. *Transactions of the Institution of Mining and Metallurgy* **82**, B74–76.

SMITH, G. F. H. (1907) Robert Philips Greg (1826–1906). *Mineralogical Magazine* **14**, 268–271.

SMITH, R. A. (1974) *A bibliography of Lake District geology and geomorphology*. Revised edition. Cumberland Geological Society.

SMITH, W. C. (1969) A history of the first hundred years of the mineral collection in the British Museum. *Bulletin of the British Museum (Natural History), Historical Series* **3**, 237–259.

SMITH, W. C. (1978) Early mineralogy in Great Britain and Ireland. *Bulletin of the British Museum (Natural History), Historical Series* **6**, 49–74.

SMYTHE, J. A. & DUNHAM, K. C. (1947) Ankerites and chalybites from the northern Pennine ore-field and the north-east coalfield. *Mineralogical Magazine* **28**, 53–73.

SOPER, N. J. & MOSELEY, F. (1978) Structure. pp. 45–67 in MOSELEY (Ed.), 1978.

SOWERBY, H. (1850) *Popular mineralogy; comprising a familiar account of minerals and their uses*. Reeve and Benham, London. [*Collecting minerals*, by B. M. Wright, pp. 14–23].

SOWERBY, J. (1804–1817) *British mineralogy: or coloured figures intended to elucidate the mineralogy of Great Britain*. Published by the author, London. 5 vols.

SPEED, J. (1610) The theatre of Great Britain display'd.

SPENCER, L. J. (1958) Third supplementary list of British minerals. *Mineralogical Magazine* **31**, 787–806.

STANLEY, C. J. (1979) *Mineralogical studies of copper, lead, zinc, and cobalt mineralization in the English Lake District*. Unpublished PhD thesis, University of Aston, Birmingham.

STANLEY, C. J. & VAUGHAN, D. J. (1981) Native antimony and bournonite intergrowths in galena from the English Lake District. *Mineralogical Magazine* **44**, 257–260.

STANLEY, C. J. & VAUGHAN, D. J. (1982) Copper, lead, zinc and cobalt mineralisation in the English Lake District: classification, conditions of formation and genesis. *Journal of the Geological Society of London* **139**, 569–579.

STRENS, R. G. J. (1963) Pyromorphite as a possible primary phase. *Mineralogical Magazine* **33**, 722–723.

STRINGER, M. (1713) *Opera Mineralia Explicata: or, the mineral kingdom within the dominions of Great Britain display'd*. J. Brown, London. xii, 308 pp.

SWEET, J. M. (1960) British gold from the Bouglise collection. *Mineralogical Magazine* **32**, 420–421.

TAYLOR, B. J. et al. (1971) *British Regional Geology. Northern England*. 4th ed. Geological Survey of Great Britain. 121 pp.

TAYLOR, S. E. (Ed.) (1959) *The future of non-ferrous mining in Great Britain and Ireland, a symposium*. Institution of Mining and Metallurgy. London. xxvi, 614 pp.

THIMMAIAH, T. (1956). *Mineralisation of the Caldbeck Fells area, Cumberland*. Unpublished PhD thesis, University of London.

THOMPSON, W. N. (1904) The Derwentwaters and Radcliffes. *Transactions of the Cumberland and Westmorland Antiquarian and Archaeological Society, (new series)* **4**, 288–322.

THOMSON, T. (1839) Notice respecting the native diarseniate of lead. *Report of the eighth meeting of the British Association for the Advancement of Science, 1838, transactions of the sections* 46–48.

THORNE, M. G. & EDWARDS, R. P. (1985) Recent advances in concepts of ore genesis in south west England. *Transactions of the Royal Geological Society of Cornwall* **21**, part 3, 113–152.

TOOKE, A. W. (1837) The mineral topography of Great Britain. [part 2]. *Mining Review* **9**, 39–60.

TURNER, V. E. (1987) Results of survey work carried out in the Caldbeck Fells, Cumbria. *Transactions of the Cumberland and Westmorland Antiquarian and Archaeological Society* **87**, 19–25.

WADGE, A. J. (1978) Classification and stratigraphical relationships of the Lower Ordovician rocks. pp. 68–78 in MOSELEY (Ed.), 1978.

WADGE, A. J., GALE, N. H., BECKINSALE, R. D. & RUNDLE, C. C. (1978) A Rb-Sr isochron age for the Shap Granite. *Proceedings of the Yorkshire Geological Society* **42**, 297–305.

WALTON, J. (1946) The medieval mines of Alston. *Transactions of the Cumberland and Westmorland Antiquarian and Archaeological Society* **45**, 22–33.

WARD, J. C. (1875) The granitic, granitoid, and associated metamorphic rocks of the Lake District, parts I & II. *Quarterly Journal of the Geological Society of London* **31**, 568–602.

WARD, J. C. (1876a) The geology of the northern part of the English Lake District. *Memoirs of the Geological Survey of Great Britain*.

WARD, J. C. (1876b) The granitic, granitoid, and associated metamorphic rocks of the Lake District, parts III–V. *Quarterly Journal of the Geological Society of London* **32**, 1–34.

WARD, J. C. (1876–1877) Jonathon Otley, the geologist and guide. *Transactions of the Cumberland and Westmorland Association for the Advancement of Literature and Science* **2**, 125–169.

WARD, P. (1977) Recent developments in work at Roughtengill mine in the Caldbeck Fells. *Russell Society Newsletter* **4**, 17–22.

WATSON, J. Y. (1843) *A compendium of British mining, with statistical notices of the principal mines in Cornwall . . .* Privately printed, London.

WHELLAN, W. (1860) *The history and topography of the counties of Cumberland and Westmoreland*. W, Whellan, Pontefract. viii. 896 pp.

WILDRIDGE, J. D. J. (1975) The instructions given by the Company of Mines Royal to George Bowes and Francis Needham and the resulting report. *British Mining* **1**, 25–40.

WILSON, G. V., EASTWOOD, T., POCOCK, R. W., WRAY, D. A. & ROBERTSON, T. (1922) Barytes and witherite. *Special Report of the Mineral Resources of Great Britain* no. 2, Memoirs of the Geological Survey of Great Britain.

WILSON, P. N. (1954) Forgotten mines. *Country Life* 6.5.1954.

WIRTH, M. (1989) Native silver from Red Gill mine, Caldbeck Fells, Cumbria. *Journal of the Russell Society* **2**, 49.

WISEMAN, W. G. (1987) The medieval hospitals of Cumbria. *Transactions of the Cumberland and Westmorland Antiquarian and Archaeological Society* **87**, 83–100.

WOODWARD, J. (1728–1729) *An attempt towards a natural history of the fossils of England; in a catalogue of the English fossils in the collection of J. Woodward . . .* 2 vols. London.

WRIGHT, B. M. (1875) Mineralogy. See JENKINSON, H. I. (1875).

YOUNG, B. (1987) *Glossary of the minerals of the Lake District and adjoining areas.* British Geological Survey, Newcastle upon Tyne. 104 pp.

ZAV'YALOV, E. N. & BEGIZOV, V. D. (1981a) [The new bismuth mineral ingodite Bi$_2$TeS]. (in Russian) *Zapiski Vsesoyuznogo Mineralogicheskogo Obshchestva* **110**, 594–600 [*Mineralogical Abstracts* **33**, 82M/3350; *American Mineralogist* **62**, 855 (1982)].

ZAV'YALOV, N. & BEGIZOV, V. D. (1981b) [Once more on the problem of grünlingite]. (in Russian) *Zapiski Vsesoyuznogo Mineralogicheskogo Obshchestva* **110**, 633–635 [*Mineralogical Abstracts* **33**, 82M/3316; *American Mineralogist* **62**, 855 (1982)].

ZAV'YALOV, N., BEGIZOV, V. D. & TEDCHUK, V. YA. (1984) [Additional data on the composition of ingodite]. *Zapiski Vsesoyuznogo Mineralogicheskogo Obshchestva* **113**, 31–35 (in Russian) [*American Mineralogist* **70**, 220 (1985)].

MANUSCRIPT AND OTHER UNPUBLISHED SOURCES

The principal manuscript sources quoted in this book are those of the late Arthur W. G. Kingsbury in the Department of Mineralogy, British Museum (Natural History). Although several original documents of the Elizabethan period have been examined, in all cases in the text quotations from such documents are taken from previously published transcripts. The Cumbria Records Office at Carlisle contains, or has access to, a considerable archive relating to the mining history of the Caldbeck Fells; unfortunately the material collected by the local miner W. T. Shaw, and of considerable value regarding twentieth century mining in the area, is restricted to study only and cannot be published. The Public Record offices for Northumberland (Newcastle-upon-Tyne) and North Yorkshire (Northallerton) also have Caldbeck mining documents in their archives. The former also administers the archive of the Newcastle Mining Institute.

KINGSBURY, A. W. G. (MS 1) (1953 or later) *Investigation of the minerals of the Lake District, especially the Caldbeck area, in collaboration with J. Hartley. List of minerals found by us at many localities examined 1947–.* [A hardback notebook containing lists of species by locality with occasional notes and descriptive detail].

KINGSBURY, A. W. G. (MS 2) *Notes on the occurrence of gold in the Lake District.* [A spiral bound notebook containing what appears to be the mss for a proposed paper, with a historical introduction followed by detailed descriptions of Kingsbury's own discoveries].

KINGSBURY, A. W. G (MS 3) *Notes on mineralogical field-trips to the Caldbeck Fells area of the northern part of the Lake District, Cumberland in Aug. 1949 & April 1950.* [Minutely detailed accounts (61 and 45 pages respectively) of two of Kingsbury's early trips to the area accompanied by H. Neumann or P. G. Embrey].

KINGSBURY, A. W. G. (MS 4) [A 6 in to 1 mile Ordnance Survey map of the Caldbeck Fells with copious handwritten annotations by Kingsbury listing and localizing many of his finds].

KINGSBURY, A. W. G. & HARTLEY, J. (MS) *New occurrences of rare minerals in the northern part of the English Lake District: part 1* [An unpublished 39 page typescript of a paper given to the Mineralogical Society on 8 March 1951. Several of the species detailed here were to become the subject of separate papers published in later years. Many of the remaining species were not listed until Hartley's summary paper of 1984; much of the descriptive information quoted in the present work has not been published before].

EIGHTEENTH CENTURY MINING DOCUMENTS

The state of mining in Caldbeck in this period is poorly known. Much of the information we give has not been published before and it was thought useful to give a full account of the documents used to enable others to follow the story. The cited items are with the Cumbria Record Office in Carlisle.

BENSON MSS The items from this archive consulted by MPC consist of papers brought together during a contest over land rights on the south side of Carrock Fell in 1797, between Isaac Harper of Haltcliffe, Caldbeck and Edward Hasell of Dacre. By 1797 the mining rights had been transferred to Lord Pomfret. The items relevant to the mining story are as follows, the reference number being given first:

D/Ben/3136 'Instructions for Plea' in the case Isaac Harper *v.* Edward Hasell, a draft copy, with an accompanying map of Carrock Fell (D/Ben/3115).

D/Ben/3134; 3150; 3162: Correspondence concerning the Wharton mining accounts in the possession of Lord Pomfret and others.

D/Ben/3116: Thomas Hillary's '*Bargains*' book giving costs of working, ore produced, etc. during 1724.

D/Ben/3117; 3118; 3122: Various accounts for materials, labour, and cash received at the Caldbeck mines dated between 5 April 1724 and 25 December 1726. See also Leconfield MSS.

D/Ben/3120: An annotated sketch map '*Discription of Brandygills Vein and Workings &c August the 25th 1724 by Mee Tho. Hillary*'.

D/Ben/3119: *Thomas Smale's orders to Hillary* June 1st 1726.

LECONFIELD MSS D/Lec/219: This reference covers several items relating to mining in Caldbeck, including:

1 A letter from one Anthony Pratt containing '*An acct of those places wee have taken notice of in Caldbeck . . .*' (referred to above as PRATT, MS). It is dated to *c.*1700 on internal evidence (style, handwriting etc.) but this date may be subject to substantial error.

2 Five variously-titled account sheets for expenses of mining in Caldbeck. From 12 September 1724 to 15 January 172[5], in part repeating entries in the Benson MSS D/Ben/3116; 3121; 3122.

PRATT MS (SEE LECONFIELD MSS)

WALKER MS '*A map of the great lead silver mine of Golden Vugh* [sic] *and Silver Gill. Belonging to the Rt. Hon. Thos. Lord Wharton in his liberty of Caldbeck in Cumberland . . . by Mr Walker March 11th 1710*'. [Quoted on the authority of a tracing of this simple mine section in the W. T. Shaw archive, Ref. D/Sh/31(b); the original has not yet been found.]

MAPS OF THE AREA

TOPOGRAPHICAL
1:50000 Ordnance Survey Sheet 90. Penrith, Keswick, Ambleside area.
1:25000 Ordnance Survey Sheet NY 23/33. Caldbeck.
1:10000 Ordnance Survey Sheets NY 23 SE, NE; NY 33 NW, SW.

GEOLOGICAL
1:50000 Geological Survey Sheet 23. Cockermouth (Solid and Drift editions).

ACKNOWLEDGEMENTS

Many people have contributed towards this book. They have allowed access to their collections and provided information, facilities and support without hesitation or complaint. To all who have helped, the authors offer their grateful thanks; and their apologies to anyone omitted from the following list.

MUSEUM AND UNIVERSITY COLLECTIONS
British Museum (Natural History), Department of Mineralogy: Peter Embrey, Alan Criddle, Andrew Clark, Bob Symes, Peter Tandy, Alan Hart, Ruth Bradford-Harris, Paul Hicks and the late John Fuller.

Cambridge University: David Price (Sedgwick Museum); Graham Chinner and Keith Millar (Department of Earth Sciences).

Leeds University, Department of Earth Sciences: T. Findlay Johnson.

Leicester Museum, Department of Geology: John Martin and Gill Weightman.

National Museum of Wales, Department of Geology: Richard Bevins, Bob King (now John Moore Countryside Museum, Tewkesbury), Jana Horák.

Nottingham University, Department of Geology: Ron Firman.

Oxford University Museum, Department of Mineralogy: Brian Atkins and Monica Price.

Tullie House Museum, Carlisle: David Clarke.

PRIVATE COLLECTIONS
Wim van den Berg
Peter Braithwaite
Richard S. W. Braithwaite
Peter Briscoe
John Cooper
John Dickinson
David I. Green
David R. Hacker
Neil Hubbard
Jim R. Knight
Mike Leppington
David R. Middleton
Mike Rothwell
Roy Starkey
Ralph Sutcliffe
Norman Thomson
George Wilson
Max Wirth
Trevor Wolloxall
Joop and Anneke Wolters
Avril Woodburn
Beverley Yates

ANALYTICAL WORK
British Museum (Natural History), Department of Mineralogy: John G. Francis, (XRD); Frances Wall, Alan Hart (EPMA).

Leeds University: David I. Green (XRD)

Leicester University, Department of Geology: John Faithfull (XRD and EPMA).

National Museum of Wales, Department of Geology: Jana Horák (XRD).

UMIST, Department of Chemistry: Richard S. W. Braithwaite (IR).

Unilever Research, Port Sunlight: Mike Rothwell and John Reid (EPMA and SEM).

PHOTOGRAPHY AND ILLUSTRATIONS
Principal photography is by MPC and Frank Greenaway (BM(NH)) with other pictures as list below:

MPC: Frontispiece and Figs. 1, 3, 16, 19, 20, 24, 26–28, 31, 32, 34, 36, 39, 42, 44, 46–48, 52–55, 57, 59–62, 64–70, 76, 78–80, 82–101, 105, 106, 108–110.

Frank Greenaway: Figs. 40, 45, 50, 71, 74, 81, 103, 107, 111.

CJS: Figs. 11, 13, 14, 49.

Mike Rothwell (Unilever Research) SEM photos Figs. 63, 77, 104.

Don Claugher (BM(NH)): SEM photo Fig. 75.

Additional document photography by members of the Photographic Unit, BM(NH).

We would also like to thank the following for permission to publish pictures from their collections or archives:

Beamish Open Air Museum for Fig. 29
British Geological Survey, Newcastle for Fig. 12 (BGS ref.: D3950)
Jack Hartley for Fig. 22
Lord Egremont for Fig. 21
Solo Syndication for Fig. 18
Victoria & Albert Museum, London for Fig. 43

GENERAL
John Adams, Peter Embrey, Bob King, Bob Symes, and Brian Young read all or part of the draft manuscript and made many useful suggestions, and the manuscript was improved by Dr A. C. Bishop (formerly Keeper of Mineralogy, British Museum (Natural History)).

John Adams' assistance with the mining history was invaluable. Maureen Allen, Bill F. Davidson, and Jack Hartley helped with aspects of the mining and collecting history. Wendy Williams translated foreign language articles. We are grateful to the staff of the Carlisle Public Record Office and the Mineralogy and Palaeontology Libraries (BM(NH)) for their help. Also, to Mrs J. M. Dickinson, Cockermouth, and Denis Perriam (Beamish Open Air Museum) for permission to use the Shaw and Perriam archives respectively. Marion Lowe (BM(NH)) kindly word-processed a substantial proportion of the manuscript.

CJS is grateful to GTDG; to the late Amy and Joe Waite of Mosedale who kindly provided cheap accommodation on many field excursions to the Caldbeck Fells; also to the University of Aston in Birmingham for funding in the form of a studentship and to Professor D. D. Hawkes (Birmingham), Dr J. W. Gaskarth (Birmingham) and Professor D. J. Vaughan (Manchester).

MPC would particularly like to thank Jim Knight for his first trip to the Caldbeck Fells in 1965; the staff of the County Library, Angel Row, Nottingham for their good humour and professionalism; and, above all, his wife, Catherine Foley, without whose forbearance and enthusiasm this book would never have been completed.

Mick Cooper

Chris Stanley

INDEX

Including the names of the mines, minerals, rocks, people, and places referred to in the text. Italic numbers indicate *figures* or their *captions*. Locality names in Appendix 1 are indexed but mineral names are not; *vice versa* for Appendix 2. Literature citations and *personal communications* are not indexed. 'Collectors' are grouped together. For fast access to minerals by major localities see Appendix 1; for localities by mineral see Chapter 6 'The minerals'.

157